New Connections 2008

PLAYS FOR YOUNG PEOPLE

Arden City

Burying Your Brother in the Pavement

Fugee

He's Talking

It Snows

My Face

The Peach Child

Scenes from Family Life

A Vampire Story

ff

faber and faber

First published in 2008
by Faber and Faber Limited
3 Queen Square, London WC1N 3AU

Typeset by Country Setting, Kingsdown, Kent CT14 8ES
Printed in England by CPI Bookmarque, Croydon, Surrey

Information regarding applications for performance
will be found preceding the individual plays

A CIP record for this book is available from the British Library

978-0-571-24489-8

2 4 6 8 10 9 7 5 3 1

Contents

Introduction

The first decade of the twenty-first century is a mere eighteen months away and the art of theatre is thriving in a race to re-identify itself. With short plays and theatre pieces which comprise an amalgam of forms becoming so prevalent they're almost *de rigueur*, the National Theatre's 'New Connections' tenth season presents the zenith of the zeitgeist. Concocted in 1993 in response to an acute thirst for exciting plays for teenage actors, the potent combination of acclaimed writer with young actor is as heady as ever. These nine new plays draw on the traditions of classical drama, the stories of Shakespeare and the trends of nineteenth- and twentieth-century theatre. They are all propelled by the thrill of the new, both stylistically and in content. Pioneering in their forging of new possibilities in the art of theatre, they've proven to be galvanic scripts inspiring thousands of young performers to create world premiere productions this year across the nation.

The search for identity pulses through these ten 'New Connections' plays: for acceptance and survival in modern Britain, for racial equality in 1960s South Africa, by deception in magical allotments, during a white-out in a snow blizzard, through parenting, or by comic mistakes in social networking.

In *A Vampire Story*, by Moira Buffini, two young women arrive in a nameless small British town. Their names are not their own. They don't declare their ages. Are they sisters, as their assumed identities declare? Or are they mother and daughter? Are Ella and Claire vampires? Or are they troubled young women on the run?

Timberlake Wertenbaker's *Arden City* is a contemporary *As You Like It*: a story about love, identity and freedom. Rosie and Sally are two cousins who escape from home after difficulties with Sally's father. Rosie dresses as a boy for safety and the girls find their way to an allotment. Orlando also flees because his brother Oliver wants him killed, and finds his way to the allotment with Adam, his younger friend.

Burying Your Brother in the Pavement is a play with songs by Jack Thorne. It conjures a wacky panorama which envelops the central character Tom, who is grappling with grief. As the play begins, Tom's brother is dead. He was killed by a broken bottle to the neck. This has upset a lot of people but it hasn't upset Tom. Or rather, it has upset him, but in ways he can't explain. Tom really didn't like his brother, but without him he faces a chasm he must explore and conquer.

Abi Morgan's *Fugee* is set in London, but could unfold in any sprawling, seemingly heartless metropolis. Kojo is fourteen, but no one believes him; he's just one of the unaccompanied minors arriving in the city, abandoned on the streets of the UK. Ara is from Baghdad and still hears the bombs at night. Cheung can do back-flips and is from a village in China that is more than a thousand years old. Orphans in London, they are the only family they have. Together they tell Kojo's story: a story of lost childhood, tall trees and a murder in motion: a murder by a child that everyone says is a man.

He's Talking, by Nicholas Wright, cunningly tells a tale of a group of politically active young people in the 1960s. It's a fact-based fiction about an anti-racist bombing group in apartheid South Africa. Luke, the leader, is seized and questioned. Every word he speaks will have a lifelong effect on his young friends and on himself. What

would you do if you were caught and interrogated?
Would you betray your friends? One year later, they all
meet up. Or some of them do. Or only a few. It all
depends on whether he talked . . . or not.

It Snows is by Scott Graham and Steven Hoggett, artistic
directors of Frantic Assembly, and Bryony Lavery. It's the
same old story. Boy doesn't meet Girl. Girl doesn't meet
Boy. The threat of the terrifying Lads Gang. The threat of
the awe-inspiring Girl Gang. Mum and Dad have declared
war against each other. There's a weird neighbour in the
building opposite. It's the usual ordinary gloominess.
Then, one day, it snows. And everything changes.

In Nigel Williams's comedy *My Face*, Susie decides to hold
a party for all her My Face internet friends, but things
go disastrously wrong as the virtual people become real.
Mark is in love with Susie, but Susie is more concerned
with the fact that Lou is in love with Sam. But Sam
(although he doesn't know it) is in love with Emma and –
to make things even worse – Lou may be in love with
Susie's brother, Pete. Disaster!

Scenes from Family Life, by Mark Ravenhill, is an expres-
sionistic landscape in which young adults are growing up.
Jack and Lisa are two ordinary teenagers who want to
have a baby. The only problem is, Lisa keeps vanishing –
literally – into thin air. Their friends Barry and Stacy, who
is eight months pregnant, have the same problem. Soon,
everyone in the whole world is dematerialising. Six
months on, Jack and Stacy find they are the only boy
and girl on the planet. For Jack it's a dream, for Stacy a
nightmare. And when the vanished start to return, Jack
has to learn how complex adult relationships are.

The Peach Child, by Anna Furse, was commissioned
with the Little Angel Theatre company, for whom Anna
originally created the piece for audiences of four- to seven-

year-olds. Based on a well-loved Japanese legend, the play offers opportunities for a visual approach, puppetry and object animation. One day, as a poor, childless Old Woman washes kimonos in the river, a giant peach mysteriously floats by. She takes it home to her husband. As she cuts the flesh a baby is born. They call this miracle Momotaro – 'Peach Child'. At fifteen, he leaves his adoptive parents on a quest to overcome the evil Ogre. He has many adventures, then triumphs and returns home to restore peace in the land.

It's been an especially productive year for the 'Connections' programme at the National. As well as these ten plays receiving their premieres in two hundred venues around the UK, the National presented professional productions of *Baby Girl*, *DNA* and *The Miracle* in the Cottesloe and our hugely successful productions of *Chatroom* and *Citizenship* toured the UK and visited Hong Kong.

The 'New Connections' 2008 portfolio has been performed in fifteen festivals around the land prior to the festival at the National. This year festivals have taken place in Theatre Royal, Bath; Pavilion Theatre, Brighton; Edinburgh Lyceum; Kendal Brewery Arts Centre; Arcola and Hampstead Theatres, London; Kildare Riverbank Arts Centre; Clwyd Theatr Cymru; Newcastle Theatre Royal; Northampton Royal and Derngate; Norwich Playhouse and Garage; Plymouth Theatre Royal; Salford Lowry Centre; Stephen Joseph Theatre, Scarborough; and the Nuffield Theatre, Southampton. 'Connections' programmes continue to grow and thrive overseas in Brazil, Italy, Norway, and Portugal.

The 2008 season culminates in the National Theatre Festival, 3–8 July, which for the first time takes place on all three of our stages, the Olivier, Lyttelton and Cottesloe. There will be productions of all these plays performed by young companies from across the UK, and four punchy new plays created by young people telling stories from the front line of their own experience, followed by debates driven by those working closely with teens of today.

I hope you enjoy reading these plays, and if you would like to become part of the programme go to the website, www.ntconnections.org.uk.

ANTHONY BANKS
Associate Director Education,
National Theatre, July 2008

ARDEN CITY

Timberlake Wertenbaker

Timberlake Wertenbaker's plays include, at the Royal Court, *The Grace of Mary Traverse*, *Our Country's Good* (also on Broadway, 1988, Olivier Play of the Year Award and 1991 New York Drama Critics' Circle Award for Best New Foreign Play); *Three Birds Alighting on a Field* (Susan Smith Blackburn, Writers' Guild and London Critics' Circle awards), *The Break of Day* (also on tour), *Credible Witness* and *Divine Intervention* (also BBC Radio 3). Elsewhere: *The Love of the Nightingale* at the RSC (Eileen Anderson Central TV Drama Award); *After Darwin* at Hampstead Theatre Club; *The Ash Girl* at Birmingham Rep; *Galileo's Daughter* for the Peter Hall Company at the Bath Theatre Festival; and *New Anatomies* at the ICA. For Radio 3: *Dianeira*. The most recent of her many translations and adaptations is Gabriela Preissova's *Jenufa* at the Arcola Theatre.

Author's Note

The first inspiration for this play came from my daughter, then fifteen. I told her I'd been asked to write a play for young people and I wasn't sure what to write about. 'Why don't you do one of those Shakespeare things but, like, modern,' she said. 'Like that film about those twins and the girl has to be a boy and play football.'

I wanted to write about two girls who had to fend for themselves and I'd always liked the character of Rosalind in *As You Like It*, so that was the starting point.

The next inspiration came when I was looking for a setting. I wanted it to be urban, but I'd discarded the idea of a cardboard city. That's when I came across the Manor Garden Allotments.

The allotment gardens were at that time occupying about four and a half acres between the River Lea and Channelsea River in Hackney Wick, East London. The gardens were established in 1900 by the philanthropist Major Arthur Villiers (director of Barings Bank) to provide small parcels of land where the local people of that deprived area could grow vegetables. The allotments were to be maintained in perpetuity. Until 2007 they were indeed tended by a tightly knit community. Some passed on the plots from generation to generation, but there were also many newcomers coming from the diverse ethnic backgrounds of the community, finding ways to cultivate the plants of their homeland. Despite the original pledge, the Olympics Committee decided it needed a concrete walkway between the two planned stadiums and the allotment holders were forced out.

I came to the allotments as a metal fence was beginning to enclose the area. I was one of the last visitors allowed in.

I really did step into a realm out of time. Leaving the traffic of a typical East London road, I went through what seemed like a magic gate, over a small bridge and suddenly found myself in what felt like the middle of ancient countryside, surrounded by trees, tall plants and with beautiful plots dotted with varied-coloured huts. Some had already been abandoned and there was a sadness hanging over the area as well. And yet there was an extraordinary sense of community as we drank tea, ate fabulous food and I was taken on a tour of the plots and met some of the plot-holders. It was indeed like a Forest of Arden or an Eden right in the middle of London, and an obvious setting for the play. Some weeks later it was closed off for good and eventually demolished, one of the saddest consequences of arbitrary planning I have encountered because I understood that with a little imagination, the concrete concourse could have circumvented the allotments.

The final inspiration came from the Camden School for Girls.

I wanted to explore how young people view gender differences these days and Max Stafford-Clark, the director of Out of Joint, and I organised a workshop with Josephine Fenton, who taught the sixth form drama students at Camden School. We spent a couple of days exploring what they considered 'male' and 'female' behaviour and what it might mean for them to switch genders. The students were open, imaginative and delightful.

As I was writing the play, I became once more indignant at power used arbitrarily, as it almost always is, whether by an individual or a committee. I neither could – nor would – want to offer a philosophical or psychological explanation or suggest political solutions in what I hope is essentially a fun and playful piece about adolescents stretching their limbs. However, the observations are there. For me, the use of arbitrary power remains infuriating but also, well, sad – in both old and new senses of the word.

As I write, other allotments are under threat, as they tend to be on prime building sites and used by people with little power. The story of Manor Garden Allotments is not over either, and anyone looking for information can go to their website www.lifeisland.org. If you go down to the area now, you would not believe such a place existed, and you might think I took dramatic liberties, but I promise you, I invented nothing.

Characters

in order of appearance

Orlando
the son of Roland Bryce and brother of Oliver

Adam
possibly from a new immigrant family

Oliver
son of Roland Bryce, older brother of Orlando

Che
a wrestler or kick-boxer

Sally
daughter of Frederick, cousin of Rosie

Rosie
niece of Frederick and of Valerie;
her mother is dead

Lebeau
a hanger-on

Frederick
older brother of Valerie,
whose business he has taken over;
father of Sally and uncle of Rosie;
he is a young father but older than the rest

Valerie
sister of Frederick, aunt of Rosie,
young but not a teenager

Ricky and others
Frederick's mates and associates, male or female

Amien, Julie, Mickey, others
friends and business associates of Valerie
who come with her to the allotments,
male and female

Colin
a boy on the allotment

Sylvius
a boy on the allotment, fourteen or under

Jay
a singer-songwriter, friend of Valerie,
who comes with Valerie to the allotments

Phoebe
a girl on the allotments, fourteen or under

*All characters are in their mid- to
late teens, unless otherwise indicated*

Notes on Staging

There are seventeen spoken parts. Some doubling is possible.

We are in the present as London prepares for the Olympics. The action takes place on a city street, in a city square and on the allotments. The scenery should be absolutely minimal to avoid scene changes: some benches, a few gardening implements for the allotments. A bucket. Clothes can be more imaginative, especially in the transformations of Rosie and Sally.

The allotments that inspired this play are called Manor Garden Allotments. Google for information or go to www.lifeisland.org. The allotments do not have to be replicated, but it's worth researching them.

The wrestling depends on what's available in the company and must be carefully choreographed. It can be stylised and short.

The music should be written by someone in the company. Jay can have companions who are musicians but no spoken lines should be added.

*Special thanks to Max Stafford-Clark;
Josephine Fenton and the sixth form of
Camden School for Girls; Julie Sumner at
Manor Garden Allotments; Irina Brown*

SCENE ONE

The street. Orlando and Adam.

Orlando When my father was dying, he told him to look after me. The first thing he did was take me out of school. He said it was too expensive. He doesn't give me any money to do anything, not even to buy trainers.

Adam Why are you telling me all this?

Orlando I want you to know.

Adam Knowing doesn't help. I have to work for him.

Orlando He looks after those big dogs of his better than me. All I do is walk the streets, hang around. I've forgotten anything I knew. I'm even forgetting who I am.

Adam Look, here he comes.

Orlando Keep yourself hidden and listen.

Adam leaves. Oliver comes on.

Oliver What are doing you here?

Orlando Nothing, I don't know how to do anything.

Oliver Then get out of the way.

Orlando The streets are free.

Oliver I'll have you arrested for loitering.

Orlando I wouldn't loiter if I had something to do. Oliver – our father told you to look after me.

Oliver I feed you and house you, that costs.

Orlando Give me some of the money my father left. I'll go to another city and you won't ever see me again.

Oliver He left you in my care.

Orlando How have you cared for me? You've turned me into a yob.

Oliver That's what you are, Orlando. Now move or you'll get yourself into more trouble. Out of my way!

Orlando (*physically threatening*) I'm stronger than you –

Oliver Are you threatening your brother?

Orlando No. Our father never hurt anyone. I am still my father's son.

He goes.

Oliver No way you're ever getting anything out of me, little brother. The sooner you're out of the way the better.

SCENE TWO

Che, a professional kick-boxer, comes on.

Che I've been looking for you. I've heard your brother is going to challenge me in a kick-boxing contest. Now look, I don't practise Peacenik Judo but the real thing. This is Sanshou and it's tough. A kid can get hurt. So you've got to convince your brother to forget it and fight with people his own age.

Oliver He won't, Che. He's stubborn and vicious. I've done everything I can for him and all he does is threaten me.

Che OK. I'll teach him a lesson.

Oliver Watch out. He'll probably have a knife, and when you're not looking he'll take it out and kill you. I won't hold it against you if you have to do the same in self-defence.

Che I don't need a knife, there are places you can kick – and it's over. It's against the rules, but it can happen by accident.

Oliver I don't like to say this, because he's my brother, but if you win, he'll never forget it and he'll find a way to kill you.

Che OK.
Oliver Whatever you do, make it quick. And final. I don't
  want him to linger in pain.

Che leaves.

I'm going to be rid of the little brother at last. I hate him.
I don't know why. He always reminds me –

Adam comes on.

How good is Orlando at this kick-boxing?
Adam I don't know.
Oliver Well: go and find out.

They leave.

SCENE THREE

An urban square. Rosie and Sally.

Sally Come on, Rosie, try to be more cheerful.
Rosie I'm being more cheerful than I feel cheerful about.
Sally Try harder. Let me help you.
Rosie Help me to forget my brilliant young aunt. I
  dreamt of her again last night. She took me in when
  they found my mother. Helped me through all that.
  Then she's thrown out of business by her own brother
  – my uncle, your father. What kind of world do we live
  in, Sal? Everything seems so arbitrary.
Sally You don't love me as much as I love you, Rosie. If
  it had happened to me, I would still have been happy
  because we're together. And I'd try to forget the grown-
  ups because most of the time they don't know what
  they're doing anyway.
Rosie My aunt knew what she was doing. She had the
  sauce recipe from her grandmother. She started
  bottling it. She went on that programme to raise

money, now it's sold all over the world. And she's disappeared.

Sally It happens all the time, doesn't it?

Rosie That doesn't make it right, does it?

Sally I'm my father's only child. I'll inherit the business and I'll share everything with you. We'll call it Rosie and Sally Associates. Please, Rosie, cheer up. You're as much fun as an estate agent.

Rosie Sorry. Let's have a laugh, then. What do you want to do? Fall in love?

Sally I wonder what that's like.

Rosie I imagine it's like slipping on a banana peel. You're walking normally and suddenly you're floored.

Sally And if it's happening to you, it's not funny but unlucky.

Rosie Or lucky. What's wrong with lying on the floor?

Sally Then let's make fun of luck.

Rosie Luck makes fun of us. Some are lucky, some are not, and luck doesn't care very much either way.

Sally I think you make your own luck.

Rosie How? If you're born ugly and poor or in a country where there's war, how do you make your own luck?

Sally Rosie, we're supposed to be having fun.

Rosie Sorry. I'm not myself today. Or maybe I am myself. I don't know.

Sally We're still at school, we can't save the world yet.

Rosie Somebody's going to have to.

Sally Now I'm really depressed.

Rosie Look, there's Lebeau. We can make fun of him.

Sally He looks so serious.

Rosie So important.

SCENE FOUR

Lebeau enters, trying to be cool.

Rosie What's new, Lebeau?

Lebeau is about to speak.

Sally It has to be new.
Rosie And interesting.
Sally Something to do with luck.
Rosie So? We're waiting.
Lebeau Haven't you heard?
Sally We've just heard your voice.
Rosie Asking if we've heard.
Sally We've heard lots of things.
Rosie Amazing what you hear in a short life.
Lebeau I'm talking about the wrestling. It was amazing.
  You missed it.
Sally You mean we didn't hear screams of pain? We're
  gutted.
Lebeau Let me tell you what happened. There was an old
  man and his three sons.
Rosie Sounds like a fairy tale, I'm going to sleep.
Lebeau The men are young and strong.
Rosie Most young men are young and a few are strong,
  yes?
Lebeau They wrestle in turn with Che. The first gets it in
  the knees. He's been taken to hospital. With the second
  and the third it's the ribs.
Rosie And that's what we were supposed to hear? The
  click of cracking knees, the whack of broken ribs –
  you think we like the rhythm or something?
Lebeau The boxing's not finished. Once the ambulances
  came they wanted to stop it. But there was one
  challenger left, he looks like a schoolkid. So everyone's

coming into the square and if you stay you'll have the best view.

Rosie I'm not really keen on broken ribs. I'm more interested in Adam's rib, spare ribs, true ribs, floating ribs –

Sally Barbecued ribs.

SCENE FIVE

Frederick, others, Orlando, Che.

Frederick Are you two girls here to see the fight?

Sally Yes, Dad, if you don't mind.

Frederick Maybe you could persuade that kid there not to fight. He's much too young, but he won't listen to us. He might listen to girls his own age.

Sally Lebeau, bring him over here.

Frederick (*moving away*) I'll keep out of the way. Try your best, I don't want child murder on my hands.

Lebeau brings Orlando to the girls.

Rosie (*to Orlando*) We're told you've challenged Che. He's the most famous wrestler around here.

Orlando I want to try my strength.

Sally You've seen how strong he is. And he's much older than you.

Rosie No one will despise you if you call it off. We'll speak to Frederick.

Orlando I'd love to give in to you but I can't. At least wish me well. If I make a fool of myself, I'm the only one who'll suffer. If I die, no one will miss me. The space I take up in the world can be better filled by someone else.

Rosie I have very little strength but I'd give you whatever I have.

Sally Me too.

Rosie Goodbye – I hope you are not what you seem.

Che Where's this kid who wants to join the others in
hospital?

Orlando Here.

Frederick Only one fall.

Che He won't be able to get up after the first one.

Orlando (*to Che*) You should boast afterwards, not
before.

Rosie I wish you strength, I wish you strength.

They fight.

Rosie Look! He's so quick.

Che is thrown.

Frederick Stop!

Orlando I'm not tired yet.

Frederick How is Che?

Lebeau He can't speak.

Frederick Take him away.

Che is taken away. Frederick approaches.

What's your name? I've seen you around.

Orlando Orlando Bryce. May father was Roland Bryce.

Frederick I knew your father. He took my sister's side,
and tried to ruin my business. You're brave, that's for
sure. You've done well, but you should have asked for
another father. I'm keeping the prize money.

*He goes with Lebeau and others. Sally, Rosie and
Orlando remain.*

Sally If I were my father, I wouldn't have done that.

Rosie My aunt was a good friend of his father's. I
remember the name.

Sally Sometimes I don't understand my father. He gets
so – arbitrary. (*To Orlando.*) You were amazing.

(*Teasing.*) If you're as talented in other ways, you'll make someone very happy.

Rosie I have this necklace, it's not too girly. Will you wear it? I wish I could give you more.

Sally/Rosie Bye –

Orlando remains speechless. The girls begin to move off, slowly.

Orlando Couldn't I even have said thank you? Something happened to me in that fight. I can't speak.

Rosie (*to Sally*) I think he wants to say something to us. Let's go back.

They do.

Did you call us? You fought really well. You slayed him. And not just him either.

Sally It's time to go, Rosie.

Rosie Bye . . . See ya . . . maybe.

They go, Rosie reluctantly.

Orlando My tongue stayed glued. And she wanted to talk. Stupid, stupid, stupid. Uncool. Uneducated. Un— anything. That's me. But she did want to talk.

SCENE SIX

Lebeau comes on.

Lebeau Run, Orlando, you're in trouble. Frederick is acting very strange.

Orlando Who are those girls?

Lebeau The shorter one is Sally, Frederick's daughter. The other one, Rosie, is the niece of his sister. Frederick kicked his sister out of their business and he threatened her too. So she disappeared. They say she lives on the edge of the city and they have allotments or something. And now Frederick is furious with Rosie for some reason. He's very arbitrary, Frederick. You've got to get out of here.

Orlando Thank you, Lebeau. It's kind of you.

Lebeau I'm not kind, I just like to be in the middle of things.

SCENE SEVEN

Sally and Rosie come on.

Sally You haven't said a word.

Rosie I couldn't even throw a hello to a dog.

Sally No one's asking you to waste your words on a poodle, just throw some words at me. Your silence is doing my brain in.

Rosie Find me the thesaurus that expresses what's happened to me.

Sally Seriously, after seeing him just the once, you've fallen in love?

Rosie Well, my aunt loved his dad.

Sally That doesn't mean the niece is supposed to love the son. Am I supposed to hate him because my father hated his father?

Rosie How could anyone hate someone who was so – so –?

Sally Handsome?

Rosie Internal.

Here comes your father.

Sally Looking angry. Whoops.

Frederick comes on.

Frederick (*to Rosie*) I want you to leave this house immediately.

Rosie But why, Uncle? I haven't done anything wrong!

Frederick That's what everyone says when they're guilty. You're my sister's niece. That's enough.

Rosie But I was your sister's niece when you took me in. Doing wrong isn't genetic, and anyway my aunt didn't do anything wrong.

Sally Dad, listen to me.

Frederick (*to Sally*) I only kept her in the house because of you.

Sally When you took her in I didn't know her and I didn't care. You were the one who felt guilty. But now I know her – we're cousins, we're friends, we share the same room, we play together, talk into the night, study together, share our meals, we laugh and cry together and when you're off on your business trips, she's here, keeping me company. At school, they call us the bubble twins – because we're always bubbling over –

Frederick She shows you up. (*To Rosie.*) I want you out of the house tonight.

Sally Then I'll leave too.

Frederick Don't be a fool. (*To Rosie.*) Don't let me find you here when I come home.

Frederick leaves.

Rosie I'd better pack.

Sally Where will you go?

Rosie I'm not the only girl who's been made homeless. I'll manage.

Sally I'm frightened.

Rosie Why should you be frightened? You have a home. A father. You're rich. He owns half the street now. He's got power.

Sally Don't you know that when my father throws you out of the house he throws me out too? I can't be a daughter to this father. So now, let's get ready.

Rosie I'm going to wander the streets, Sal, it's not much
of a life. Anyway, your father will find you
immediately. I'd better hurry or he'll have me hurt.

Sally We could go find your aunt.

Rosie I don't know where she is.

Sally Didn't she ever manage to get in touch with you?

Rosie For a while I had text messages but then that
stopped.

Sally Where did she say she was in the messages?

Rosie Something called Arden City. She said they'd
found some allotments hidden in the middle of the city.

Sally Arden City? I've heard about it. I was researching
this project on wilderness in the cities, remember, and
they talked about these allotments in London and they
were going to be destroyed.

Rosie Well then, she won't be there.

Sally No, there were protests, a reprieve, there's even a
map – we'll Google it. Where's your computer?

Rosie How will we get there?

Sally Trains, buses – hitchhiking if we have to. I know
where my father keeps some cash.

Rosie He'll come after us.

Sally People disappear all the time. They're never found.
We'll get disguised. We could dress as boys.

Rosie No, one boy and one girl, it's safer I think. I'll be
the boy because I'm strong and I play football. I'll cut
my hair and wear baggy trousers and a big shirt, no
one will know. A cap. I'll speak in a low voice. All
I have to do is grunt – like most boys we know. And
I'll walk all male like. Look.

Rosie tries.

Sally Your hips are wrong. You've got to have your hips
out and roll on your feet.

Rosie Yeah, swagger. Cool. How's that?

She practises.

Sally Better. I'll be your sister. I can cover my face too. Scarf, a veil even. What shall we call ourselves?
Rosie I'd liked to be called Garry. Garry Lost.
Sally I want to be called Alien.
Rosie You can't call yourself Alien!
Sally Liena, Leina. That's good. Garry and Lena Lost. We'll have to throw away the mobiles because we can be traced, but we can take the laptop.
Rosie They're not going to have plugs in an allotment.
Sally Well, until the battery runs out.

SCENE EIGHT

Arden City. A large selection of allotments in an East London wilderness. Valerie, Amien, Mickey, Julie, others. They're in rough clothes: they've been fishing.

Valerie What I like about nature is that its power is immense but not malicious. When the cold freezes my bones it's not because it's out to get me but because I happen to be here. Nature is not jealous of my existence or success as my brother was. But it demands respect. I was successful so young that I despised everything. Now I take time and I pay respect to what's in front of me.
Amien I'd pay respect to a hot bath.
Valerie Cold water is better for the skin. Mine's never been so smooth.
Julie I still miss the excitement of the city.
Valerie What excitement? The rat race? Who's thrown out on a television show, the stock market? Fashion? There's excitement watching the changes in the trees as they drape themselves in different colours through the seasons – but you have to slow down and look.

Amien I used to love watching the news. That's because I love disaster.

Valerie The news always made me feel angry and powerless. What do we need to know? That there's enough water in the rivers right now for us to fish, but we have to be careful. The water's getting polluted by the clearings going on.

Amien What if we have to move?

Julie Yes, what about these Olympics?

Valerie If we can do something, we will.

Amien And if not?

Valerie Greed and glory are old and powerful human drives – hard to stop. But there are other, newer drives in us, like the ones we've found here. Let's trust those.

Mickey I like being here, Valerie. I mean if someone had told me I'd find vegetables interesting, I'd have laughed. But the land around us is being cleared, a warehouse was burned down the other day, the fish are disappearing and we don't have a plan.

Valerie When I had my business I planned years ahead but I didn't see my brother's plots right in front of me. What's in front of us right now? It's getting dark and we need to eat.

Julie And I'm tired of fish.

Valerie What about some pigeon breasts? We can cook them with figs. Add watercress . . .

Amien You'd better talk to Jay about the pigeons. He says no living thing should be sacrificed to our greed. He says we're like a foreign invasion massacring those who were here before us.

Valerie Let's go find him, I love to talk to him when he's in this mood.

They leave.

23

SCENE NINE

Frederick, Lebeau, Ricky.

Frederick Didn't anyone see them?

Lebeau When the cleaning lady came in she saw the girls hadn't slept in their bed.

Ricky I overheard them talking about how wonderful that young wrestler was. I bet they can be found with him somewhere.

Frederick I knew that boy was bad news.

Ricky There's an older brother. He's helped us before.

Frederick Find him and bring him to me.

SCENE TEN

Orlando, Adam.

Adam Orlando, run. When your brother heard about the boxing and how amazing you were, he got very angry. He's asked me to burn down the garage where you sleep with you locked in it, so it looks like an accident. What a world we live in: you do something well and instead of being admired for it, you're hated. Go, before your brother gets back.

Orlando Go where? I have no money. I can't go on the streets and beg. Let my brother have my death since that's the extent of his brotherly love. I'm tired.

Adam Your father was always kind to me because he knew I had no family. Before he died, he gave me a hundred pounds. I never used it because I started doing errands for your brother. Take it. And let me come with you. I know you think I'm too young and ill and I know I can't walk very fast, but I'll keep you company. I can't work for your brother any more. I've

closed my eyes to a lot, minded my own business to
survive, but there's a limit.

Orlando Why put yourself in danger because of me?
Oliver will come after us.

Adam It's not that I believe in right and wrong or
anything – but there's a limit. I'm coming with you.

Orlando We'll have to move to another city.

Adam I've lived on these streets all my life, doing some
pretty bad things, I didn't want to know, but it's finished
now. Somehow I reached the limit. Funny, isn't it?
What's a limit?

SCENE ELEVEN

Near Arden City, a building wasteland.
  Rosie and Sally come on, exhausted and limping. Rosie
wears baggy trousers, a cap, etc., and moves from being
boyish to girlish. Sally is well covered.

Rosie I'm a boy, I don't cry. I'm going to disgrace myself
and start snivelling like a girl.

She resists snivelling.

Sally I can't go any further.

Rosie We're lost.

Sally All these high fences, and no one around. I'm
scared.

Rosie We can't go to sleep, it's too dangerous. Show me
the map on the computer again.

Sally I have twenty minutes of battery left.

They open the computer.

Rosie It's all changed from what they show here.

Sally (*looking*) There's the bus depot. But where's the
alley?

Rosie Look. The sign was knocked over. There's supposed to be a little gate.

Sally I hear a noise!

Rosie Two men – coming from over there.

Sally They're going to kill us!

Rosie We can hide here. Keep still.

Enter Colin and Sylvius. Sylvius is very young. Colin is a little older.

Sylvius If you only knew how I love her.

Rosalind (*to Sally*) Phew! Their minds aren't on robbing us! Anyway, they're about twelve.

Colin I was in love once.

Sylvius No one has ever loved as I love. What crazy things did you do?

Colin I can't remember.

Sylvius I'm sure you never talked about the girl you loved for hours and hours the way I talk about Phoebe. Oh, Phoebe, Phoebe, Phoebe. You never left your friends just to be alone and say her name: Phoebe, Phoebe, Phoebe.

Rosie I know those feelings . . .

Sally Maybe they'd give us some food – go and ask them, Rosie . . .

Rosie goes, very boyish.

Rosie Hmm. You – yeah, you.

The two boys on the defensive.

Colin What do you want?

Rosie Uh – we've been travelling. Like – how do you buy food around here?

A moment. They measure each other.

Colin We don't buy any food, we grow our own. On the allotments.

Rosie There are allotments? You have an allotment?
Where?

Colin I don't own an allotment, I work on someone else's.
But he's decided to abandon it. There's some food
stored away. I'm happy to give you what we have.

Sally comes forward.

Sally Did you say there was an abandoned allotment?

Colin Yeah, it has a good hut on it and some chickens –
with a special cage so the foxes don't get them. But all
this land is being cleared for the Olympics, we don't
know what's going to happen, so people are giving up.
Technically you should deal with the council, but the
way things are . . .

Sally Go tell your boss I'll buy his tools and anything he
cares to leave behind. And you can stay and help us.
I don't know anything about growing food and I've
only seen chickens in packages in the supermarket, but
I'd be happy to learn.

Colin You'd better come and see the hut and make sure
it suits you. I mean . . . it's just – a hut.

Sally Just – a – hut sounds perfect.

Colin I hear some people, come quickly.

*Sally, Colin, Sylvius and Rosie leave. Orlando and
Adam enter.*

SCENE TWELVE

Adam I can't go any further, Orlando. I'm sorry. I'll just
lie down here and die. I don't mind. There's a limit.

Orlando I promise that if there's any food in this weird
place I'll find it.

Adam They stole all our money on the train. Why? Just
because there were a lot of them and that made them
stronger?

Orlando There must be some food somewhere. Don't give up. Please.

Adam You know I'm going to die pretty soon anyway – that's what the doctor said before I stopped going to him.

Orlando No one knows the future, Adam.

Adam He said it would take a miracle for me to get through the year.

Orlando A miracle is just a future no one has yet imagined. Come over here and keep quiet, no one will see you. Here's my jacket. Try to sleep.

Orlando takes Adam off.

SCENE THIRTEEN

The allotments. Valerie, Jay, and all.

Valerie Jay, we don't see you any more.

Jay I was talking to that old gardener.

Valerie Hassan?

Jay What a gardener.

Valerie He has great plants. Opening those figs is like staring into a hidden galaxy. And his aubergines –

Jay He has great words. He told his plants stories of when they were small shoots and now they've grown and soon they'll be ripe and perfect and then they'll rot. And the plants listen quietly and don't move. I want to become a gardener. I'll cut back the show-offs and encourage the shy ones. No bullies in my garden.

Amien You should talk, you were the biggest bully on the street.

Jay I had to be. But it doesn't work with plants.

Valerie It doesn't work with humans either.

Jay I'm not so sure about that.

Valerie In the end.

Jay But when's the end?

Orlando comes on with a knife.

Orlando Don't touch that food.

Jay We haven't touched anything yet.

Orlando It's mine.

Jay What kind of a cave have you come from, big bully?

Valerie Are you looking for food or for trouble?

Orlando I'm not a thug. I wouldn't behave like this if I weren't hungry. DON'T TOUCH THAT FOOD!

Valerie Why don't you ask politely? It'll save you a lot of energy.

Orlando I'm starving.

Valerie Well, sit down and eat with us, there's plenty here.

Orlando I thought everyone lived rough here and looked after themselves.

Valerie We do look after ourselves, that's why we look after others.

Orlando I don't know who you are or where I am, but if you've known what it's like to be treated badly and to go hungry, if you've known better days, if you've hoped someone would take pity on you and they haven't, then – please help me and give me some food!

Jay We've all known better days. Although those words don't mean much. How do you define a better day?

Valerie You're welcome here. Help yourself.

Orlando is about to throw himself on the food.

Orlando Wait. There's a young boy who's sick and can't walk. He's followed me and he's fainting with hunger. I have to feed him first. I'll carry him here.

Valerie You look faint yourself. Where is this boy? We'll take our food to him. And then you'll tell us what happened to put you in this state.

Orlando, Valerie, and the others go.

SCENE FOURTEEN

Frederick, Oliver and Frederick's mates.

Frederick What do you mean, Orlando has disappeared?

Oliver He left in the night.

Frederick How do I know you're not hiding him?

Oliver I would never hide him. I hate him. I wish him dead myself.

Frederick What kind of a brother are you? I hated my sister but I didn't wish her dead. I just wanted what she had. That's normal. You're not. Go and find your brother and don't let me see you until you've got him. And the rest of you: ask around the train station, the buses, but make sure the police don't get involved.

All leave.

SCENE FIFTEEN

Arden City.

Orlando (*with a can of spray paint*) ROSIE. I'm going to paint every tree with your name. Wait, these woods are beautiful. (*He looks at the tin.*) It's OK, it's washable paint. (*He paints.*) ROSIE. WHERE R U ROSIE? I need to find something better. What rhymes with Rosie? Nosy? That's no good! Posy? I'm so prosy. There's something people drink in magical places – ambrosie: that rhymes. But I think it was ambrosia. Why do words always disappear over the edge when you run after them?

Leaves. Sally, Colin.

Colin I left home when I was eleven. I was in trouble with my stepfather. I was on the streets for a while,

that was rough. Then I found the allotments. I helped
this guy Phil. He kept some bees and I helped him.
Then I made some of my own hives and now I have a
colony.

Sally Don't you miss the city?

Colin I never go except to sell the honey.

Sally But what about the cinema, music, clubs, pubs?

Colin There's always lots going on here.

Sally The telly? You don't even have a computer. How
do you find out what's going on in the world? What if
there's a war?

Colin If you're quiet enough you can feel things. We
knew something happened when there were those
bombs. Something changed.

Sally But there's nothing to do.

Colin I don't always have to do something to be happy.

Sally Yeah, but how do you pass the time?

Colin I don't pass the time. I stay with it.

Sally Yeah, but at night?

Colin I watch the weather.

Sally The weather. Wow.

Colin Have you ever watched the weather?

Sally I can't say I have. I mean, I know when it rains.

Colin You see everything coming, you watch the clouds
move, change shape, you see them fill with rain, then
sometimes it does rain, sometimes it's not enough, they
move away. When I was on the streets, I never saw
colours.

Sally Yeah, well, maybe . . .

Colin I don't have exams or an office job, nobody's my
boss, I don't clock in or answer registration. I do what
I want. I think.

Sally About what?

Colin Why people are so easily bored when there's so
much around. And I worry too. You know, whether the
bees are going to disappear. Whether they're going to

destroy this allotment to make way for their Olympics. It's not even for a stadium, it's for a concrete walkway. I'll show you the hives. The bees won't sting as long as you don't step between them and the sun.

They leave, Rosie enters.

Rosie Who's sprayed paint over all these trees? Hang on. It's my name. My name in all these different colours, 'WHERE R U ROSIE?' I'm 'ere. But who wants to know?

Sally comes in, running, jumping up and down.

Sally You'll never guess, you'll never guess, you'll never guess.

Rosie That you've gone mad?

Sally Three guesses, ten guesses, a hundred, try. Have you noticed your name on these trees?

Rosie Rosie must be a very popular name.

Sally You can't think who's done it?

Rosie Who?

Sally Serendipity.

Rosie Who's that?

Sally Amazing coincidence, fate, luck, serendipity, fatal attraction.

Rosie What are you talking about?

Sally Amazing, amazing, totally amazing. He's found the allotments.

Rosie Who? A man? What kind of man? Is it an old greybeard of a pervert who fancies my name?

Sally No, I think he's too young to have a beard.

Rosie Well, he'll grow one eventually, so who?

Sally Haven't you guessed?

Rosie I'm going to scream like a girl if you don't tell me.

Sally It's Orlando. The one who wrestled and floored you.

Rosie Orlando! Here? Oh my God. Where? What am I going to do looking like this? My hair! What is he

32

doing here? Did you speak to him? What did he tell you? Did he ask where I was? What did you tell him? When will you see him? Tell me now, quickly, in a word.

Sally I'd have to be a giant with a giant's mouth to answer all that.

Rosie Is he still the same?

Sally Well, I saw him under a tree and he looked the same.

Rosie Lucky tree: it drapes its branches over him.

Sally Will you listen?

Rosie Yes, yes, tell me, tell me quickly, now.

Sally He was stretched out on the ground.

Rosie Lucky ground to feel his weight.

Sally Rosie! Will you let me finish? He was fishing.

Rosie He'll hook my heart.

Sally You're like a scratched CD. I can't say a thing.

Rosie I'm so excited.

Sally Act like a boy and go all silent and cool, please. There he is!

Orlando and Jay come on.

Jay I have to ask you to stop defacing the trees with your paint.

Orlando It washes off.

Jay Meanwhile I have to see it.

Orlando You don't have to look.

Jay So her name is Flower.

Orlando Rosie!

Jay Violet's a better name.

Orlando No one thought of consulting you when they named her.

Jay How tall is she?

Orlando She comes up to my heart.

Jay If she came up to your throat she could keep you quiet.

Orlando Actually, I couldn't speak to her.

33

Jay I don't think much of love. No one deserves love any more than they deserve to be flooded out of their homes. That's what happens, isn't it? Love floods in and sense climbs the roof.

Orlando If she has sense, she won't love me. I have all these faults. I don't know anything.

Jay Your worst fault is being in love. Love is boring.

Orlando Only to those who've never felt it.

Jay Plants are more interesting. They grow, they rot. Like love, but they make less of a fuss about it. I'm off to see mine, Bye-bye, sweet lover.

Jay leaves. Rosie, to Sally.

Rosie I want to talk to him. I'm going to pretend I'm a rude crazy boy and see what happens. Do you think he'll recognise me?

Sally He only saw you once.

Rosie (*to herself*) Right: I'm a boy, I'm cool, I'm a boy.

Rosie pulls her cap down. She goes to Orlando. Scuffs around.

Rosie Hey – got the time?

Orlando I don't have a watch but I think I can tell by the sun.

Rosie If you don't have a watch you don't know what love is.

Orlando Why?

Rosie How can you count the minutes you're waiting for this one you love if you don't have a watch? Time won't seem slow enough.

Orlando Time is always the same

Rosie No. It moves at different speeds – would you like to know how?

Orlando Sure.

Rosie There are two light bulbs and they're going on at the same time. But if you move towards one of the light bulbs it goes on before the other. In your measurement. That's special relativity. Apply that to love. In a crowded room the one you love lights up faster. Time has speeded up. But if they're moving away from you then time moves very, very slowly. And if they disappear, time stops altogether. And sometimes it moves normally like when you're – euh – normal. I read all that somewhere.

Orlando Where do you live?

Rosie Here, on this allotment.

Orlando Aren't you in school?

Rosie Not any more. I live here with my sister, and we grow our own vegetables and pass the time thinking.

Orlando Thinking?

Rosie My lot belonged to an uncle of mine, he was very wise and he taught me to think clearly.

Orlando About what?

Rosie Well, for example about how awful girls are these days, and he told me never to fall in love because it would be a disaster. And he taught me how to cure anyone who was even thinking of falling in love. It's a disease, but it's not terminal.

Orlando No one could cure me.

Rosie Do you want to bet? I'll cure you in two weeks.

Orlando No, because the girl I'm in love with is Rosie.

Rosie You don't look like someone in love.

Orlando How am I supposed to look?

Rosie You should look sort of shy and ruffled, walk weirdly, and your voice should squeak. You look too sure of yourself.

Orlando I have to look that way to survive. What's your name?

Rosie Garry.

Orlando Believe me, Garry. I'm in love.

Rosie You might as well try to make that Rosie of yours believe it.

35

Orlando She would believe me. But I don't think I'll ever see her again.

Rosie Then I might as well cure you. I've done it before.

Orlando I don't want to be cured. I like thinking about her, even if it's painful. I enjoy the pain. It makes me hold on to her.

Rosie Sounds like you're at a critical stage, but I like a challenge.

Orlando Well, it'll pass the time.

Rosie It'll pass what time? Atomic time? Universal time? Time . . . Poor time? Quality time? Dynamical time? Terrestrial time? Greenwich Mean Time? How do you measure time? And why let it pass? That's sad. Let's get hold of it. Now the way I cured this other boy was by pretending I was the girl he loved.

Orlando You! Pretend to be Rosie? What a joke.

Rosie You have to use your imagination a little. You're probably imagining her all the time anyway, so you can imagine her more like me. I'm not bad looking, am I?

Orlando I don't know. I don't really care. You talk a lot.

Rosie And you think that Rosie of yours would be silent?

Orlando I don't know. I don't think so. We didn't have time to speak.

Rosie Some people say time is reversible. Pretend I'm her and you can go back to the time you met her and say what you want.

Orlando There were so many things . . .

Rosie Have you got yourself a hut? Show me where it is.

Orlando Garry – I don't think this is going to work.

Rosie Call me Rosie.

They go. Jay comes in and sings a solo of about two minutes on the theme of time.

SCENE SIXTEEN

Rosie and Sally come on.

Rosie I'm going to sit on these plants and cry.

Sally Boys don't cry.

Rosie I have a right to cry. He's a liar. You can always tell by a boy's hair.

Sally Even by his voice.

Rosie What's wrong with his voice? It's a beautiful voice. And actually his hair isn't bad either. So why isn't he here this morning when he said he'd come?

Sally Maybe he just lied.

Rosie So you do think he's a liar?

Sally He may not lie about most things, but when it comes to love maybe he doesn't know the difference between nice words and really loving someone. What is the difference anyway?

Rosie He was definite about being in love.

Sally In love some of the time, out of love another time.

Rosie Orlando. Orlando. Orlando. There's no one like Orlando.

Sally No one like him to say he's in love, no one like him to forget he's in love, no one like him to make promises, no one like him to rip them up like so much useless paper – he sprays your name on the trees but the paint washes off in the first rain.

Rosie That's ecological.

Sally And logical: he leaves no mark. Oh look, here's Colin, he's teaching me about planting.

Colin enters.

Colin You remember when you first came here you saw that boy who kept mooning over the girl he loved?

Rosie Yes, I remember, she was called Phoebe.

Colin They're both coming here – or rather she's coming here and he's following her. You'll see how horrible she is to him.

Rosie Let's hide and watch. I need a distraction.

Enter Sylvius and Phoebe. Phoebe is very young, but a little madam.

Sylvius You don't have to love me, just say you don't hate me.

Phoebe Why don't you just leave me alone?

Sylvius I can't. Even when you kill me with your looks.

Phoebe Right. Now: it's all my fault, is it? I have eyes, I can't help that. Maybe they're beautiful eyes. I can't help that either. They look at you. Well, if I'm killing you with my looks, why don't you die? Go on – die. You see, you're not dead, so don't say I'm killing you.

Sylvius One day maybe you'll know what it is to have a heart.

Phoebe When that happens, Sylvius, you can talk to me, until then leave me alone. Go!

Rosie comes out.

Rosie How dare you speak to him like that? You haven't even finished growing! And you're not even that attractive if you ask me. (*To Sylvius.*) Why do you follow her? The only attraction she has right now is the fact you find her attractive. As for you, girl, you should go down on your knees and thank God someone finds you pretty, because there won't be many, let me tell you. I'd catch this one while you can. I'm off.

Phoebe No, stop. Tell me more. About how awful I am. I don't mind. I sort of like it, coming from you.

Rosie He sees you as something you're not, and I believe you see me as something I'm not. Why are you staring at me like that?

Phoebe I wouldn't hurt you for the world. What's your name?

Rosie Garry.

Phoebe That's sort of a very cool name. Garry.

Rosie And Sylvius sounds too gentle? Take my advice: see what's in front of you and don't look at me. I don't like you anyway. You're nothing more than a spoiled child. (*To Sylvius.*) Come to us anytime, we live in the hut next to the big fig tree.

Rosie and Sally go.

Phoebe Now I understand what you're talking about when you say you loved me at first sight.

Sylvius Oh, Phoebe, be nice to me.

Phoebe I will, now.

Sylvius Really? If you could love me, we'd both be happy.

Phoebe That's asking too much. But at least I understand you. That boy! All he did was insult me. It's the novelty that shocked me. And he spoke well. Well, not that well, because what he said was so rude. But it was rude in an interesting way. Some girls might like that kind of behaviour or think he's handsome, not me. Actually, I hate him and I'm going to write to him and tell him how much I hate him. Will you take the letter?

Sylvius Yes, of course I will. You'll tell him you hate him?

Phoebe Yeah. I'll be really rude to him, that'll show him.

They go.

SCENE SEVENTEEN

Jay, Rosie and Sally.

Jay Let's talk, you seem pretty intelligent.

Rosie I'm told you're always depressed about everything.

Jay It's better to be depressed than to laugh stupidly when there's nothing to laugh about. Look at this world.

Rosie What's the point of being depressed? It's an excuse for not doing anything.

Jay There's not much we can do. Better be depressed than stupid.

Rosie Better be a stone then.

Jay Look, I'm not depressed because I'm not rich, or because my music isn't in the charts, or because I'm not strong enough to fight bullies, or because I'm in love, which combines all of these. I'm just depressed. I moved around a lot and I didn't like what I saw.

Rosie You should have stayed at home.

Jay I saw a lot.

Rosie You may have seen a lot but it doesn't mean you learned a lot. And now you don't have anything to show for it.

Jay I have my depression.

Jay leaves. Orlando comes on.

Rosie (*pouting*) Oh, you. What's brought you here?

Orlando I told you I'd come at this time. I'm only an hour late.

Rosie An hour late by the clock, an eternity late by Rosie's time, and if you were in love you wouldn't be a second late by any measurement of time.

Orlando I'm sorry.

Rosie I'd rather go out with a tortoise.

Orlando Why?

Rosie Better a plodder than a runner.

Orlando I am a runner. What's wrong with that?

Rosie You'll run after me, you'll run circles around me, you'll run away from me, you'll run after someone else. I want a tortoise.

Orlando I ran here as fast as I could. Rosie would understand.

Rosie Pretend I'm Rosie and we'll see about that.

Orlando You're nothing like her. She was so gentle and patient.

Rosie Patient! Rosie? Really? Let's pretend then: how would you convince Rosie you loved her? What would you do first?

Rosie/Garry goes very girlish, looks at her nails, etc., ignores him. They mime a silent encounter.

Orlando No, it wouldn't be like that. Not with her. I'd just look at her, take her in, and then, well, I'd kiss her.

Rosie Girls like to talk. Mostly about themselves. Say something interesting, like some observation about her, and then when you run out of things to say you can kiss her.

Orlando I'll never run out of things to say to Rosie.

Rosie Don't be so sure. Boys find girls interesting when they first meet them, and pretty soon they find them very boring.

Orlando I'll never be bored with Rosie.

Rosie I'll be asking you every five minutes whether you love me and why aren't you paying attention to me and I'll burst into tears and complain you don't understand me. And if you want to watch the telly, I'll be jealous. I'll get cross when you want to go out with your mates, I'll expect you to stay with me every minute until of course I'm bored with you and I want to see my own friends.

Orlando You might be like that if you were a girl, but not Rosie.

Rosie She'll be exactly like me, I promise you.

Orlando She's different, she's very intelligent.

Rosie Then she'll be better at nagging you. You'll always be in the wrong whatever you say, she'll turn everything around.

Orlando I like a girl who can speak for herself.

Rosie Until she sleeps with your best friend.

Orlando How can she excuse that?

Rosie She'll say it was to share your tastes. She'll always have an answer.

Orlando But she'll know it's wrong. I can feel what's right and wrong in me and I know she will too.

Rosie Maybe right and wrong are as relative as time.

Orlando No, because time is felt in the head but right and wrong are felt deep down in the gut. Just as you know when someone's right for you.

They stare at each other. A moment.

Rosie You were saying you'd kiss her.

Orlando Yes.

Rosie Well?

Orlando Well.

Rosie Why don't you kiss me?

Orlando No way.

Rosie I'm Rosie, remember. You can kiss me.

Orlando considers.

Orlando No. I can't.

Rosie You're never going to get anywhere if you don't pretend.

Orlando The thing is, I keep thinking she's watching or she's here or something. Like I'm hallucinating. It must be all these vegetables I'm eating.

Rosie Go with the veggies.

Orlando I promised Valerie I'd meet with her now, I'll come back in two hours.

Rosie Two hours? I can't be without you for two whole hours.

Orlando I promise I'll be on time.

Rosie You can't be on time. Don't you remember the light bulbs? You'll move away from me so you'll

42

always be late. I knew you didn't love me. I'll just have to love someone else.

Orlando What happens if there's a third light bulb and you're always close to it because you carry it with you?

Rosie That's completely unscientific.

Orlando Maybe it's a new law.

Rosie Alright, but if you're a minute later than two hours – and I mean a minute – I'll know you never mean a thing you say, you don't deserve Rosie and you never loved her anyway.

Orlando I promise – on my life.

Rosie No – don't promise on your life, that's too dangerous, just promise and don't break your promise, promise you won't break your promise. Two hours!

Orlando goes.

Sally What a great way to talk about girls, he'll hate the lot of us before you're finished. What is this, anyway, you wear blokey clothes and you start acting like the worst of the lot?

Rosie Oh, Sally, if only you knew. I thought love would be something easy and soft, in my heart, but I feel it in my mind, and I feel it in my body, and I feel it everywhere, burning like insanity, I can only think of Orlando, see Orlando in front of me, feel Orlando in the air. How do you get through two hours when time is standing still?

They go.

SCENE EIGHTEEN

Sally, Rosie, Sylvius.

Sylvius (*to Rosie*) I've been looking everywhere for you. I have a letter. You won't like it.

Rosie Then why give it to me?

Sylvius Phoebe insisted. I watched her writing it. She looked really angry. I'm afraid she says in it that she hates you. I'm sorry, I don't hate you. But I guess I'm glad she hates you.

Rosie (*opens the letter*) Nobody writes letters these days.

Sylvius We don't have phones here.

Rosie Yeah, it's like going back to the Ice Age, except it's so hot.

Sally They've never had so little rain in autumn.

Sylvius We can't control the weather.

Rosie Any more than we can control love. (*She reads quickly.*) Although we should try on both counts. Why do you love that girl? I don't think this is her handwriting anyway – you wrote this letter.

Sylvius She did. She told me it was to tell you she hated you.

Rosie And you believed her, and like a nice boy gave it to me. Why don't you read it?

Sylvius She said they were 'haikus of hate'.

Rosie hands the letter to Sylvius.

Sylvius (*reads*)
I did not know what love was
Until you came and
Broke open my heart

Who are you, mysterious boy
Who has turned me into
A sighing girl?

He brought you this letter
Not knowing its secret
I'm yours if you want

You said rude things to me
The face I saw was kind
Love me or I'll die

44

Rosie These haikus may be hateful but they're not haikus of hate.

Sally You poor thing.

Rosie Why do you pity him, Sal? It's his fault for not seeing what kind of a girl she is. (*To Sylvius.*) Tell her that she should try to see what's in front of her and love you, although if you saw what was in front of you, you wouldn't love her, but there we are. Now go, because I see someone else coming. I hope it's not another letter.

Sylvius goes, Oliver comes on.

Oliver Can you help me? I'm looking for a small hut, almost hidden by apple and plum trees, not far from a stream.

Sally Follow this hedge of honeysuckle until you get to the wild roses, turn left and you'll see the hut. But no one's there now – can we help you?

Oliver I think you are the people I am looking for. A boy who looks and speaks a little like a girl.

Rosie (*rough*) Who said that?

Oliver And his sister, a little smaller, more tanned and very beautiful.

Sally That's definitely me.

Oliver I have a message from Orlando.

Rosie Where is he?

Oliver And a handkerchief.

Rosie Handkerchiefs are for tears.

Oliver I'll explain. I hope you won't hate me when you hear my story.

Sally We left hate at the gate of the allotment.

Oliver Orlando had promised to be here at a certain time.

Rosie He's four minutes and forty-seven seconds late.

Oliver He was on his way here when he noticed a well-dressed man sleeping in a hedge at the entrance to the

45

allotment. The man was lying on his face, and Orlando
went to see if he was alright. Just then two boys
with knives appeared, the man sat up and Orlando
recognised –

Sally Who?

Oliver – his brother. A brother who had always been
cruel to him. He was about to leave – let the man be
robbed and beaten or killed as he deserved – but
Orlando couldn't help feeling pity . . .

Sally You're his brother.

Rosie You're the brother who tried to have him killed.

Oliver I was that brother, I am not that brother, I am a
different brother. I left the other brother at the gate of
the allotment.

Rosie But the men, the knives –

Oliver Orlando ordered them away but they attacked
him. He was wounded. This handkerchief –

Oliver shows a bloody handkerchief. Rosie faints.

Sally Garry! Really!

Oliver A boy shouldn't faint at the sight of blood.

Rosie recovers.

Sally Let's take you to our hut. Help me.

Rosie Orlando?

Oliver Orlando is fine. They got his arm, but he's very
strong. He's being bandaged by Valerie, but he told me
he was playing a game pretending this Garry was a girl
he loved, so he told me to send you this handkerchief
to show you he wasn't breaking his promise.

Rosie Yeah, it's a fun game, we pretend a lot and you'll
tell him I pretended to faint and I was really good at it.

Oliver It looked real to me.

Rosie It's all pretence. I feel sick again. Isn't this brilliant
acting? I'm completely identified with my part.

She retches.

How many people can do that?

Sally Let's get you home.

Rosie Make sure you tell Orlando how amazing I am at
pretending.

The three leave.

SCENE NINETEEN

Jay with friends and Adam.

Jay You get attached to something and it's immediately
threatened with disappearance. We've found refuge in
these allotments and they're about to be bulldozed to
make way – not even for a stadium, but for a concrete
pathway. They've existed hidden for a hundred years,
a piece of wilderness in a big city. Let's sing a song for
disappearances, all change is not to the good. I never
thought much of nature, of the planet. Now that it's
disappearing, I'm falling in love with it.

Adam That's how I feel about life.

Jay I better write a song about all this.

Jay leaves.

SCENE TWENTY

Orlando and Oliver come on with Adam.

Orlando You looked at her, fell in love, you told her you
loved her and she told you she loved you, and now you
both want to live together in a hut here? That's fast.

Oliver How do you measure the speed of love? Ask
Valerie if we can take over one of the huts. I'll sell the
business and you can have all the money.

Orlando But you know this place is under threat.

Oliver We'll find a way. Sally loves it here. And we'll look after Adam if he wants to stay with us.

Orlando (*to Adam*) You should be in hospital.

Adam I don't want to.

Oliver He's looking better than he used to.

Adam I feel better. Not because I think I'm going to live any longer, but because the time I have left, whatever it is, stretches out so much here it doesn't feel like it's passing at all, so it means I live longer, see? Even for ever if I keep stretching time. I'm not limited.

Rosie comes on.

Rosie (*to Oliver*) Ho, brother.

Oliver Brother.

Oliver and Adam leave.

Rosie (*to Orlando*) I hear you've been heroic. They say a knife was plunged into your heart.

Oliver Just the arm. My heart bleeds for other reasons.

Rosie I hope your brother told you what a great actor I was when I fainted at the sight of blood. I'm doing Hamlet next.

Orlando He told me it was real.

Rosie Is anything real in this allotment? Look what's just happened: he came, he saw, he conquered. She was here, she saw, she conquered back. And now they're setting up hut together.

Orlando I'm happy for my brother, but sometimes it's hard – Rosie's probably forgotten me by now.

Rosie Am I not good enough?

Orlando I can't keep pretending, Garry – it's weird. Also, I'm beginning to feel confused. I mean, I really like you.

Rosie So? It's a good game.

Orlando No, I really like you as Garry. So, maybe I'm gay, which is fine, but what about Rosie? And also,

I don't know what you feel about that . . . I know you
like pretending to be a girl – this is a bit confusing, you
know.

Rosie What would you do if Rosie appeared before you
now?

Orlando I'd tell her I love her.

Rosie Are you sure?

Orlando Well, I'd want to get to know her.

Rosie What do you want her to be like?

Orlando Well, sort of like you, you know, fun and full of
life. I – really like being with you – maybe –

They stare at each other for a moment.

Look, I need some time to work this out.

Rosie I think it's time to help you find Rosie.

Orlando The thing is, I'm not so sure any more. How
would you do it anyway?

Rosie That uncle of mine taught me how to find people.
You do want her? There may be a price: you can't get
something without losing something.

Orlando As long as I don't lose you. I've never had a real
mate before –

Sylvius and Phoebe come on.

Rosie Not you again.

Phoebe How could you show the letter to him? That was
unfair.

Rosie Are you fair to him?

Phoebe How can I love him if I love you?

Rosie What do you know about me? What do you know
about love?

Phoebe (*in haiku mode*)
A leaf flutters in a raging storm.
I am the leaf. Garry's the storm.

Sylvius I see Phoebe everywhere in the allotment – in the
flowers, the trees, in the water and the clouds. When

she's cross, I feel the winter. When she smiles, it's like a summer afternoon I hope will never end.

Orlando She's like a song I heard once and can't forget. One day, I'll learn all the words to her.

Rosie And what do I feel? I can't begin to feel until I am what I am. Enough. We sound like doves taking a cooing exam. We try to catch love with words but it slips out of our definitions. Even the experience slips through time.

So now, listen carefully: Phoebe, promise that if you ever decide you don't want Garry, you'll have Sylvius.

Orlando, promise that if you find Rosie you won't treat her like some alien from another planet but stay the way you are now.

Sylvius, promise you won't blame me if you get Phoebe.

Let's all meet this evening under the fig tree.

They leave.

SCENE TWENTY-ONE

Jay and Valerie and others.

Jay We have to protect what we have.

Valerie How?

Jay Make it known, use the tools we had when we were in business.

Valerie We don't have computers here or the internet.

Jay We can get these – campaign, fight.

Valerie I fought all my life, Jay. I only lived for the future and I was always angry. I never want to feel anger again. I want to preserve my energy and enjoy the present. In animals it's called optimal foraging: you only displace yourself when it's energetically worthwhile.

Jay This is no longer a refuge or an escape, it's our life.
Even if we don't stay, this is a magical island in a cruel
city, why should it be destroyed? By delusions of
grandeur? Rigid architecture flattening the curves of the
seasons? A hundred years of growing bulldozed for
four weeks of competition? Tell me, is that
energetically worthwhile?

Valerie Maybe the world can't preserve its own energy,
but the allotments show us a future. They flourish
despite the city, like little streams that bypass obstacles
and then slowly wear them down. And sometimes
streams go underground, spring up elsewhere. The
allotments may re-emerge.

Jay In a hundred years. If there's no drought. And we
won't be there. Does it matter? Then why these tears?
There's a song in that somewhere. By the way, what
are we doing here at sunset?

Valerie Orlando asked me to come here to help Sally and
Oliver organise one of the abandoned huts. But he says
Garry has promised all kinds of things. I've hardly seen
this Garry, he keeps away from me – what's he like?

Jay A clever boy who appeared out of nowhere and is
probably not what he seems. He's like the rest of us –
we leave our old selves at the gate, become something
else, maybe more real, maybe not. What he was I don't
know, I'm not even sure he was a he, I don't ask
questions any more than I answer questions. If nobody
labels you, you can be what you want. Maybe even
what you truly are.

Orlando enters.

Valerie Orlando, you're sure this Garry can do what he
promised?

Orlando I don't know. I'm afraid to believe too much.

Rosie enters, very much as Garry.

Rosie Valerie, I know we're not supposed to ask questions, but do you have family?

Valerie I have a niece, I had to leave her with my brother. I often dream of her.

Garry/Rosie If she suddenly appeared magically before you and you discovered your niece and Orlando were in love, you wouldn't object?

Valerie She's still very young.

Garry/Rosie What's young?

Valerie OK.

Garry/Rosie And you, Phoebe, if you decide you don't want me, you'll go with Sylvius.

Phoebe Sure.

Garry/Rosie And Sylvius, you'll have Phoebe?

Sylvius Yes, at any price.

Garry/Rosie Orlando, you still want Rosie? Even if she's not the one you dreamt of.

Orlando Yes, I want Rosie.

Garry/Rosie I have promised to make things right. Wait here, disturb nothing.

Valerie What a strange boy.

Jay Look how the sun's rays sweep like searchlights over the golden leaves. While we're waiting, I'll sing a song.

Orlando Sing about love.

Jay No. I want to sing about what vanishes. Maybe that's love.

Jay sings a short verse. Colin and Oliver come on and listen or sing with the music.

SCENE TWENTY-TWO

Rosie enters as a girl, with Sally.

Rosie (*to Valerie*) Hi, Auntie.

Valerie Is it Rosie? You've grown so much! I was dreaming of a little girl. I find a new Rosie, but still my sweet Rosie.

Rosie (*to Valerie*) Yours and not yours. (*To Orlando.*) Orlando, I promised . . . I'm yours – if you want me.

Orlando You were here all the time and I didn't see you. I was dreaming, I'm not dreaming now but it's still a dream.

Rosie You lose Garry.

Orlando Do I?

Rosie (*to Phoebe*) Anyway, I'm not for you.

Phoebe You're not the one I dreamt of, well . . . there's nothing wrong with loving a girl, is there? Except girls can be so mean. If they're like me, that is. Sylvius . . .

She turns to Sylvius. Lebeau suddenly enters.

Sally Lebeau! You've found us. Does that mean my father's on his way? (*To Valerie.*) Will you help us? We ran away . . .

Lebeau Your father found out where you were and came here to get you back. But when he arrived in the allotments, the first man he spoke to invited him to share a meal and began talking to him about all sorts of things and about happiness. Frederick's never been happy before, he was always in a hurry, but he spent days with this man, not far from here, and now he's completely changed. He's decided he wants to live here and study things – happiness, gardening. (*To Valerie.*) He's giving all the business back to you and to his daughter. He's coming here to tell you this himself.

Valerie So: our exile is over. But will we be able to remember what we became here?

Jay Who did you say Frederick spoke to? Take me to him. I'll and match my depression against his happiness. And then the world will be balanced.

Valerie You girls have to finish your education.

Orlando I want to as well.

Sally I don't want to leave.

Oliver We'll come back, I promise.

Colin (*to Sally*) I'll save my best honey for you.

Rosie (*to the audience*) Well, it's not exactly a happy end, going back to school. Or is it? You'll answer according to who you are. As for me, I don't know whether to speak as a boy or a girl or whether there is much difference. I leave that for you to decide. And now it's time for you and for us to leave this beautiful allotment. We hope you liked it as much as we do. I can already hear the bulldozers. But let's hope they'll never succeed in wiping out the memory of the magical time we spent here.

Frederick comes on. Everyone on stage.

End.

Production Notes

Whilst the allusions to *As You Like It* are obvious, *Arden City* stands alone as a dramatic work. The choice whether or not to reference the play back to its Shakespearean roots rests with the director.

The play starts at an immense pace (the first four pages contain a murder plot and a potentially fatal fight). It asks questions about the perceived nature of progress, family and identity. It confronts the relativity and the nature of time and feelings.

THE SOUNDSCAPE OF THE PLAY

The action of the play takes place in the City and on the allotments. Music will determine the accent of the play and to an extent the meaning of the piece. It could help you decide what kind of a play you think it is.

Please consider the following:

ONE In the text, the presence of music (Jay's songs) is referred to for the first time as we arrive at the allotments. This is part of the make-up of the allotments and could be expanded upon.

As an exercise, it would be vital to question and explore the absence/presence of sounds and music in the city. How would this affect the meaning of the play?

TWO Jay's songs: these could be sung by Jay alone or accompanied by other characters.

How do they express or affect the character of the allotments?

- *Lyrics* could be inspired by thematically appropriate sections from the preceding scenes, such as:

  Orlando Well, it'll pass the time.
  Rosie It'll pass what time? Atomic time? Universal time? Time . . . Poor time? Quality time? Dynamical time? Terrestrial time? Greenwich Mean Time? How do you measure time? And why let it pass? That's sad.

- *Music* could be written by the acting company during rehearsals so that the flavour of the score emerges organically through the overall creative process.

- *What is the voice of the allotments?* It is a meeting place of many different cultures. Many different people from different places settling here for different reasons. A melting pot of different nationalities and different languages.

EXERCISES

OBJECTIVE *Getting to know your character's story from your partner's point of view.* Read through with each performer, reading the part of his/her partner where possible (e.g., Orlando reads Rosie; Rosie reads Orlando).

OBJECTIVE *Familiarising oneself with the story structure and creating awareness of the physical shape of scenes and movement within the story.* Five or six chairs are to be placed in one part of the room, the rest are set in a semi-circle at the other end. All performers sit in a semi-circle watching, as those who are present in the scenes sit on the chairs on stage and read the scenes.

THE INITIAL EVENT

Can we identify one event which sets the whole story into motion and affects every single person in the play? One event, which occurs before the play starts and makes this story inevitable?

If identified precisely, this will unlock from the beginning of the play the underlying connection between every single scene, and help you understand the physical and psychological momentum of the story.

Here is a proposed line of questioning which could help:

- Why does the play start today? What is different in every character's life today as compared to the day before?

- Why is it today that Oliver wants to get rid of Orlando?

- Why is it today that Frederick kicks Rosie out?

- Why have all the characters been pushed to their limits today?

- Is it Orlando's challenge to Che, a seemingly insignificant event, that sets the cogs of the plot into motion?

All the stakes are higher today.

STORY AND CHARACTER RELATIONSHIPS

Exercise: the Picture Gallery

OBJECTIVE *A visual and physical exercise to uncover the intricacies of the story through the interrelationships of all the characters and discover how these reveal and reflect the world they live in. This exercise is an in-depth exploration of the given circumstances, interpersonal conflicts as well as wants and desires of every single character in an interactive and playful format.*

Keep the group sitting in a semi-circle in the audience position, facing a few chairs or benches on stage to be used as required. Props could be employed. Every single family member, their friends and dependents mentioned in the play are to be represented. As the story develops, let the performers present what happens to characters (e.g., they die). This seemingly simple game will open up and lead to complex questioning of the story. Keep it simple at all times. Use 'freeze-frames'.

Take it all the way through the play, investigating the changes as the story progresses. Here's an example for the beginning of the game:

FIRST FAMILY TREE

SECOND FAMILY TREE

Rosie's (don't forget the grandmother and her famous recipe, the mother who died, etc.)

Outcome of the exercise

The first half of the play takes place in a broken world: a modern city world.

- Relationship between Frederick and the late father: the polar extremes of the story.

- Pivotal changes in the story after Orlando's father dies (Valerie loses to her brother, goes into hiding, etc.).

- *Oliver's character*: Oliver has become unnatural even in Frederick's eyes as he wants to have his brother *killed*.

- When looking at the relationships in the city, it is important to note the lack of parents.

- The powers and hierarchies in the city are either not present or not working as they should be.

- The exercise reveals that although most of the characters are intertwined through business or family connections, these connections have disintegrated through death or exile. The dynasties breed arbitrary aggression. It is an URBAN JUNGLE, where every man is out for himself.

- The exercise reveals in a palpable form key differences in relationships of the city inhabitants and of those who live in the allotments. Notice the *arbitrary* nature of many events in the city, especially those perpetrated by Frederick.

THE FIGHT

The fight is an event within the community. Its results are brutal and predictable: challenges are made, the contenders fight, Che wins and the losers are sent to hospital.

- The outcome of Orlando and Che's fight is unexpected. This is not one of the usual fights that are extremely violent but entertain the crowd: this one could be fatal. The fight and the build-up to it should be rhythmically structured to create the intensity required by the story. The stakes are high: Orlando's life and Che's reputation are at stake. This should be reflected in the staging.

- Kick-boxing doesn't have to be the fighting style in the play. Other martial arts can be used to suit the capabilities of the actors and the choice of the director. The fight could be stylised or heightened in a number of ways.

The unpredictable outcome of this fight changes the future of everyone in the city:

- Orlando fails to get his prize money despite his victory.

- Frederick's behaviour gets visibly arbitrary and violent: he confiscates the prize money and throws Rosie out.

THE ALLOTMENTS

Set up a new Picture Gallery Exercise

- In the allotments, there is no business; in fact there is no room for commerce. In the allotments everything that happens does so because of responsibilities and necessity. The fight in the allotments is a fight to sustain the community rather than individual self-advancement. The allotment people don't work for money or business, they work for survival.

- The allotments are a haven. This is a magical world with a more sensible way of life. An alternative to the urban jungle.

- The allotments offer you time and space to find out who you really are – your true identity.

- Life on the allotments is not easy. It is not a pastoral idyll, but a challenge.

- The allotments are not a geographical notion: they are an idea, a feeling and a state of being passed on from one resident to the next.

- Everything that happens in *Arden City* is relative; the inhabitants adapt and change.

- All the characters in the allotments have crossed over, they have walked through the gate – the place where

Oliver is attacked, the border where these two worlds collide. It's like stepping through the looking glass.

- Examine the difference between the characters who have always belonged to the allotments (Phoebe, Sylvius, Colin, Hassam) and those in self-imposed exile.

The journeys to the allotments – and of leaving them – are not over at the end of the play. All the characters, as well as the allotments themselves, are in a state of change and transition. The play ends at the beginning of a new life, whether it's going back to the city or waiting for the bulldozers at the allotments.

STAGING

The scene changes should be instantaneous. The staging can be minimalist. An empty stage. Use lighting, props and costumes to change the place of action and atmosphere. The pace and momentum of the play is fast.

The change between the city and the allotments is an important junction for the transition of meaning – the meeting of two worlds.

Rosie should try to look as masculine as possible when she is playing Garry. She could use costume to signify her gender roles. When she goes back to being Rosie, a little bit of Garry should remain.

NOTE FROM TIMBERLAKE

Arden City also plays with gender differences and similarities. Even though Rosie is the only character who crosses gender in the play, this affects everyone and it's a major theme.

The actors should explore what is 'masculine' and what is 'feminine' behaviour. A good way of doing this is to have all the boys walk around the room and interact with each other as girls, while the girls watch; and then have the girls be boys, while the boys watch. In both cases, those watching can comment on what is convincing 'masculine' or 'feminine' behaviour. What is the difference? How great is it? How do girls walk and sit? How do boys walk and sit? What's the difference in the way they interact as friends and as enemies?

Another area to explore is what happens when two people fancy each other, again playing with gender. Have a girl be the boy and a boy be the girl, then a boy pretending to be a girl (and a real girl) and a girl pretending to be a boy, etc. It's great fun finding the many permutations. This should help the actors define their characters along the gender spectrum.

From a workshop led by Irina Brown
with notes by Irina Brown and Daniel Rollings

BURYING YOUR BROTHER
IN THE PAVEMENT

Jack Thorne

Jack Thorne's plays for the stage include *When You Cure Me* at the Bush, in New York, and for BBC Radio 3; *Fanny and Faggot* in Edinburgh, at the Finborough, the English Theatre of Bruges and Trafalgar Studios; and *Stacy* at the Tron, Arcola and Trafalgar Studios. His radio plays include *Left at the Angel* on BBC Radio 4. His TV writing includes episodes of *Skins*, *Shameless* and the thirty-minute drama *The Spastic King*. His short film *A Supermarket Love Song* was shown at Sundance 2006. Jack Thorne is currently Pearson Writer-in-Residence at the Bush.

Author's Note

At my grandad's funeral recently I found myself laughing. A hymn had been chosen that no one knew how to sing. It was one of those hymns with two possible tunes – my step-grandma (my grandad's third wife – go go, Grandad) chose it because of one of these tunes, the organist chose to play the other. It was genuinely really funny; if you've never heard a small crematorium desperately trying to mumble their way through a hymn while remaining respectful, you should: 'We plo-t-fie and scaaaaaaaaater the o-ee o-the grooooound . . .' Lots of vowels, occasional consonants and that brief moment every verse when everyone knew what note they should be singing and got excited. I like comedy, particularly unusual comedy. This was definitely unusual comedy. I laughed.

But I was standing by my dad, who'd lost his dad, I was twenty-eight years old, and my grandad was dead in a box less than six feet in front of me. I should have known better. I wish I had it on tape now because I'd probably play it to most of my friends, but . . . it was wrong.

Anyway, I was thinking about it (a lot) afterwards (mainly because I felt pretty bad about it, partly because I hadn't talked to my dad about it – still haven't – and I figure he might have noticed, and slightly because I had a long train journey home), and sort of worked out that I don't think I've ever had an honest response to someone close to me dying. I've had a few people die that I really really love – aunties, teachers, friends, best friends – and some deaths that have been truly tragic, and I haven't laughed in any other funeral. In fact, I've forced out tears at a few. But it's always felt pretty unreal to me, death, and I've got to be honest – in 'grief' I've probably cared more about other people's reaction to how I'm reacting than my own. And I don't think I'm on my own in that. And I think that sort of distance, between what we want to feel, what we feel other people will want us to feel, and what we actually do feel is really interesting. In life generally, actually, but particularly in grief. So I've tried to get into that in this play. I don't think I've got very far, but that's what I've tried to do.

The other sort of inspiration (I hate the word 'inspiration', I prefer stimulation, but that's a word that seems to carry a whole load of other unnecessary images along with it – at least in my head) for this play is Aubrey Phillips. He was my best friend when I was a kid. He isn't any more – I haven't seen him for at least ten years. But when we were kids he was really important to me.

He was (and probably still is) amazing – once we were playing some sort of tag / bulldog / decapitate / garrotte / murder game thing in the playground at school. I think we were about nine. Anyway, he was standing facing the wall (part of the game) and I ran right into him (by accident) and he smashed his head against the bricks. He'd need six butterfly stitches for the cut – which is sort of something, when you're nine – but he still turned around, no crying, no nothing, blood running down his forehead, and he said: 'It's OK, Jack, it'll be fine.' Why did he do this? Because he knew I was ridiculously sensitive (I had to be taken to see *The Jungle Book* three times as a child because every time Baloo 'died', I cried so loudly I had to be removed from the cinema) and he worked out that his injury would probably upset me more than him.

It remains one of the most genuine acts of generosity I've ever seen close up. Because, like grief, I don't think I do generosity very well either (I'm increasingly realising writing this that I should perhaps consider becoming a monk or something). I fake it. Aubrey didn't – there was much more benefit in that moment to being upset (girls, sympathy, future guilt-tripping), but he was heroic and stoical and like a cowboy. Don't get me wrong, Aubrey wasn't a total angel – me and him would frequently steal off his mum the day her benefit came in (and go down McDonald's, where Aubrey had the enviable talent of being able to regurgitate at will – we'd eat our 99p burger-chips-and-a-drink meal, and then he'd regurgitate some of it onto a tray for the McWorkers to clean up. I later worked in McDonald's so regretted that behaviour slightly) and when he got a bit older he did beat me up once (I was friends with Jacob by then, it was complicated), but in terms of making a shy and sensitive kid feel wanted and at home at that time in my life, he did that job and more. He's sort of the model for Tight. And this play is dedicated to him. Though I suspect he'll never know. And possibly wouldn't care if he did.

Characters

in order of appearance

Tom
Mr Wilkins
Courtney
Mum
Boy
Aunty Helen
Friendly Phil
Uncle Gerry
Tight
Martin
Luke
Simon
Sandra
Leo
Libby
Ricky
JK
Drunk Bill
David McPhee
Miss Hands
Pushchair Mum
Babyfather
Estate Agent
Stanley Burrows
Client
PC Bob
PC Bill
Underwear Man

plus ensemble

Notes on Staging

The cast can be as large as a stage can contain, and has been performed by casts ranging from four to sixty. Aside from Tom, Tight, Luke and Courtney, the parts are not gender-specific. No parts are racially specific.

Musically, it would be brilliant to either have live music or someone sound-mixing live onstage with the actors. The more either the musicians or the sound guy can be brought into the action the better.

The most important thing is that this play is kept scruffy – nothing is beautiful, everything is quick and swiftly accomplished. This should look like a piece of theatre achieved on the bounce and stuffed full of life. This means two things. Firstly, if you happen to have a brilliant roller-blader in your cast, then use her; and add a triple lutz somersault to the 'Dairy Lea' song number. Secondly, don't let the technical overwhelm. I specify a lot of spots in the first few pages – but these could easily be torches held up to people's faces, and, in fact, might work better like that. Scene changes should be incorporated into the action. The whole stage and auditorium should be used.

Robbie Williams was a popular entertainer in post-war Britain. Jesus Christ was less popular, but equally entertaining in pre-war Galilee. Planning Law is both popular and entertaining.

ONE

*It's dark. Very dark indeed. Tom lights a torch. A
pathetic torch. But it's almost blinding in this darkness.*

*As our eyes adjust we take in his surroundings . . .
Tom is underneath a table – a small table, so he's had to
squeeze himself underneath. The table is in a large dusty
attic.*

*Tom is an ordinary-looking boy in his early teens. He
is wearing the hand-me-downs of a cooler older brother.
But he wears them slightly wrong. Too many buttons
done up on a polo shirt, that sort of thing . . .*

Tom I first had the idea that I was the son of God, when
I was nine. I'd just read the Bible.

Not the whole Bible, not cover to cover, but, you
know . . . extensive dipping . . . Anyway, the more
I read, the more it sort of made sense, that I was the
second coming. Jesus Christ. Two.

The sequel.

I mean, my mum a virgin? Well, looking at her, you
could certainly believe so. Check. Dad not my real
dad? We never did have much in common. Check. Me
leading a sad-and-tortured-life-where-everyone-hates-
me-and-I-have-to-die-for-the-good-of-humanity-who'll-
be-sorry-when-I'm-gone?

Check.

But then I tried to cure a leper – well, a kid with
really bad eczema . . . it didn't work. He just bled a
lot. I tried to – rip some of his skin off and . . .

Beat.

I first got the idea I might have Aids after a particularly aggressive sex ed class – you know, the sort of class where your teacher just repeatedly shouts –

Spotlight – a harassed-looking teacher in a tatty-looking blazer. He's spitty.

Mr Wilkins You must never have sex. Never. Ever. Ever.

Spotlight off.

Tom I mean, talk about premature, I hadn't even persuaded a girl to kiss me yet. But he always was premature, Mr Wilkins.

Spotlight. Mr Wilkins in flagrante (tastefully) with a blow-up doll.

Mr Wilkins I'm not normally like that. I'm a good lover, really I am . . . Oh, don't look like that.

The blow-up doll looks back, the same open-mouthed expression on its face as always.

Tom So, Aids – me? Unlikely! But then I had a tetanus shot and it took them ages to find a vein and I thought – well, maybe I had a mutated version of Aids, the sort where you don't get to do anything good to catch it. 'I caught mine through drugs.' 'I caught mine through sex.' 'I just, well, I just sort of got it.' 'Why?' 'Because I'm unlucky.'

There are loads of other examples – the time I thought I'd developed a cure for blindness in biology class because I seemed to be able to see things with my eyes closed – the time when I thought I may have inadvertently started a war between Korea and the Isle of Sheppey with some stuff I'd written on my blog – the time when I thought I'd accidentally castrated my dog –

A dog howls in the distance. Tom frowns.

OK, well, I sort of did castrate my dog. That's a long
story . . . my point is this . . .
     It's normal to be the centre of your own world, in
your head, star of your . . . And me . . . I don't just star
in my head, I kind of suffocate all other forms of life.
But this – finally – I've got the opportunity to actually
be some kind of star and I'm . . .

*Tom hears something. He freezes and turns off the
light. He indicates us to be silent, takes a deep breath
and holds it.*
     *Courtney opens up a hatch in the attic floor and
light immediately spills into the room. She looks round
aggressively with a torch of her own.*

Courtney Tom . . . Tom? If you're up here, you little
turd . . .

*The light passes across Tom's face: it is racked with
fear.*

Tom? Don't be a shit, OK?

*She twirls the torch through one more tour. It sees
nothing.*

No, Turd's not in the loft, Dad . . .

*She closes the hatch. And the light goes with it. We're
back in the dark.*
     *Tom breathes out, counts to three, steadies himself,
opens his eyes and then turns on the torch again.*

Tom They're – having a funeral downstairs.
     I'm supposed to be there. Down there. With them.
     I mean, it's not like a guy missing his own wedding –
I mean, it's not my funeral, obviously. *Tada*! I'm
alive! So, but . . . still . . . I'm expected to be there.
And not here – hiding under a table in my attic.

He chews a finger and looks contemplative.

Luke – my brother – always used to come up here when he was upset. I was . . . too afraid – always thought there was something living up here. Something swimming in the water tank, sliding through the pipes, nestling in the insulation. But now – well –

Tom looks around. He shines the torch around.

Funerals – fune–er–rals, from the Latin meaning 'the rule is'. The rule . . . is fun. Great news for my little cousin Kevin, who has jam around his mouth and mayonnaise in his hair and likes randomly launching into his world-famous impression of Robbie Williams. And less good news for my mum who just wants to cry – on me.

Spotlight – a mother, in tears. Tom looks at her carefully. She looks up at Tom. They hold for maybe fifteen seconds, just looking at each other. Then the spot flicks off and Tom is staring into blackness.

My brother died. Badly. It's that simple really . . .

He chews a finger and looks contemplative.

You know why they call them wakes? It used to be a time when people sat by the body waiting to see if it woke up. Before doctors knew what they were doing. Some bodies did wake up – in which case they were alive and mourning was kind of pointless. Others didn't – in which case . . . well . . . Either way, everyone got drunk.

   I know that I can't stay here. I didn't mean to – I was panicked up here when an auntie I barely knew licked my face and told me I was a good boy and then tried to give me a deep-fried mushroom thing from Iceland. And it . . .

Jesus didn't have to deal with this rubbish, did he?

Tom looks around. He shines the torch around.

I need to get out of here. I mean . . . here. I mean, all of
here. I mean, the house . . . I mean, the funeral . . .
I need to get out.

*He waits a second and then turns out his torch.
Silence.
Slowly light spreads across the stage to reveal a
typical middle-class living room. Knick-knacks, paddy-
whacks, comfortable sofas and too many standing
lights. The room is musty and filled with gloom.
A lad – preferably a boy soprano – steps out alone
into the centre of the room. He takes a moment to
compose himself. He has a small cough to himself. He
sits on a stall in the centre of the space. He opens his
mouth to sing. But thinks better of it.
He gets off the stall and walks over to the sideboard.
There is a glass of water on it. He drinks from it. He
sits back on the stall. He opens his mouth to sing. But
thinks better of it. He opens a drawer from the telephone
stand and pulls out a fork. He clinks the fork against
the glass. It makes a ringing noise.
He opens his mouth to sing. But thinks better of it.
He drinks some more from the glass. He pulls out
the fork and clinks it again. Again it rings, but this
time at a slightly higher pitch. A pitch that reverbs
around the audience. He smiles. That's the note he was
looking for.*

'WHEN YOUR BROTHER'S DEAD'
A Music-Hall Number

Boy (*sings*)
When your brother's dead
Your mouth should taste of lead

And your eyes should feel
Like marbles.

So when that's not the case
You have to fake your face
To make relatives believe you're
A good boy.

And while everyone cries
You quickly rub your eyes
To make them red like everyone
Else is.

And you shut out
The niggling in your snout
That you're a nasty bastard
With no feelings

Cossssssssssssssssssssssssssss . . .

He holds the note a very long time . . . He touches an item of furniture onstage – a light fitting. It grows into a man. A normal-looking man wearing a lampshade for a hat.

The man joins the boy singing. The song is sung more slowly now:

When your brother's dead . . .

And a candlestick holder is touched, and similarly grows into a man, with candlesticks for hands. Slowly we discover that all the furniture is similarly alive. (Think Beauty and the Beast. Or IKEA on a school night.)

Your mouth should taste of lead . . .

And another voice joins in. And a sofa unfolds itself to reveal a baritone within.

And your eyes should feel like marbles . . .

And slowly, the stage fills with people, all dressed as items of furniture: soprano telephones, and tenor televisions. The stage is suddenly a very exciting place.

So when that's not the case
You have to fake your face . . .

Tom appears at the side of the stage and begins to attempt surreptitiously to move through the throng.

Auntie Helen (*a bookcase*)
Tom! We've found you!
   I've found Tom everyone!
   How are you bearing up?
   Such a lovely boy . . .
   Such a loss . . .
   Vol-au-vent? Mini-quiche?

Tom wilts. She turns him around, do-si-do style.

Singers
To make relatives believe you're a good boy . . .

And now the cast start to dance, a slightly hypnotic waltz. The stage is alive with lights and furniture people, all waltzing around the stage. All pushing and prodding Tom as they do. Who is now desperate to escape them.

Friendly Phil (*a rug*)
Tom, where did you disappear to?
   Need a hug? Feeling left out. Wishing it was you?

Singers
And while everyone cries
You quickly rub your eyes
To make them red like everyone
Else is . . .

Uncle Gerry (*a painting*)
TOM! Your brother dead. You live? Where's the punchline?

Tom begins to scrabble through, under and out of the mêlée. And the mourners transform into passing trees and cars and people – he runs through them all, desperate for freedom. All the while the singing gets more intense. A descant is put into effect, and a base line and a tenor line. It sounds kind of great, a wonderful swelling noise.

Singers
And you try to shut out
The niggling
In your snout
That you're a nasty bastard
With no
Feelings
With no feelings
Wiiiiiith no feeeeelings . . .

Finally, Tom manages to escape and runs from the pursuing furniture, out of which Courtney slips.

Courtney (*she stays as herself*) Tom! Tom. TOM!

He turns, looks at her a second, and then turns back to fleeing. And then suddenly everyone falls flat. Taking all remaining props down with them.
And Tom is free.
And breathless, and confused.

TWO

A wet summer's night. Not that it is wet now, but it has been. The weather feels intense. Tom is sitting on a wall, not sure why he's there.

Tom (*as he catches his breath*) I've always liked running. I'm not fast, but I like it. It makes me feel weightless and numb and I like being out of breath. And I've always liked stopping – and that feeling where your blood suddenly surges all over your body – where the numbness gets replaced with something else . . . But I never expected to stop here . . .

He clicks his fingers, a light snare-drum plays, and the cast lying on the floor stand up.

The Tunstall Estate.

The men in the chorus flick up their suit jacket collars. They look like 1930s gangsters now.

Not a –

The chorus exit in different directions, with a sort of menace.

Well, not a place many would choose to run to. Choose to run from, yes. But run to? No.
   We did a school local history project on the Tunstall. In the 1950s, believe it or not, this was a place of hope, somewhere where you . . . but that changed. Rot problem. They didn't build the estate on the right land, you see and, so some of the foundations sunk, uh . . . And then they had problems with the riots . . .

Tom stops talking.

A young lad walks across the stage, listening to some R&B on his mobile phone.

He doesn't stop, he doesn't look at Tom.
When he's left, Tom – scared by this kid – checks
he's gone and counts to three.

The 1980s riots – all electrical appliances, including
    lighting fixtures, were ripped out and no one really
    replaced them right . . . And now they're –

Tom stops talking again.
    The young lad has reappeared at the side of the
stage. He looks at Tom closely. Tom tries to act casual.

Tight You hands-free, or you just talking to you?
Tom What?
Tight (*slow, as if talking to a foreigner*) You hands-free
    or you just talking to you?
Tom Oh, uh, no . . . I was talking to myself . . . Sorry . . .

Tight considers this thought.

Tight Riiiiiight.

Tight nods and exits.
    Tom counts to three.
Tom The 1980s riots –

Tight re-enters. He thinks and then approaches Tom,
with a pimp roll. Tight thinks he knows where it's at.
He's wrong, he has no idea where it's at. But he's kind
of sweet.

Tight (*under-his-breath*) You wanna buy a travelcard?
Tom What?
Tight I got some travelcards, you wanna buy one?
Tom No. I'm OK.
Tight Give you great price?
Tom No. I just, I'd rather be – on my own . . .
Tight I ain't a generous guy normal. I am known round
    here as 'Tight', cos I'm like . . . tight. But for you – my

business associates would literally kill me for this – but
I could be prepared, on this occasion, and on this
occasion only, to give wholesale prices, just cos – well
– you look like a kid who just got given a teddy and
realised it's full of used syringes and condoms –

Tom (*starting to get annoyed*) A kid? How old are you?

Tight (*cough*) How old I look?

Tom I don't know . . . fourteen.

Tight (*high*) I never do! (*He coughs so as to speak lower
and manly.*) I never do. I mean, sixteen, yeah, I'd buy
sixteen if you were offering. But fourteen? You are
talking to a guy who like regular – reg–u–lar – gets
served for Marlboro Lights.

Tom How old are you though?

Tight considers.

Tight Fourteen. But that ain't the point.

Tom says nothing.

Tight You sure about the travelcard?

Tom Look. I don't know who you are. And . . . and . . .
Just. Leave me alone will you?

Tight I would . . . but I'm too nice. This ain't the place
for a boy like you. Take a travelcard, go somewhere
better. I mean, boy 'bout your age got stabbed here less
than a week ago. With a bottle. You know what I'm
saying?

Tom Yeah.

Tight I mean, you is in Tunstall land now, this place is
the definition of rough – look 'rough' up in your
dictionary, you'd get a photo of this place. I mean, we
is basically sitting on a murder here, serious! This area
supposed to have all dem 'Police, Don't Cross' signs
and stuff round it. Yellow tape, you know, with the
black stripes, looks pretty cool, yeah? But someone

83

nicked it. That's how dangerous this area is – we don't just get told we're dangerous, we nick the tape that tells us it. Rah!

Tom Right.

Tight thinks, coughs and then tries anyway.

Tight You don't want any 'Police, Don't Cross' yellow tape, do you? Cos I just happened to come into a little bit of it myself recently. Very good price.

Tom I'm OK.

Tight But you won't stay here, yeah? It's too – it's not right for a boy like you – here.

Tom What is a boy like me?

Tight No offence, but a posh boy . . .

Tom (*offended*) I'm not posh! I go to my local school . . . comprehensive school . . .

Tight But you're in top-set maths, I can tell . . . and your school is one of dem nice ones – still free and that – but you don't get kids like me going . . .

Tom thinks.

Tom Thanks, for being worried and everything, but I kind of got to stay here.

Tight Why? You broke your legs? Cos they look fine to me.

Tom My brother was killed here, last week. Stabbed with a bottle.

That's shocked Tight.

Tight Oh.

Tom Yeah.

Pause.

Tom I just, I wanted to come here and . . . I don't know . . .

Tight You – his brother? No, you ain't.

Tom Um. Well, yeah . . . I am . . .

Tight grabs Tom's face to study it. Harder than he should do.

Tight You don't even look like him.
Tom (*ping*) Hang on . . . You knew him?

Tight stops again. He's spotted something – something beautiful. He stares at Tom now. He lets go of Tom's face.

Tight (*soft*) Just then – OK. Yeah, just then. When the lamp caught your face just then . . . Yeah, I can see it . . .
Tom How did you know him?

Tight thinks. Processes. And considers. You can almost see the cogs turn.

Tight I gotta go. Got fifteen travelcards to pimp before the last tube runs – and these Oysters, man, they're playing with my trade. Still – (*He takes a golden card out of his pocket and blows it clean of dust.*) Want you to have this. (*He points to various things on it.*) My mobile. My pager. My only-to-be-called-in-extreme-emergencies-cos-my-mum-gets-well-mad-when-my-mates-ring-the-house number. People know me as Tight – or – if you're speaking to my mum – Tre, but you don't get to call me Tre – cos no one does. I'm just saying, case you speak to her, you know?
Tom How did you know him? Please. Tell me.

Tight considers telling him, but decides against it.

Tight You need anything. Anything. I mean, I ain't gonna get you stuff for free. But you know, give you a good price. Cos look . . . Laters.
Tom Hang on – how did you know my brother? Please. PLEASE!

Tight thinks, and then rolls off the stage. But the walk is less confident now. He hesitates and turns around one final time before making his exit.

Tight Another time, bro, another time . . .

And then he finally goes.
Tom sits back on his wall. He looks around. He shivers . . .

THREE

The sound of a baby crying. Not wailing, but snuffling, making noise, doing what babies do. In the background the sun is setting. Maybe a few windows are opened and today's washing brought in from the night sky. The smells of cooking dinner are brought out, and there are some exotic tastes out there. Sausages from one kitchen mix with saffron from another and sage from another as well.
Tom is staring at the ground, he looks up at the audience, astonished.

Tom There's a stain on the ground. I didn't notice it when I first . . . a bloodstain, I think.

He bends down as if to touch it, but pulls his hand away. He looks at his hand.

Maybe I'm supposed to be solving the case. I always thought I'd be a good policeman. You know, a maverick one. Like Columbo. Or Dennis Waterman. Maybe I'm here to solve my brother's murder and go home to my parents the conquering hero on the back of a white unicorn . . .
Or maybe I'm here to make people feel bad. This is a pretty open place to die at, isn't it? Someone must have heard or seen . . . my brother dying . . . Maybe

86

I'm a torch to shine and pressure and . . . make the
people who live here apologise, and then I'll go home
to my parents on the back of a white . . .

    Or maybe I'm nothing. Just a mixed-up kid sitting
on a cold wall. Looking at a – stain on the ground.

He sniffs, it's cold now.

We were ten months apart. Which means, as my friend
Martin put it –

Martin stands up from the audience.

Martin Must have got pregnant the first take. First take.
Cos women, yeah, they won't let you sleep with them
just after they have a baby. So . . . your dad must be
potent. Po–tent. You know what I'm saying?

Tom Martin doesn't have many friends. Nor do I. We're
in computer club together. We run computer club.
We're the founder members . . . We're the only members.
And no, he doesn't really know what potent means . . .

*Martin sticks his thumb up at anyone who looks, and
then sits down again with a smile.*

We weren't supposed to be in the same year – me and
Luke. It's just, I got put forward a year. Mum wanted
Luke to be put forward a year too – for sort of – for
symmetry. But they pointed out he wasn't clever
enough . . .

    It sort of made sense . . . because up till then we'd
always . . . I mean, he'd sat in the cot beside me, he sat
in the pushchair, he'd only just finished breastfeeding
when I started clamping. He – he was always there to
copy – when he started walking, I started walking,
when he squeezed his first word out, well, I'd seen how
he did it. I mean, I think that's why I got put forward a
year . . . I was just . . . copying. And now –

A kid – Luke – steps out onto the stage. He walks around beside Tom.

    They begin to move in time with each other, just a really simple mirroring dance, framed under lights. Underneath a refrain of 'When Your Brother's Dead' is gently hummed by the chorus from the wings.

When he's –

Luke falls flat, Tom continues dancing for a moment until he realises he's alone. Then he stops and looks at where Luke fell.

Killed by a bottle. What do you do then? Who do you race then? If racing's all you're used to, that is –

Slowly people come on stage and throw down flowers where Luke lies, as if leaving flowers at a road traffic accident. Some from the audience, some from the stage. Martin also approaches from where he was sitting.

Bill They were really different. I mean, they did everything different.

Martin Tom was more . . . academic.

Simon Geek. He was a geek. And he looked so neeky man. He kind of breathed neeky. You know? Like, I don't know even how neeky breathes – but kinda lemony, you know?

Sandra Luke was hot, I know they were s'posed to look similar, brothers and . . . But – they was living proof of it ain't what you got, it's how you use it. And Tom – no offence – used nuffink.

Leo Luke was in a band, you know? Tom was in computer club, you know?

Martin It was the way Tom wore his shoes. It was everything. I mean, I'm not criticising . . .

Sandra It was the way Luke swung his hips.

Libby It was the way Luke opened his baby blues.
Ricky He just had something – Luke did . . .

*The kids pick up Luke and carry him like a coffin, on
their shoulders.*
  Tom watches them as they do.

Martin It'd have evened out in time. I mean, Tom was
  going to go to University. He definitely would have got
  there. And I'm not sure Luke would have . . .
Sandra Luke was exciting. Such a rubbish word. But –
Martin It would have evened up in the end.

They exit the stage, carrying Luke.

Sandra Just cos you're a geek too . . .
Martin Not as bad a geek as Tom is . . .
Sandra No one's as bad as Tom is . . .

*Tom stares off to where Luke has been taken. Still not
sure how to react.*

FOUR

*It's night now. The milky black of a streetlit night. The
sort of night where you can smell the pollution of the
day.*
  *Tom takes off his jacket, sits down beside the wall, and
tries to use the jacket as a blanket.*

Tom I don't know how many people have tried sleeping
  on the street. A pavement for a mattress, a wall for a
  pillow, a jacket for your duvet. It isn't easy. And I
  don't know how many have tried sleeping on the
  Tunstall Estate, but it's . . . loud – and – more awake
  at odder hours – and there's a smell too, a smell of
  anything can happen here . . .

Somewhere in the distance, a dog barks, a car engine revs and a bottle is smashed.

JK OI! . . . COME BACK!

JK comes running onto the stage.
Drunk Bill comes from the back of the auditorium.

Drunk Bill (*singing*)
I'm a tramp, and they love me . . .

He swigs from a bottle, smiles and then faints dead away.

Tom And I don't know how many people have ever tried sleeping on the exact spot where their brother died. But it's . . . tricky. I mean, I don't even care he died, or I don't seem to, but I still get . . . And I'm too old for fairy tales, but I still get pavement elephants –

The sound of an elephant trumpeting.

– coming to trample me, and sky dragons –

The sound of a dragon exclaiming.

– come to –
Courtney WHAT – ARE – YOU – DOING?

Tom sits up with a start, and wipes his eyes.

WHAT – ARE – YOU – DOING?

Tom wakes with a stretch and immediately flinches when he sees his sister.

Tom Oh. Um. Hi. Courtney.
Courtney WHAT ARE YOU DOING?
Tom I was – sleeping – I think . . .
Courtney It's three a.m.!
Tom I reckon it's more normal to be asleep at three a.m. than shouting.

Courtney You just ran off. Mum and Dad have been
ringing round the hospital wards for the last five
hours. They thought you'd done something stupid.

Tom Well, I haven't.

Courtney YES YOU HAVE! Luke's funeral, and you pull
this stunt. What? Worried you weren't getting enough
attention . . . ?

Tom It's not about that.

Courtney Don't try and pretend you cared about him . . .
You hated each other.

Tom I know.

Courtney So why are you here?

Tom I don't know. Felt right.

*Courtney picks him up by the arm and starts pulling
him offstage.*

Tom What are you doing? Oi! Oi!

Courtney You're *coming with me.*

Tom *Let me go, Courtney. Or I'll scream!*

*Courtney thinks and then screams, an ear-piercing
scream. And then she screams again.*

Courtney RAPE! RAPE!

*They look around the estate, not the slightest attempt
has been made to help the damsel in distress. Courtney
looks at Tom with a world-weary grin.*

Some good it'll do screaming round here.

She takes his arm and starts pulling him off again.

Tom LET GO! LET GO! COURT!

*He pulls her hair in an attempt to get away from her –
not a light pull, but a full-hearted yank. She
immediately responds by kicking at him. They throw
each other onto the floor and have a fight. And yes –*

*it's boy v. girl but it's also brother v. sister, and so it's
sort of OK. And she twists and she turns him, but
finally he pins her to the ground. Both are breathless.*

Tom Submit? . . . Submit?

Courtney Well, would you look at that? My little
brother, finally able to beat his sister up . . .

Tom Submit?

Courtney No.

Tom SUBMIT?

Courtney considers her predicament.

Courtney OK. Submit.

*He loosens his grip on her slightly.
    She wriggles out a little. Tom tries to explain –
softly.*

Tom I need to stay here, OK? Will you tell them that?
I know you don't understand, but I really need to stay
here, OK?

*Now he fully lets go of her. She stands up and brushes
herself down.*

Courtney Can't believe you beat up a girl. Actually, can't
believe you beat up anyone.

Tom I know.

Pause. She finally looks at him with compassion.

Courtney You are . . .? You are . . . OK . . . aren't you?
I mean, not mental or . . .

Tom Yeah. I'm OK . . . Will you . . . tell them where I
am?

Courtney considers. She looks around, she shivers.

Courtney Of all the places to choose to go . . . No. I
won't tell them. It'll only hurt them. But I'll say you're

safe. They'll shout at me to get me to tell . . . But I won't . . . You got three days, OK? Three days to get home, or I'll tell them exactly where you are and I don't care who it hurts. Deal?

Tom Deal. Thanks.

She hesitates and then exits. Tom thinks, then takes off his jacket and readies himself for sleep again.

And for some reason, sleeping becomes a lot easier after you've beaten up your older sister. A lot easier. No pavement elephants . . .

An elephant sounds. Tom frowns.

No pavement elephants. No . . . nothing . . .

Tom is asleep.
Blackout.

FIVE

The gentle mist of eight a.m. Windows open, and the sound of radios being tuned and then blared out around the estate. Maybe a seven-year-old having a screaming fit after being told of Teletubby massacres also massages our eardrums.
Tom sleeps through this. He's a good pavement sleeper.
A line of schoolkids comes out from the wings and either stands on or by the wall. Preferably the line should span the width of the stage.
The kids wake Tom with a start.

'DAIRY LEA'
A Marching Song

The School Chorus
School – school – School – school –School – school –
School – school –School – school – School – school –

93

School – school – School – school – Schoo-schoo-
schoo-schoo-school.

*Tom wipes his face with his hand and tries to get
awake. And actually, it's not as difficult as he thought,
he wakes easily. But he is slightly bewildered by all the
noise.*

Tom The Tunstall estate at day is very different from the
Tunstall at night. Filled with noise and colour, it's quite
the place to be. Night is about the people who come
out at night, day is about the mothers . . .

*The Mothers, with tea-towels nattily tied around their
heads like headscarves, come on singing. They are
carrying brushes with which they brush in symmetry
with one another. And maybe a few of these Mothers
are men, and maybe they aren't. The School Chorus
continues underneath throughout.*

Mothers
He was twelve
When he said
He'd have nothing on his bread.
But Dairy Lea
Dairy Lea . . . (*Repeated in overlap by other Mothers.*)

Tom And, despite my pavement mattress and my wall
pillow, I feel quite refreshed, and full of very odd ideas.
Actually . . . STOP!

Everyone does. Tom takes a deep breath.

I've had an idea. I know what I want to do for him.

*Everyone looks at Tom, a few quizzically – and then
set back on their 'Dairy Lea'.*

Mothers
I tried Edam
I even tried ham

94

But he said, give me my
Dairy Lea . . . (*Repeated in overlap.*)

When I
Asked him why
He spat me in the eye
And said –

Boys break from their chorus to sing:

Boys
MUM, GIVE ME MY DAIRY LEA
DAIRY LEA (*In repeat.*)

David McPhee, dressed in a suit, clutching a briefcase, comes in as if being attacked by a hail of bullets. One of the boys walks slightly too close to him and he flinches away. This is not his natural habitat.
   Mums re-take song, but it's slower now.

Mothers
So I do
As I'm told
Wait for him to get old
Prayin' he'll no longer want
DairyLea

David (*muttering to himself*) Go on a site visit, they said. Get out of the office, they said. Get some fresh air, they said. Chance to prove yourself, they said. Who knows, maybe tomorrow you'll make us do your photocopying rather than the other way round.

He bumps into another member of the School Chorus and leaps away with a cry.

I knew this was a bad idea. Of all the places . . .
Tom Mr McPhee?
David Arrrgh!

David jumps two feet in the air, turns pale and starts quivering. Then, looking at Tom the entire time, basically moon-walking backwards, he starts unloading things from his pockets.

David Take my wallet. Take my wallet.

Tom My name's Tom.

David Take the wallet! Just don't – whatever you do – PLEASE DON'T SHOOT ME!

He drops to his knees.

Tom I'm not going to shoot you. I don't have a gun.

David Why would you tell me if you *did*?

Tom Mr McPhee, I phoned and made an appointment –

David TO SHOOT ME!

Tom Do I really look like someone with a gun?

David Oh, uh . . . (*He looks up.*) No. You don't really. Actually, you look really like this kid we used to pick on in school . . . I forget what we called him, but by God we gave him hell.

Tom sits on the wall. David's got it in one.

Tom Yeah. That sounds about right.

David It was something to do with ice cream, some terribly clever pun on ice cream, eczema and the Irish potato famine . . . Lord knows why, I don't think he was Irish . . . Sorry. For a moment I thought you were one of them . . .

Tom One of who?

David (*covertly, through his teeth*) Them. THEM. There was a kid got stabbed with a bottle here last week. Them. The ones that killed him. I mean, they could be – oh my God, they could be all around me, levelling their gun sights so as to take a clean shot at me. (*He drops to the floor.*) Take the shot. TAKE THE SHOT. I never should have come . . .

Tom So why did you?

David clears his throat and stands up. He hands Tom a card.

David David McPhee, Max Bentley funeral homes. You make the appointment. We fill it. Or, rather, we do when we're desperate . . . We're, um, bit short of business at the moment due to, uh, unforeseen . . . People are living too long. Horrible business this, uh, healthy living. Now . . . to business. How can I –?

He opens up his briefcase. It explodes everywhere. Papers literally fly out at all angles as if springloaded.

Oh no! OH NO NO NO NO NO NO! I WANT TO DIE!

David is hysterical. Tom slaps him.

David Ow!
Tom Better?
David Much. Thanks.

David bends to pick up his papers. Tom helps him.

So. Really. How can I help you?
Tom Are you . . . the work experience boy or something?
David No – I'm a – that's very insulting – I'm on a modern apprenticeship for undertaking. My mum said there'd always be jobs in death. And after I was expelled from five schools I decided she was right. Sad thing is, people seem to be stopping dying. Five a day. Absolute rubbish. Five portions of chips a day and then we might . . . DAMN YOU, JAMIE OLIVER! Anyway, no one else in the office wanted to come. And for me, it was either this or watch a body be drained and then filled with embalming fluid. So . . . So tell me, what do you want?

Tom I want to bury my brother. Here. In this pavement.
David Sorry?
Tom I want to bury my brother – here – in this pavement. Here where he died. I want to bury my brother in the pavement.

David looks down at the pavement, then up at Tom.

David Why would you want to do that?
Tom I just do.
David But – a pavement? You're a boy, is it really . . . ?
Tom I've got money. I can pay . . .

David hesitates. He licks his lips. He pulls a tape-measure out of his pocket and begins to measure Tom. He turns into a salesman.

David Would you say he was about your height and breadth? Because we've just had a superb new range of coffins . . . (*He changes his mind.*) No. What am I saying? No. No. You can't just dig up a pavement and put a body in. You need to speak to a planner. Get planning permission.
Tom Planning permission?
David Yes, planning permission. You're digging up a council-owned pavement. Call a planner. Call your mum. And, well, it mightn't be a bad idea to call a psychiatrist –
Tom I'm not mad –
David (*interrupting*) And once you have the permission, from parentals and planners and psychiatrists, then call Max Bentley Funeral Homes and we'll give you a quote. You make the call. We fill it.

He clicks his fingers, puts on a metaphorical hat and exits across the stage. Tom is more than disappointed. He lashes out.

Tom Mr McPhee? MR McPHEE!

David Yes?

Tom There's a red spot dancing on the back of your head. Don't look now, but I think it's a gun sight . . . Mr McPhee, get down, I fear you might be about to be shot.

David Oh . . . oh . . . oh . . . (*He drops to his knees and exits at a fast crawl.*) I never should have come.

Tom laughs, David turns round harshly, realising he's been made a fool of.

The only people I'm going to tell about this are those that need a good laugh. What kind of freak would want to bury their brother in a pavement, eh? What kind of freak?!

Tom considers the question with a scrunch of his face. Why does he want to bury his brother here?

SIX

Luke steps out onto the stage past David, who watches him carefully for signs of violence. When he shows none, David exits, relieved.

Luke sits down on the wall beside his brother. But Tom doesn't notice him.

Luke takes his brother's hand. But Tom doesn't notice. Tom just stares forward.

Tom We used to have this game we played when we were kids – we'd both be superheroes. I'd be Hero Man, and he'd be Skill Man. We weren't very good with names. And Courtney was the baddie, Super Bitch – though she didn't know she was the baddie, because Courtney wouldn't be caught dead playing stupid games with stupid little kids. Plus, she'd have killed us for calling her Super Bitch. So we used to pretend she knew and hide from her and beat each other up. I mean, really, that was sort of the reason for all of it, a quick game of hide 'n' seek and then a bundle – which generally meant hitting each other. It was good.

I still remember the first time I knew he didn't want me around. The year I skipped was year four. I moved up from the end of year three to the beginning of year five. Anyway, so I was brought in to meet the class, like I was a new kid, though they all knew me because I was Luke's brother from the year below. And then the teacher asked –

Spotlight on a kind teacher.

Miss Hands Do you want to sit by your brother, Tom?

Tom stands up. He wiggles from one foot to the next. He's nine years old again.

Tom And . . . and . . . Luke was sitting by someone else – Ben or someone – and shot me this look. Half a smile and half a not and half a please-don't-sit-by-me-please-don't-sit-by-me. And then he looked away and never looked up. And it sounds stupid now, but when you're nine, I mean that was one of the first times I'd figured out that not everyone would like me. You know how you think that? When you're a kid, you think, everyone likes me, of course they do, why wouldn't they? I'm great. And then you get older and you realise, no one likes me, of course they don't, why would they? I'm horrible. Anyway, Luke – that look in Luke's eyes – and then looking away – I knew he'd hate to sit by me . . . so I sat in the spare seat – beside Martin.

Luke starts balancing on the wall behind his brother. Tight enters, carrying two huge bin bags stuffed with bedding. The midday sun is high in the sky now and Tight has to shield his eyes from the sun. Not easy, when your hands are full.

You see, my brother was probably the nicest guy anyone knew – if you'd known him you'd have thought the same – I mean, everyone – *everyone* – thought he was nice and everyone would say it. Nice Luke. Not that he was that nice, just everyone thought he was. Me, I knew him as he really was –

Tight clears his throat. Both boys twist to see who it is. Luke falls to the ground like a puppet with his strings cut. Luke's body lies dead on the ground. Tom isn't sure which way to look. Tight makes him nervous.

Tom I wasn't . . . talking to myself . . . I was – OK, I was talking to myself, but there's nothing wrong with that, is there?

Tight Look at the back of my hand. You see hair on it?

Tight charges over and thrusts his hand under Tom's face.

Tom Um . . . I think you mean palm of your hand. The sanity test – whether you can find hair on the palm of your hand – but I'm not mad.

Tight Oh . . .

Tight looks at the back of his hand and then flips it over. Then laughs.

Right. Cos there is actually hair on the back of my hand, ain't there? Man, and I thought I was mad. I'll remember that. Palm of the hand. Palm of the hand.

Pause. The boys make eye contact. Tight's permanent smile droops.

Tom How did you know Luke?

Tight Yeah. That's what I come to tell you . . .

Pause. Tight doesn't know how to start.

I ain't goin' to be very good at it. Telling. And you'll
probably like – maybe get a bit mad. But – an' it could
go quite bad on me if what I say comes out in the
whole kind of . . . wider-world thing.

Tom I can keep secrets.

Tight Maybe – and maybe you ain't gonna keep this one
secret.

Tom He was on drugs?

Tight No! Just cos he was coming down here ain't to say
he was into drugs. (*Beat.*) He was in love. Said he was
in love. Went on about it. You know?

Tom What?

Tight Sorry – love is a bit . . . rubbish word innit? But he
really liked saying it . . . I mean, maybe love is alright.
No, it ain't. Cos he didn't mean it. He liked someone
a lot. He just said he loved them. You ain't gonna hit
me, are you?

Tom Who did he like? Who?

Tight Settle. Just – someone he met at the snooker club
up near the town centre. They got talking. They both
knew. Neither of 'em liked it. But they kind of – fell in
together . . . And then one of them went on about
being in love all the time, and the other was like,
whatever, and then the one that went on about being
in love got killed with a bottle. Your brother. You
know?

Tom's eyes widen. He walks forward.

Tom This is . . . Maybe this is the reason I'm here.
Maybe to find her, talk to her, find out what he was
really like. Maybe the pavement thing is all a . . . And
who cares about solving the case? I need to find her.
You need to help me find her.

Tight Yeah, you see, but it's complicated, you know? Cos she is a he. I am – it's me.

Beat.

Tom What?

Tight Yeah. This the bit where you could hit me.

Tom WHAT?

Tom gets up and walks away from the wall.

Tight Yeah. I was shocked too. What's it all dem magicians say? Abracadabra. Sorry.

Tom stands still for a long time – his body static, his mind whirring. Finally he says:

Tom My brother was . . . You're too young . . .

Tight Same age as you!

Tom I'm too young. Luke was too young.

Tight For what? For knowing what he was?

Tom For being in – for liking you. Either of you . . . You don't . . . We're too young . . .

Tight (*angry now*) You wanna tell me what I'm feeling now?

Tom No.

Tight So let me get this right. If I was a girl it was a, 'I need to find her,' but cos I'm a me, I'm 'too young, Luke was too young.' And I thought you posh boys was supposed to be – what's the word – open-headed.

Pause. Tight controls his anger. This is not the way he wants to go.

Anyway, whatever, yeah? I'll leave you be, yeah? Just. I brought you blankets. In these bags – and my mum is gonna get well mad cos I didn't ask, cos she don't give blankets to no one who lives on the street, and so I nicked them and took them on the bus . . . I thought you might get cold – at night.

Tight scratches his nose with the back of his hand. He's quickly become too scared to look at Tom, who is looking at nothing at all.

Tight We didn't . . . do sex or nothing, just – kissing and touching and – holding sometimes. I mean, but . . .

Suddenly Tom's eyebrows shoot up.

Tom Shit! This is a clue!

Tight What? Cluedo for what?

Tom We need to tell the police – it might explain everything . . .

Tom starts to make for the exit.

Tight What? No. Calm down. Tom. Tom. Where you . . .? No, no . . . You – can't . . . DON'T.

Tom I'm going to the station. No, a phonebox. Have you got a mobile? What's the number? Stupid me. 999.

Tight shouts after Tom.

Tight So he was killed by someone who hates gay men? Wow. That is one big clue that, cos most people love gay men. Specially round here. Won't be a clue. Won't be nothing. It'd . . . it'd . . . just get me in shit, OK? And your parents, yeah – think about them . . .

Tom stops walking.

You want your parents to find out like this? Thinking they didn't know their son? You want them to? Do you?

Tom (*deeply emotional*) Why not? That's how I feel!

Pause. Tom turns back to Tight.

Tom Why d'you tell me? I didn't want to know!

Tight I, uh, I . . . (*stutter laugh*) dunno. Seemed right. What? Change how you feel, does it? Cos that is –

Tom Change how I feel? It changes *everything!* We were brothers! We lived together. We went to school together. We were in the same year. I should've known. How did I not know that? Something this big and – I missed it. He should've fucking told me.

Tight hadn't considered this angle.

Tight Yeah. He should.

Pause. Both boys are trying to process quite a lot here.

Tom You're a coward for not telling the police the truth. Whether you think it'll change anything. You know they'd want to know.

Tight Maybe.

Pause. Neither boy is sure what to do.

You want these blankets, then?

Tight rips open the bin bags, rather too aggressively, and shovels the blankets out.

They ain't our best but . . . And I got you some . . .

He hands Tom some deodorant – also from the bag. Luke appears. He watches Tight carefully, and approaches.

Just something I noticed . . . I mean, you stink . . .

Pause.

I ain't a coward.

Pause. Luke walks up to Tight and puts his arms around him, and Tight melts into him. They stay like that – holding each other for a few moments.

Tom You . . . you . . . miss him too?

*Tight exits. Not looking back, because he's emotional
and doesn't want to show it.*

Tight Who d'you think was staking out this wall before
you came dancing?

Luke is left onstage with Tom.

SEVEN

*Tom sits on one of the bin bags. He looks out into the
audience.*

Tom I . . . Um . . . I . . .

*A guy on a skateboard rides across the back of the
stage, trying an olly before exiting.*

I just . . .

The boy with all the words can't explain himself.

The thing is, Luke isn't a surprising – wasn't – I mean,
that wasn't what Luke – he was straightforward. Not
that – not going too far, not doing too much different.
    I mean, he didn't . . .
    And I . . .

*He quietens as a Pushchair Mum pushes a baby
aggressively across the stage.*

Pushchair Mum No, what you said was, 'Get your hands
off my remote control, bitch, I got things to do, and
people to watch.' I was like, 'You got things to do,'
you –

Baby's Father What's with your chatting all the time?
Chat chat chat . . . Cos I tell you, I ain't even listening
no more . . .

Pushchair Mum You ain't listening? You listen, boy. You
listen strong. Otherwise I'm putting that remote

control where it hurts and you gonna be birthing it like a baby.

They exit the stage just as an Estate Agent hurries past.

Estate Agent No, I'm on my way to look at some property on the Tunstall . . . Lee Marshes . . . God no, I took the bus, I'm not parking around here! (*He laughs like a jackal.*) Well, that's why the first thing I'm going to propose is a garage extension . . . Well, the location is fabulous that's why . . . it's called gentrification, darling, and it's happening . . .

Tom is still staring into space.

Tom I've never liked surprises. When I was younger, my mum used to have to tell me what was in my presents before I opened them. She knew what I was like.

Stan comes in wearing a dapper suit and walking like the Pink Panther. He has a sort of undeniable slink to him. He's very jazz. The sun is now setting. It's magic hour, and here's the magic man. He has a theme, a light snare-drum and some baritone sax.

I mean . . . not telling me that. That's – that's spin round five times, touch the floor, bang your head on something . . . And –
Stan Hey. Kid. Planning. Me. The cat. Called. You?

Still totally absorbed by Tight's revelations, Tom spins to meet his new company.

Tom What?
Stan You don't talk jive? Thought everyone round here talked jive, man? My names Stanley Burrows, I'm from the Planning Department. You called. I came. (*He makes revving noises.*) Grrrm. Grrrm.
Tom You're – a planner?

Stan Yeah. Me. Planner. Wow. And you know what – I'm going to make something of this place. Selling it. All. Private development. Tube extensions. Transport links. Wow. Clean. Schmean. Amazing.

Tom considers what to do.

Tom I need your help.

Stan Who doesn't?

Tom I want to bury my brother in this pavement. I got told I needed planning permission. Do I? Can you give me permission?

Stan looks at Tom, his eyebrows shooting up. The street lights come on. One has a bad flicker.

Stan In the pavement?

Tom Yeah.

Stan Wow. Love to, kid. But – jurisdiction. You heard of it? Juris–d–d–d–diction. This is not a planning matter. This cat keeps his paws clean, you know? Burying brothers in pavements – planning? No, sir. Call Environmental Health. Call Highway Control. Nice meeting you. I'm off to prowl. Purrrr.

Stan's theme recurs as he sashays his way offstage.

Tom Will they let me? Do you think? Environmental . . . Bury him? Here? In the pavement?

Stan stops. He turns.

Stan Here? Pavement? Grave? Brother? Unlikely.

Tom Why not?

Stan Kiddo, schmiddo – huh . . . you need a good reason to dig up pavements. Not just anyone can do it. It affects people's access – it's a public right of way – you dig?

He attempts another exit.

Tom They dug my street up last week so as to lay a TV cable – you saying laying a TV is more important than burying my brother?

The flickering street light flickers off. Stan dinks it with the back of his shoe. It switches on again.

Stan Which brings me on to . . . cables and pipes. Gas, electricity, phone lines, cable television, sewers, water, electricity – you open a pavement, there's more cables in there than concrete. Where do you put a dead body? You dig?

He attempts to make his exit again. This time when Tom stops him, he's annoyed.

Tom I don't dig. No.

Stan Then there's Public Health – a dead body lives in a whole new way, kiddo. It disintegrates. Disintegrates over our lovely pipes and releases toxins into the atmosphere that could really jazz up Public Health. Then there's the smell – I mean, Environmental Health, say hello? Hello. Goodbye. People walk past on a hot day – sun in their face, hope in their heart, they sniff, they think, they say, 'What's that smell? Smells like dog meat gone rotten. Oh no, of course it's just that boy's brother disintegrating a bit more.' Sorry. Insensitive. Forget. Brother.

Stan makes a determined attempt at an exit.

Tom Will you talk to other people about it, see if there's any other way . . .?

Stan (*softening slightly, but determined to leave*) What I will do is give you details of a woodland burial ground. Very nice. Classy. Biodegradable.

He makes for an exit. And this time it's personal.

Tom Please . . . Wait . . . If I could explain . . .

Stan You have explained . . . Listen, kiddo, I'd love to sit here miaowing. But there's mice to be caught, kid. And this cat's gotta catch them.

He exits across the stage but stops just as he leaves. He looks around, he smells the air. He sighs contentedly.

Everything's going to change.

He exits. There's a final drum kick as he does. Tom watches him go.

EIGHT

Our Boy Chorister stands up from behind the wall. He is carrying a glass of water. He considers drinking from it, but thinks better of it and hands it instead to Tom, who takes it without acknowledgement, drinks a little, then puts it on top of the wall.

Tom open his bin bags and begins to assemble a bed for the night from the blankets inside.

'TENDER CONTEMPT'
A Lament

Boy Chorister
Lollipops and hairgrips
Action Men and dirt
Friday night TV chips
A water gun that squirts
He –

The line isn't coming.

He –
The –

The Boy looks at Tom. He doesn't know how to finish this song. Or even sing another line.

Now he's –

The Boy stops. He can't do this. He walks away. Tom looks after him.

Tom Second night on the street and it's funny how quickly you adapt to a new life. I mean, I'm not super tramp or . . . but I am warmer, cos of the blankets – well, that's not adapting, that's just blankets – but the barking dogs bother me less, and the smashing glass and . . .
  I think – I think I was scared of him.
Luke You? Scared of me?

Tom doesn't hear Luke. And he continues not to do so in the rest of this scene.
  He continues making his bed. With more gusto now.

Tom I wanted him to like me. And I knew he didn't – I knew he wouldn't – because I wasn't cool like him. I mean, even using the word 'cool' is probably uncool – I mean, I'm probably saying it all wrong or using it in totally the wrong way. I don't know.
  There was this big marble competition – the Marble Wars of 2003 we called it – about three months after I'd joined Luke's class.
  And three months in a nine-year-old's mind is like unbelievably long. I'd totally settled in by then – which means I'd been rejected by all the popular people and started musing with Martin about the kingdom we'd rule called 'Computer Club'. And we were far too old for marbles, everyone who took part – I mean, nine-year-olds, ten-year-olds playing marbles – what is this, 1950? I mean, literally some kids played with a fag in their mouth and a knife in their pocket.
Luke (*laughs*) Knife? Who carried a knife?
Tom Still – somehow marbles became important and me and Martin, we practised loads and we won and

kept on winning – shooting through the rounds –
until we got paired together in the semi, and Martin
said –

Light on Martin.

Martin No, this is totally ace, it means a member of the
Computer Club is guaranteed a place, a grand final.
It's like two English clubs pairing each other in the
Champions League semi-finals. It's perfect.

Light off.

Tom Neither of us know much about football. Oh, and
he didn't speak to me for a week when he lost. And
then suddenly it was the final – and I was in it.

*'Eye of the Tiger'-type music. The cast from offstage
wheel on huge beachballs, done up to look like
marbles. The cast are now all in tracksuits and PE
uniforms. They look terrible. They start limbering up
as if 1970s sportsmen.*

And I was facing – my opponent was – well, as it turned
out, Luke. Of course I'd practised hard to make it to
the final and he was – well, he did it on natural talent.

*Luke takes a beachball from one of the cast and lines
up his eye.*

He threw the first marble. He looked at me, and then
threw it. And it was – it was . . .

*Luke rolls. One of the cast picks up the ball and rolls
with it, placing it carefully in the auditorium. There is
some sort of musical accompaniment to this. The rest
of the cast keep playing games of their own.*

First off I was winning – and then he was – and then me
– and then him – and then . . . it came down to one
large marble –

Luke Was a butterfly marble, I remember it well . . . I'd
won it in one of the earlier rounds.

Tom – and I just needed to chink it out of the circle. I
won't attempt to explain the rules – think Curling
meets Lawn Bowls. It was a sophisticated game.

Luke We always liked making rules, more than the
games mostly.

Tom One large marble and all I needed to do was chink
out of the circle – and I'd win –

Tom picks up a beachball and lines up his shot.

– and I let my marble go with loads of wrist spin –

*Tom lets the ball go, and it is again rolled by a cast
member. The cast start paying attention to this battle
now.*

Luke You always used to talk shit about things like wrist
spin.

Tom – and it rolled and it rolled and it rolled . . .

*The ball is rolled and rolled and rolled, deep into the
auditorium. The cast are now closely watching this.
Think Scotland. Think Winter Olympics. Think
Curling.*

Luke Yours was a speckled hen. Small, compact, usually
a good aim . . .

Tom And I couldn't look at him and he couldn't look at
me.

Luke I just . . . I wanted to beat you at something just
once.

Tom And it rolled . . .

*The ball keeps rolling. Tom is breathlessly watching it.
Leaning left to encourage it to do the same.*

Luke You won every maths test, every history test.
Always top of the class when I'm always in the middle.

The ball slides past the one already placed. The crowd cheers. Tom groans.

Tom And it – and it – it slided by on the outside. It nudged but it didn't chink. I should have used a heavier marble –

Luke And I won. I beat you. The best. The kid who was younger than me, but always seemed to get there first.

Tom My wrist spin was all wrong . . . And all his mates were cheering and holding him up. Chuffed their popular champion had beaten the lonely geek.

Luke Popular? Me? They don't even know who I really am . . .

Tom And everyone wanted to touch you – to congratulate you – to tell you you're the best. And I don't even have Martin to talk to because he's still sulking . . .

Luke You reckon they'd touch me with a barge pole if they knew I liked boys? I envy you, Martin, he cares about you. No one cares about me.

Tom Luke winning was fine . . . I mean, fine. But he had this flushed look all day – like he was really pleased it was me – and I hated that. I hated that look. That wasn't fine.

Luke I loved it. Finally showing you what it was like to lose. Like I had to. Every day.

Tom (*finally spitting it out*) WHY DIDN'T YOU TELL ME WHAT YOU WERE?

Luke WHY D'YOU THINK? I needed a brother. And I didn't have one.

Tom I couldn't talk to you.

Luke I couldn't talk to you. And I had more to say.

This shocks Tom. He fades into silence. Luke reaches out to touch his brother. But changes his mind.

I still remember first day in class the teacher asked if you wanted to sit by me.

Spotlight on a kind teacher.

Miss Hands Do you want to sit by your brother, Tom?

Spotlight off.

Luke I knew you'd say no, I had to prepare myself for
you to say no, this brother who'd got brought into my
class, my world, and I knew you'd –

Tom (*shocked*) No! You gave me a look! You didn't
want me to sit by you . . . You gave me a look –

Luke What look? I didn't give you a look, and – you said
no, and went and sat by that Martin kid, and I –

*Courtney enters from beside the stage, and Luke falls
to the floor. Tom doesn't realise this.*

Tom Luke . . . Luke . . .

*Tom looks around wildly for the reason why his
brother – whom he's finally been able to talk to – has
gone. He notices Courtney watching him. He looks at
her suspiciously. She looks back with equal suspicion.*

NINE

Tom Uh. Hi. Um. Hasn't been – three days yet, has it?

Courtney No.

Tom So how come you're . . .?

Courtney I plead temporary insanity – I wanted to check
you're OK.

Tom Oh. Really? Um. OK.

Courtney I am your sister. I know you like to pretend I'm
not. But –

Tom I'm OK.

Courtney Good. And . . . uh . . . well, I bought you
some . . .

She proffers some blankets, but at the exact same moment realises Tom already has some.

Courtney Who – got you blankets?

Tom Just someone . . . I, just . . . someone . . . You wanna sit down? You can see the stars really clearly. Must be cos most of the streetlights are broken round here . . .

Pause. She looks at the spot. Realises it's where her brother was murdered.

Courtney No. I better get back.

Tom (*firm*) Sit down, would you?

Courtney Tom . . . this is – like a horror movie or something – sitting where he . . . died.

She starts to exit briskly.

Tom (*firmer still*) I want . . . I don't know enough about you, Courtney . . . like, what do you like doing? Or what do you think when you meet someone? Or what you want for Christmas? Seriously. STOP. Tell me what you want for Christmas.

Courtney turns.

Courtney What are we, eleven?! What do I want for Christmas? What do you care?

Tom I just do.

Courtney You'll start asking me about my sex life next.

Tom Please. I wouldn't ask if it wasn't – I just want to know.

Beat. She considers. She looks at her brother's sincere face. She melts slightly.

Courtney OK, maybe, just off the top of my head . . . Um . . . this is embarrassing. I don't know – maybe a train ticket, to Paris. You know, Eurostar. You reckon it'd cost too much?

Tom No.

Courtney I wouldn't want to stay. Just a day return. And not to see the shops or any of that crap. Just to buy some food from the deli or eat maybe in one of the small side-street restaurants or . . .

Tom You see, that's really interesting, I'd never have guessed you'd have wanted that . . .

Beat. Courtney sums up some serious courage.

Courtney Look – I haven't told anyone this, so if you laugh . . . I want to be a chef.

Tom Oh.

Courtney You laugh and you'll never have kids, I mean that! I'll do what you did to the dog.

Tom I'm not laughing. Chef?

Courtney Yeah. Chef. You think I'm mad?

Tom No.

Courtney Mum'll be well pissed off, 'With your GCSEs, a chef? But you could do so much better!'

Tom I like it when you cook for us. Those puddings you do – the cakes . . . You should make more of them.

A small smile slides across Courtney's face.

Courtney OK. Well. Thanks. But . . . don't tell anyone, OK?

Tom No, I won't tell anyone.

Pause. Courtney moves across and sits by him, smoothing out the blanket.

Courtney (*soft*) What are you doing here, Tom?

Tom (*soft*) I don't know. I just – I wish he'd told me what he wanted for Christmas.

Pause. Tom is thinking – hard.

The thing is . . . the thing is, I thought he was stupid.

Courtney He wasn't.

Tom And I thought he didn't like me.

Courtney I thought he didn't like you too.

Tom And I thought he was boring. Uninteresting. Not surprising.

Courtney Wasn't he? What was surprising about him?

Tom I used to think – I was the most special person I knew – which is not . . . I mean, I thought I was Jesus Christ for a bit but . . .

Courtney Jesus Christ?

Tom It's a long story. But I always thought . . . I always felt better than everyone around me. What if – what if Luke was the special one and I was too dumb to . . .

Courtney What if he was ordinary? Does that make it any way different?

Tom No. But he wasn't . . .

Courtney No . . . I don't suppose anyone is.

Pause. Lights fade.

It's not bad round here really, is it? I mean, it's bad, but not as bad as – people say.

Tom No, it's OK – this woman from the flats even came down with a tupperwear dinner for me the other day – rice and chicken.

Courtney That's nice.

Tom Courtney. Do you ever think – think death is magical? I mean, not David Blaine or people coming back to life. Just magical – you know?

Courtney I don't know. Shall we go to sleep now, you reckon? Yeah?

Tom Yeah.

Beat. In darkness.

Tom Courtney –

Courtney Yeah?

Tom Thanks for telling me what you want for Christmas.

Courtney OK.

Tom She slept by the wall too that night. And together we braved the pavement elephants that came out to dance –

An Indonesian shadow puppet dance starts at the back. A pavement elephant waltzes across it.

And the sky dragon came out to sing –

A burst of flames as a sky dragon coughs.

And the concrete sabre-tooths –

A wide, sharp-toothed mouth cracks down on the assembly.

And the creeping wall-monkeys that laughed through it all.

Monkeys laugh as they swing mercilessly around the stage.

And we were too old for all of them. Too old and sophisticated for fairy stories. Because I'd stopped believing when I was six and found my Christmas present from Santa on my dad's credit card bill. But still – we had to fight the mystical creatures and we did, and by the time the sun came up she was gone.
And I felt closer to Luke than I ever had done.

TEN

The sun rises and it's beautiful. Gently tinkling the metallic pavement with a soft glow. Luke and Tom are sitting, leaning their backs against each other.
They say nothing.
And then a loud Estate Agent with an anxious Client interrupts the serenity.

Estate Agent I think you'll find it a most vibrant place to live.

Client Well, uh, what's, uh – I mean, crime –

Estate Agent Figures. Schmigures. Breathe. Ingest. Look at this place. It's vibrant, it's exciting, it's new – and that may sound like estate-agent speak, but I'm really excited about where this area can go. And, of course, they're extending the tube line you know – which means prices will rocket –

Client Oh. Well, that does sound interesting –

The Estate Agent and Client disappear offstage. Tom watches them go.

Tom It's funny how things – two days ago I was frightened of this place. Now I'm frightened what it's going to become. Do you know what this place feels? It feels honest. And I know I sound like a patronising wanker even saying . . . I mean, I'm here for Luke, not for the scenery, but . . . I don't know, you look behind Batman's mask and sometimes things are better . . . and this place – well . . .

Two Policemen walk out onto the street. They're carrying yellow tape and some traffic cones. They're dressed in riot gear.

PC Bob You hot, Bill?

PC Bill Toasting lightly. You, Bob?

PC Bob Same as. Same as. Remind me, Bill, why we in riot gear?

PC Bill Be prepared, Bob. That's the police motto.

PC Bob No. That's the Cub Scout motto, Bill . . .

PC Bill Is it, Bob? What's the police motto?

PC Bob Dunno, Bill. Think it's in Latin.

PC Bill You can't even remember it roughly, Bob?

PC Bob At a guess, Bill, something about attending to needs. We are here today, for instance, to attend to this young man's needs.

He indicates Tom.

PC Bill And what does he need, Bob?

PC Bob Well, Bill, according to our police report, he wants to bury his brother in the pavement.

PC Bill Oh – shall I fetch my spade, Bob?

PC Bob What?

PC Bill You know, Bob, give him a hand.

PC Bob No, Bill, we're here to tell him no. And threaten him with arrest. If he stays here and keeps making a public nuisance of himself . . . we'll arrest him.

Bob starts reassembling the ribbon fence. Bill dips in to give him a hand. They assemble it around Tom.

PC Bill Just a question, though, Bob – how is threatening him, attending to his needs?

PC Bob We're setting him rules, Bill, people need rules, especially people on this estate.

PC Bill Great answer, Bob. Shall I let him know? About the rules?

PC Bob Why don't you do that?

Bill ties off the ribbon, approaches Tom, bends down, and then shouts in his ear.

PC Bill YOU WILL NOT BURY YOUR BROTHER IN THE PAVEMENT. AND YOU WILL STOP MAKING A PUBLIC NUISANCE OF YOURSELF . . . (*He sniffs, disgusted.*) AND YOU WILL HAVE A BATH . . . SOON.

Tom He was gay.

PC Bill What?

Tom The victim. My brother. He was gay.

PC Bob Do you not read the papers, boy? We know he was gay. Everyone knows he was gay. It's common knowledge, the boy was gay. We had a kid come and report it. Might help us find who did it. Probably not. But it was nice to know, wasn't it, Bill?

PC Bill It was, Bill. Very nice.

PC Bob What? I'm Bob. You're Bill.

PC Bill Oh. Yes. That's right. Sorry, Bill.

PC Bob Bob . . . Bill . . . (*Seriously confused.*) What? Listen, son. Just – you can't stay here, OK? Why don't you – go home.

Tom This is where I belong.

PC Bob Well, that's not true, unless you're a traffic cone, that is, isn't that right? (*Unsure.*) Bill?

PC Bill That's right, Bob.

They both smile, relieved to have got each other's names right.

Well, that's us. See you, kid. Stay away from the tape. Stay away from the scene.

They walk past Tight as he walks on stage. He scowls at them. Luke follows him onstage, watching him carefully as he does. Once in the middle of the stage, Tight checks they've gone, and then begins unravelling the tape.

Tight Hi.

Luke Hi.

Tom Hi.

Tight (*indicating the tape*) Don't want this, do ya? Cos I got a guy in Fulham pay good money for this. I tell you, man, eBay, man, changed my life. But if you . . . you want it?

Luke Do you like him?

Tom No.

Tight Hey! You weren't talking to yourself when I come out, that's well good, innit.

Luke It was his smile got me. He's got a great smile, don't you think?

Tom No.

Tight has now unravelled the 'Police, Don't Cross' ribbon, which he then pockets.

Tight Like this means shit. Like police mean . . . But. Still. I told 'em. I weren't no coward about it either. I went down in person to tell 'em. Face to face. That'll get back, that will. People will know it's me . . . and that'll mean, wreckage, you know?

Luke I'm not saying I'd have spent the rest of my life with him . . . But he's nice, Tom, he's really nice . . .

Tom OK. He's nice. He's nice, OK?

Tight Who's nice?

Tom (*flicked back into Tight's world*) What? I was just – I mean, brave, not nice . . . that was brave. I mean, yeah. Thanks. You're a good – person.

Tight (*smiles gently*) Yeah. Well. We ain't all drug-dealers round here, you know . . .

Tom No. I know. In fact, I can understand why Luke spent time here. I mean, it's quite a nice – I don't know. But it did . . . kill him, didn't it? This – place. So . . .

Pause. Tight's face darkens. Luke looks at him apprehensively.

Luke You'll need to listen to this bit.

Tight Yeah. 'Bout that. I don't reckon it was no gay-basher did it.

Tom Oh.

Tight (*gushing out*) Yeah, cos . . . the thing is . . . The . . . I reckon he did it himself.

Tom looks at Luke, who says nothing. Tight is finding this very difficult indeed.

Tight Yeah. Innit. He weren't that happy, your brother, kept going on about how thick he was, and how his life was gonna be shit, and how he couldn't work out how to tell no one what he was, and then I split up with him and the weather weren't great and . . .

Tom What? No. He . . . uh. No. You've got the . . . He ain't the type.

Tight (*barely listening*) I weren't even nice about it. He kept saying, 'It's cos you're scared,' and I was saying, 'You're scared too, you ain't told no one about us,' and he was like, 'You're scared,' he kept on and kept on and kept on and he was right, but I couldn't – I wouldn't – so I was like, 'That ain't even the main reason, the main reason is you're not good enough for me,' and I only said it like that cos I wanted to hurt him and I wanted the conversation done and I knew it would be done then, cos he never did think he was good enough for anyone, did Luke. It's how come everyone liked him. 'Cept you.

Tom says nothing. He's too busy computing. Luke looks steadily into the distance.

And now . . . I need – I need you to forgive me . . .

Tom You really think . . .? You think he did – himself?

Tight I need you to forgive me –

Tom Suicide?

Luke I'm sorry.

Tight – for what I done. I need you to tell me it's OK. Cos I got this cloud, man, and it won't – and I miss him, so bad and . . . He was right, I was scared, but I proved I can be different now right? I told everyone – (*he gestures to the paper*) – I weren't the coward you said I was. People'll find out was me who told 'em, you know . . . So . . .

Luke Tre told me he didn't want to see me again – you hated me – and I was standing in this cold street and I didn't want to go home, I didn't want to do anything. And we'd done that thing in biology about the carotid

arteries in the neck and so I broke a bottle and just –
and if I'd known how much it hurt . . . and . . .

*Luke's neck starts bleeding, he puts his hand up to
stop the flow.*

Tight Tom – Tom – you gone all quiet, you OK?

*The truth is, Tom's not hearing either of them, he's just
got the suicide word rebounding around his head.*

Luke I'm not saying – if I had to do it again – if I had to
do it again – I mean, it wasn't like I spent my entire
time going, 'How do I kill myself?' because I didn't –
just – at that moment – everything seemed right . . .
I wouldn't have done it any other day – or I don't
think . . . It was just – that day – seemed too hard.
I just – got a bit crushed and felt a bit – crushed, so –
I crushed myself.

*Luke takes his hand off, and lets his neck bleed. Tom
stands up to look at him carefully.*

Tight It ain't your fault, it's mine.
Tom No.
Tight How can we fix it, then? We need to fix it!

*Tom stands in the middle of the stage, finally owning
the space around him. His grief has allowed him that.*

Tom You . . . You're – the guy that can get anything,
right?
Tight Right.
Tom I . . . I need an axe.
Tight Is it?
Tom I need an axe.

Pause.

Tight I can get you an axe.

An axe is bought onstage by a glamorous-looking girl (or a boy dressed up). Tight catches it. He hands it to Tom. Tom thinks – and then hammers it into the ground. Music starts. Something substantial.

Tom It wasn't until the axe hit the pavement that the dance started . . .

The glamorous one begins to belly-dance. He/she is joined by other brick-wall princesses.
   Tom hammers the axe into the ground again.

Tom It was the brick-wall princesses that started it off – a primitive belly-dance that shook the room and then the lamp-post monkeys began to wobble and shout . . .

The lamp-post monkeys do indeed begin to wobble and shout. It begins to feel epic.
   Tom smiles and hammers the axe in again.
   A man in underwear comes running onto the stage. The music stops. Everyone turns to look at him.

Underwear Man Oi! Don't do that. You know how long it took 'em to get cable put in round here?

Tom thinks, and then hammers again. The music starts up again. Louder, more robust than before.

Tom And then the pavement elephants came out to play. And the sky dragons. And the cable moles and the pipe snakes and electric eels.

And they do.

Underwear Man Stop, stop! My Sports! My movie channels. Please. I'll do anything. My Granada Men and Motors! My Living TV! My Sci-fi Channel!

Tom hammers again.

Tom And slowly – slowly, the place became – well, magic.

Tom hammers again. As the magic and the noise continue all around, a slow fade to a spot on the middle of the stage, in which Luke stands. Still covered in blood.

Tom approaches and joins Luke in the spot. They slowly dance around each other, and then slowly Luke droops into Tom's arms. He stands there holding his brother.

Tom The night he died – they basically forgot about me. Courtney said she heard Mum crying, and woke then, and came downstairs to find out. But I didn't hear anything. He hadn't come home, I knew that before I went to bed, but I figured he was just with mates. Even Mum wasn't worried, so I slept well and slept deep. Anyway, about four a.m., I woke up and I needed a piss and a glass of milk, so I went downstairs. And Mum was in tears and sitting in a corner of the kitchen on the floor and Courtney was standing crying and Dad was just really really angry – saying things like, 'Well, what the hell was he doing down there?' And there was a police officer making everyone tea and trying to look unobtrusive and I – was – seeing all this was like . . . I just – and I didn't know what had happened.

Anyway, so I ask, 'What's going on?' and they all turn and look at me. And they didn't want to explain it all again – my parents didn't – so the police officer said, because she knew they didn't want to explain it again, 'I'll take him in the living room, shall I? Let him know what's happening.' And Mum just nodded.

They'd told Courtney themselves, but that was probably because they knew she'd have a better reaction than me, and they wanted to hug her and stuff. I was never the sort of boy that people hugged, Luke was that sort of boy, I was – I'm the sort of boy people pat.

On the back, head, or arm . . . Anyway, when the police officer told me and I asked, 'Are you sure?' and she said, 'That's a strange response,' and I said nothing and that I probably needed to go to my room for a bit and she said OK, and then I went and sat in my room and played solitaire on my computer. And –

He's not going to be buried here. They've put him in the ground already. They're hardly going to dig up the body to put it in a concrete hole. But this is – my burial, isn't it? The time I'm burying him, for me. And I know him now, and I know what I'm burying and I know what he means to me now, I know that I love him.

You know that, don't you? I love you. You know that? And I'm sorry. I'm so sorry.

Courtney slowly approaches Tom and helps him lower Luke's body to the ground.

Courtney Yeah. He knows you are.

Blackout.

EPILOGUE

A full cast blow-out:

Chorus
Burying your brother in the pavement
Seems such a stupid-weird thing to do.
But when your mind's a pit
It seems like a bit
Of a way to make things feel less through.

Burying your brother in the pavement
Oh what funny people are we
But actually it ain't bad

Actually it ain't mad
Just a wave to those we've let free.

Burying your brother in the pavement
I got a plot picked out for me
For it's such a way
To deal with the day
When I go on to what may be.

Tom is placed in handcuffs by PCs Bill and Bob, as the chorus sing. He tries to wave goodbye. He's handcuffed. He can't. Everyone else gets their bow. As if escaping, Tom runs in to take his too.

Production Notes

- There is a challenge to find a coherent theatrical language for the play. The play needs a theatrical language that binds it together physically. The 'step forward' could take you anywhere, but the 'step back' is important and must be linked with the overall language of the production.

- The music that companies achieve in their productions should be based on the particular musical talent they have in their group.

- A synthesis of the physical and musical – but be careful that the show doesn't become a 'ragbag'.

- The play is 'epic theatre', not 'dramatic theatre'.

- How can we develop the physical relationship between the two brothers? How might the naturalistic moments move into something more poetic with the physical moments?

- Not a 'gay suicide' play, but a play about a boy who didn't feel that he fitted in, despite the assumption that he did. It's not about *why* Luke committed suicide, but *how* all those around him didn't realise he was unhappy.

- There is a truism in theatre that 'You cannot dramatise grief', but that is what is achieved with this play. What is grief like for a young person and how does one deal with grief?

- This is a play that goes at 'the speed of thought'. Running length should be about an hour.

- Some plays have very particular stage directions, but *Burying Your Brother in the Pavement* is the opposite of this.

- Directors must be aware that each 'number' has a narrative effect and the challenge is to locate and unlock it.

- What is important for the play is how to get Tom through the narrative journey. How do we make this 'geeky kid' the centre of attention?

- The choreography and movement challenges in the play are about finding a 'physical movement language'. So is there a physical theatrical language that links each 'number'?

- This is a serious story which the characters have great fun telling.

- Tom should ideally be kept at fourteen years old as there are great differences of age between twelve to sixteen. If there is not a fourteen-year-old actor, he should still be played as fourteen.

EXERCISES

Tom and Luke's physical relationship

- Find a partner of similar body shape and size. Standing side by side, experiment with giving each other some of your weight. Then try to move around the space with these two rules in mind:

  1 You must keep a point of physical contact at all times.

  2 You must give each other your weight at all times.

- After experimenting, take ten minutes to try to come up with a short routine or sequence.

- Find the natural resting points where both can breathe. These resting points may be moments for a narrative insert. Think also about how you breathe together and melt together. Think about how certain moments of the movement feel (soothing, dangerous, frustrating) and what story they may tell. What is the context of the movement within this mini-narrative?

- What was effective? Dramatic changes of pace? The relationships between the characters. Support and attack? How do these interact? Between sleeping and waking? With trust? How do we direct such movement to tell a story?

Tom and Luke's physical relationship: mirroring

- Get into pairs.

- Together create a mirror sequence and take licence with how this might work (i.e., be synchronised, rather than copying).

- Decide who is Luke and who is Tom. Luke may be following Tom (as in the play, Tom cannot see Luke but Luke can see Tom). Each may play a different verb (e.g. Tom is 'actively anguished' and 'in crisis'. Luke is 'soothing and loving' towards his brother.) Play with who leads the sequence, and then take it on a journey to see what story or narrative may arise from it.

- Add in a moment where Luke tries to touch Tom and narrowly misses. One character wants to make contact, but can't.

- Try to make the sequence build emotionally to a point of frustration, with moments of missing each other. Here 'stings of movement' become effective.

- In the search for a language of movement, it can be useful to establish rules for an exercise – then break them and interrogate the results. Always keep the exercise fresh and alive but keep your eyes open for technical 'hooks' upon which the sequence may rest.

MUSICAL 'NUMBERS' IN THE PLAY

Some important points about the musical numbers:

- They offer the challenge of how to show Tom's emotional state through movement and music

- They must be tailored towards moving the narrative along; they must have an anchor-point to focus the audience – it may be in the pauses of these physical sequences that the dialogue falls.

- The larger musical numbers offer a stimulating contrast to the smaller, lyrical exchanges between Luke and Tom.

- Don't apply one rule to the numbers: each has its own narrative place and style .

- Be lean with interpretations so as to retain narrative and context over style and spectacle.

- The audience are left in a different place after each song than they were before.

- They are part of the narrative of the play, and shouldn't be seen as light relief or a break from the story.

- The musical numbers are about Tom's confidence – they are reflective of his emotional state. So in the first half of the play there are more numbers, to reflect a time where Tom expresses more control over his situation. The songs become fewer toward the end of the play as Tom's emotional state changes. In a similar way, the boy soprano's lack of confidence in singing his opening note before 'When Your Brother's Dead' reflects the way Tom doesn't really know what he is doing or feeling at this moment of the play.

EXERCISE   *Exploring the musical numbers and possible physical languages in the play.*

The following was a company exploration of Tom's journey from the loft into the estate, undertaken in a workshop.

- Find a space and begin a waltz sequence: 1-2-3 (forwards) and 1-2-3 (backwards), moving around the space and enjoying the 'swing'.

- Play with the possibilities of this movement (going lower, higher, moving like a robot, varying precision).

- Take the movement into 1-2-3 (up) and 1-2-3 (down). Experiment with unison and freestyle.

- Each member of the company takes an object (a chair, jumper, handbag) and begins to continue the waltz movement with this object as their 'partner'.

- The leader may shout 'freeze' in order to regiment and explore the movement.

- Form two circles: an inner (moving clockwise and up) and an outer (moving anticlockwise and down). Give more flow to the movement by making steps longer, maintain precision and experiment with moments of stillness.

- Tom is positioned centre stage, and these circles form around him. Tom attempts to get offstage but is trapped.

Here the manic quality of the physical movement should signal an important narrative point: according to him, at this point in the play, Tom feels trapped and utterly bewildered by his mad family.

- This sequence leads to a chase, as if Tom has escaped from his house and is making a run for it. Tom is kept as the anchor-point within the seeming chaos of the ensemble movement around him. Tom's journey though the streets is shown by him running on the spot and the chorus running past him in two adjacent lines, as if to represent lamp-posts and trees passing as he runs (as on a conveyor belt). The speed of this chorus procession past Tom should be varied to indicate different speeds and phases of his leaving the loft.

THE CHALLENGES OF PLAYING TOM

- It is possible to 'break up' Tom for multiple actors.

- Explore Tom's thoughts, and how to 'place' each one somewhere in the auditorium – a particular thought planted in a particular place. Consider what thoughts might go 'up' into the air (often the more searching thoughts).

- Decide if the character cares what the audience thinks of him at different points. Does Tom want to be answered? Will the audience agree with what Tom says or will he have to persuade them?

- The moments that were most exciting were when we saw Tom having a change of thought or a revelation.

What is the pressure or impulse to speak? Why does Tom speak to the audience? It is not so much 'Why does Tom speak?' as 'Why are other characters there at this point and how are they connected to what Tom is thinking/ feeling?' Is Tom 'grieving outwardly'?

How might the 'frame' of the space be broken and what effect would that have (e.g., leaning on the proscenium arch)?

EXERCISE *Direct address*

Young actors were sent away to pick a number between one and ten and asked to deliver the line: 'To be or not to be? That is the question'. One represented very low confidence or status while ten represented very high confidence and status. The company tried to guess which number was being played.

Repeat the exercise with one representing a character who really needs the audience's help, and ten being a character who doesn't need help at all.

This highlights a vital distinction in direct address: the difference between *showing* the audience that you need them (for example) and a character having a relationship with/to the audience and *feeling* towards them. The character should never be 'non-active' or 'passive' in relation to the audience.

CASTING

TOM (14) should be somehow other-worldly. • Can hold the stage. • Is not a conventional leading man. • Doesn't quite know how to hold himself. • Sees things in an epic way. • Is immature, as he was put forward a year (has the mental age of 12). • The music begins to disappear as he stops finding the fun in things. • The actor must be able to understand the journey that Tom makes in the play and understand the way the play works around him.

TIGHT (14/15) Genuinely cool. • Vulnerable. • Good comic timing. • An actor who can deliver something underneath the surface.

STAN Someone who has to believe he is someone, because nobody else does.

ADULTS All the adults are Tom's perceptions of them. • All kids are normal. • All adults are weird.

ENSEMBLE There could be a living ensemble present throughout the play, 'dressing' the world of the play and giving it a wider life.

Sex of characters can be changed if necessary, though ideally Tom, Luke and Tight should be male.

TEXT

The text should not be cut or changed except in the following two instances:

1. Companies can tweak references that are specific to London in the text to make it appropriate to their town, city or region.

2. Companies can alter swearwords to prevent offence. The suggestion made was to use the *Battlestar Galactica* technique (the current series, not the Dirk Benedict original) in which 'frack' is substituted for 'fuck' and so on . . .

From a workshop led by Josie Rourke
with movement by Dominic Le Clerc
and notes by Sam Yates

FUGEE

Abi Morgan

Abi Morgan's award-winning plays include *Skinned*, *Sleeping Around*, *Tiny Dynamite* and *Tender* and *Splendour*, recently broadcast on Radio 3. For TV she has written *My Fragile Heart*, *Murder*, *Tsunami – the Aftermath* and *Sex Traffic*, a multi-award-winning drama for Channel 4. Work for film includes *Brick Lane*, an adaptation of Monica Ali's bestselling book. *White Girl*, a ninety-minute film for BBC2, was broadcast in early 2008.

Author's Note

Fugee came out a period of research for a television drama I was working on based around immigration and asylum. It became apparent that the stories of unaccompanied minors were vital and needed to be told. There seemed no better opportunity to place these lives immediately centre stage than in the NT 'Connections' project.

Ben Okri says: *'We plan our lives according to a dream that came to us in our childhood, and we find that life alters our plans. And yet, at the end, from a rare height, we also see that our dream was our fate. It's just that providence had other ideas as to how we would get there. Destiny plans a different route, or turns the dream around, as if it were a riddle, and fulfils the dream in ways we couldn't have expected.'*

Fugee is a play about lost dreams, lost countries and a generation of lost children walking the pavements of London. This play is for them. I cannot think of a more appropriate cast of players than those from the youth groups, schools and colleges that have taken on this play. It was a privilege to write this for them and for the two thousand or more unaccompanied minors who come into this country every year seeking asylum.

Characters

Kojo
Ara
Cheung
Hassan
Roza
Mother
Father
Brother
Young Woman with Buggy
Dying Man
Street Cleaner
Market Trader
Girl One
Girl Two
Woman with Boyfriend
Passport Controller
Refuge Manager
Social Worker
Translator
Refuge Counsellor

Kids with Guns

Ticket Collector

Man in Hotel

Boy in Burger Bar

Father in Burger Bar

All the parts are to be played by young people.
Age/nationality is not applicable to any part.

SCENE ONE

An urban street, frozen mid-moment like some dark, classical painting.

Two young Girls, mouths gaping in horror, craning their necks to see:

A Woman averting her eyes.

Her Boyfriend, jacket removed, trying to cover the body of a Man stabbed on a pavement.

A Market Trader desperately trying to make a call on his cellphone.

A Street Cleaner looking up from heaving a refuse sack out of a dustbin.

The blur of human traffic, frozen mid-step, all around.

Kojo, a young boy, suddenly illuminated.

Kojo My name is Kojo. The person playing me is an actor. I don't exist. Except in this story. This is my story. I choose where it starts. It starts now –

Suddenly the scene springs into action.

Trader Fuck fuck fuck –

The Woman is screaming.

Girl He's gone, man. Dat man's gone.

Boyfriend Please can someone please get help?

Cleaner Turn him on his side. Turn him on his side. There's stuff coming from his mouth, bro.

The scene freezes again.

Kojo points to body of the Man stabbed on the pavement.

Kojo That man. The man on the ground . . . I don't know his name. (*Pointing to Woman.*) There's a woman screaming.

The Woman starts screaming again and then freezes, silent.

She's screaming a lot.

The Woman starts screaming again.

Right in my ear. Someone needs to shut her up . . . . Only I'm not here.

The Woman stops screaming, now gone.

I'm running. I'm running with this –

Kojo holds up a bloody knife, out to the audience.

Young Woman Oh my God . . .

A Young Woman walks into the scene with a buggy, freezing on seeing the knife in his hand.

Kojo Back . . . Stay back . . .
Young Woman I've not fed her yet. Please no . . .
Kojo It's OK . . . It's OK . . .
Young Woman Get away . . .
Kojo I'm not . . .

The Young Woman starts crying, shielding her baby.

Young Woman Don't hurt my baby . . . Don't you fucking touch her.

The Young Woman starts screaming.

Kojo And I'm running again.

The Young Woman stops screaming, now left far behind.

There's something you should know. When I speak, no one understands me. I don't speak your language. I come

from the Ivory Coast. It lies in the middle of the
tropical rain forest. So I miss trees. I really miss trees –
les arbres.

Don't worry. Even if I am speaking my language, the
actor makes it sound like English. The others won't
understand me. But you will. And you're the people
I want listening to me.

The screech of a car horn –

Driver For fuck's sake. Dickhead.

Kojo So I'm running. Don't know where. Where am I
going? I'm passing . . . a burger place . . . a man with
a kid . . .

*A Man looks up from eating a burger, staring blankly
at Kojo.*

He's got ketchup dripping down his chin . . . His kid
keeps . . . tapping on the glass . . . Got a little plastic
monster . . . with his burger . . . The kid's –

*A Little Kid holds up a plastic toy, smiles, tapping on
a window.*

– happy.

The Little Kid is pulled away by his Father.

I'm gonna be . . . sick . . . I've still got . . . It's all slippery
in my hand.

Kojo drops the knife. He's shaking.

I can taste . . . metal . . . It's blood.

*Kojo bends over, starts throwing up, crying, a total
mess, snot and tears pouring down his face.*

It's his blood.

SCENE TWO

A children's refuge.
A young girl, Ara, stands by a bunk-bed.

Ara (*to audience*) My name is Ara. I'm from Kabul.
I don't know where the actor is from playing me. It
doesn't really matter. It doesn't really matter if she
looks nothing like me. She is speaking my words.
She's good isn't she?

Kabul is in Afghanistan. Population 31,889,923.
Afghanistan is the only nation whose name begins
with an A but doesn't end in an A. I know a lot of
facts. Not the actor. Me.

Africa . . . Asia . . . See . . .? See?

Kojo turns suddenly, hiding something in the back of
his trousers, pulled out from under a bunk-bed.

This bit happened before . . . before all the other stuff.
This bit is important. Because it's when he met me.
When Kojo met me –

The distant murmur of a TV.

It's *X-Men. X-Men.*
Kojo Huh?

Kojo, a beaten-up holdall next to him, dishevelled in a
too-big T-shirt.

Ara *X -Men.* Downstairs?
Kojo Cool.
Ara They show videos on Friday. Except when they
break down. They always break. Then there's ping
pong. Ping pong?

(*To audience.*) We don't speak the same language.
Where we are, no one speaks the same language. This

is a refuge. It's where they bring all the fugees. All the fugees who have got here, here into this country, your United Kingdom, on their own or even with someone and maybe they are now on their own.

Unaccompanied minors. That's him. That's me. I came in a lorry. (*Beat.*) To stay here you have to be under sixteen.

Silence.

What you got?
Kojo Huh?
Ara Behind your –

Kojo hesitates, holds out a photo. Ara takes it, smiling on seeing –

That your –?

Kojo's Brother enters, a football under his arm. smiling, as if posing for a photograph.

Kojo Brother.

Kojo's Father enters, joining Kojo's Brother, a look of surprise, hand over his eyes, as if squinting in the sun.

Ara Abba.
Kojo Papa.
Ara You've got his ears. (*Gesturing.*) Ears.
Kojo No.
Ara Yeah.

Kojo laughs. Ara laughs. Kojo points to the photo.

Ara She's pretty.

Kojo's Mother enters, face freezing mid-laughter, the photo taken.
    Kojo nods.

Kojo holds out his hand. Ara hands him back the photograph. Kojo's family exit.

Ara Don't put it on the wall. The other kids . . .
Kojo Huh?
Ara Keep it in your pocket . . .

Ara points to Kojo's pocket.

Pocket. The other kids nick photos.

Kojo holds out his hand. Ara hands back the photo. Kojo's family exit.

Kojo I don't know what you're saying.
Ara Huh?

Ara laughs. Kojo laughs.

You should come down?
Kojo Huh?
It's noisy. It's too noisy.
Ara What?
Kojo Downstairs. It's too . . .

Kojo mimes head-thumping.

Wah . . . wah . . . wah . . .
Ara It's just a dumb movie. (*Beat.*) Kojo?

Kojo is surprised.

Ara You're name's written up on the wipeboard.
Kojo Huh?

Ara laughs.

Ara It's where they write up the names of the new kids.
  Ara.
Kojo Cool. Cool. (*To audience.*) Did she say . . .? I don't
  get a word of what she's saying?

Ara (*to audience*) This is his story.
Kojo Kojo.
Ara Did anyone ever tell you –
Kojo Huh?
Ara – you've got really big hands.

SCENE THREE

An urban street.
  The Young Woman with the buggy screams.

Young Woman (*to audience*) Hi. I'm the girl with the
  buggy, the one earlier?

  The Young Woman screams to demonstrate –

It's really hard to do that. You can really damage your
  voice if you're not careful. Don't worry. It's not a real
  baby.

  *The Young Woman pulls back the blanket in the
  buggy, holds up a pink plastic doll.*

A real baby is much bigger than this. I don't know why
  they want me to speak. Just that I was there. Not me.
  Because I'm an actor. But the girl I'm playing. She was
  there. I thought I should have had way more gold
  jewellery and nicer clothes, but they put me in this
  tracksuit. I don't know why. I mean, look at me? I'm
  fifteen, right. Just cause I'm a kid with a kid. They
  don't have to dress me all up nasty . . . But I'm not
  important. I'm just someone who was there. I've got
  eighteen lines . . . So far . . . That's not bad for someone
  who was just there.

  *The Young Woman with a buggy starts screaming at
  Kojo, the bloody knife in his hand.*

Because this is his story. The kid. The kid with the knife . . .
The one who's about to kill me.

The Young Woman starts screaming again.

Kojo It's OK . . . It's OK . . .
Young Woman Fuck off.
Kojo I'm not gonna . . .

The Young Woman starts crying, shielding her baby.

Young Woman Fuck off. Don't hurt my baby . . . Don't
you fucking touch her.

The Young Woman starts screaming.
*Kojo starts running, leaving the Young Woman
behind.*

Young Woman (*to audience*) That's it. My job done.
That's all you'll really see of me.

*The Young Woman exits. Kojo stops, leans against a
wall, bends over, throws up, crying . . .*
*Cheung, a young man, runs past him, pulling at
Kojo's hoodie, urging him on.*

Cheung Run, bro . . . Run . . .

Sirens. Lights. Kojo running.

SCENE FOUR

Heathrow Airport.
*Kojo stands waiting in line at passport control. He is
carrying a beaten-up holdall.*

Kojo (*to audience*) This bit. This bit comes a bit earlier.
Like a lot earlier.

*A Passport Controller sits in a glass booth, barely
looking up –*

Controller Next . . . Step up to the line.

Kojo hesitates, steps up to the line on the floor.

Passport.

Kojo stares at him.

Do you have a passport?

Kojo shakes his head.

Are you travelling alone?

Kojo hesitates.

Are you on your own?

Kojo hesitates, nods.

Kojo *Oui.*

The Passport Controller makes a phone call. Kojo rocks gently back and forwards on his feet, waiting.

SCENE FIVE

A children's refuge.
The slam of doors.
Distant sound of shouting. Laughter. Music on a radio.
Kojo follows the Refuge Manager along an endless corridor. He is carrying a beaten-up holdall.

Manager Bathroom. Showers. TV room. Bedrooms. Six to each room. I've put you a towel on your bed.

Kojo enters a long dormitory, a bunk-bed, a towel folded waiting for him.

It's fish, beans and chips for supper.

Silence.

It's a bit scary the first night. Some of them are a bit of a
rough bunch. Just mouthy, but you look like you can
handle yourself. How old are you? How old? Never
mind. I'll get one of the counsellors to come and talk
to you tomorrow. Do you speak any English?

Silence

English?

Kojo hesitates, shakes his head.

Is that all you've got?

Silence.

You can pick up some more clothes tomorrow. We've got
a store downstairs in the office. Nothing to get excited
about, they'll be trousers and clean T-shirts and pants
if you need them. They your only shoes? (*Pointing.*)
Shoes.

Kojo looks down at his worn trainers, nods.

You can get some more trainers downstairs. Where are
you from? Home?

Kojo Africa.

Manager We've got a couple of kids from Africa. Congo,
I think. The other boys will be up later. Have a shower.
You're nice and early. The water should be hot . . .
You've chosen a good day to arrive. It's Friday. Friday's
video night . . . *X-Men.*

Kojo Huh?

Manager That's what they're showing tonight. Supper's
at five. Alright, lovey?

Kojo nods.

Gillian.

Silence.

Make yourself at home, pet. Do you like fish? There's veg
   lasagne if you don't.

   The Refuge Manager exits.
      *Kojo sinks down on his bed, pulling out things from
   his holdall. A book. A few clothes. A photograph.*
      A football rolls past.
      Kojo's Brother passes.

Brother Hey Kojo. You want to play?
Kojo Nah, after homework.
Brother Your loss.
   *Kojo's Brother dribbles the ball, kicking it backwards
   and forwards.*
      The slam of the ball, repetitive, Kojo watches until –
      Kojo's Mother passes, singing.

Mother You see your father yet? Run and meet him.
   Don't dawdle. There's chicken for tea. You hear me,
   Kojo?
Kojo Yeah –
Mother And pick me up some Coca-Cola. You listening,
   boy?
Kojo Yeah.
Mother The sun's so strong today.

   *Kojo's Mother holds a hand up to her eyes, squinting
   in the sun.*

Don't sit out here all day, dreaming.

   Kojo's Mother and Brother exit.

Cheung Hey, new boy.

   Kojo looks up, Cheung stands in the doorway.

What you looking at?

SCENE SIX

A park.
Ara stands, staring at Kojo, hands smeared with blood holding the knife, Cheung by his side.

Ara No . . . No . . . No . . . Kojo . . .

Kojo goes to touch her. Ara pulls away. The scene freezes.

Cheung (*to audience*) She's a bit upset.

The scene springs back into life.

Dump it, man. Dump it.

Kojo hesitates, unsure what to do next, He hurls the knife into a distant bush.

What you going to do?
Kojo Huh?
Ara Kojo, why? What were you thinking of?
Kojo He looked at me –
Ara Who?
Kojo He was looking at me. He kept looking at me.
Ara Talk to me. You're not making any sense.

Kojo starts crying.

Don't cry . . . Don't cry.
Cheung Where you get the knife?

The scene freezes.

(*To audience.*) From a kitchen. It's a kitchen knife. From a place you haven't seen yet. (*Pointing to himself.*) Cheung. Two years here. I'm fourteen. Little for my age. That makes it easier. I can do tricks. He can't, the actor playing me. But if he could, if he was actually me, he could backflip across here and balance on one thumb. His whole body on one thumb. But he's just an actor, playing me. He's also Chinese. Even if he's not. He is. Because he's playing me. And I'm Chinese. From Zhongshan. A village that's a thousand years old. In Zhongshan I did tricks for money. Except no one had any money. Five months. Five months it took me to get here. To the United Kingdom. At the refuge, they never questioned me. They never questioned my age. Not everyone is so lucky. They don't have many places. It's just what they do. If you're not sixteen, then they don't have to look after you. If you don't look sixteen then they'll find a way not to have to deal with you. But look at me . . . OK, the actor playing me is taller than I would be, but I look like a kid . . . Even when I'm forty. I'll still look like a kid.

I can fold myself up so tight I can fit in a little box. You're going to have to imagine it.

But this isn't about me. This is Kojo's story. This isn't about me.

The scene leaps into action.

You're a dead man.

Ara They'll never let you back. They'll never let you back now, Kojo.

Ara starts to weep. Kojo grabs a bottle of water, rinsing his hands.

Have you gone crazy? Crazy? Kojo. Why?

Kojo Huh?

Ara Why? Look at me . . . Look at me . . . I don't know you . . . I don't know who you are . . .

Ara runs away, leaving him behind.

Kojo Ara . . . Ara . . . (*To audience.*) This bit. This is the worst bit. This bit is really . . .

Cheung You're fucked, man.
Kojo (*to audience*) Let's go back. I want to go back. Go back to before all this.

SCENE SEVEN

A dusty road.
Kojo is standing alone, two bottles of Coca-Cola in his hands.

Kojo (*to audience*) Standing in the road near my house . . . The place where I am from . . . Where I have come from . . . Côte d'Ivoire . . . Remember . . . Good . . . good . . . You can see . . . trees . . . and a river . . . And the Coca-Cola stall. Just a plastic crate, really, with a woman selling drinks from a bucket . . . I walk along this road to meet my father. Today I have bought Coca-Cola for my mother. Two bottles. I'm a bit nervous. It's nearly dusk. We need to be home before the curfew. The military are already out. Their trucks rumble past . . .
Today is my eleventh birthday . . .

Kojo's Mother, Father and Brother enter.

That is my mother, that is my father and that is my brother. Tamba, It means second born. They're also played by actors.

Kojo's Mother, Father and Brother smile at the audience, throwing a little wave.

My father was a bit taller. My mother was a bit fatter. My brother . . . Actually that's quite a good fit for him. Today is very important. Today is my eleventh birthday.

Kojo's Mother produces a birthday cake.

Mother Make a wish.

Kojo blows out the candles. Everyone cheers and claps, singing 'Happy Birthday'.

Father You're getting too big for birthday cake.

Kojo shakes his head.

Kojo No, that's not what he said.
Father Capital of Botswana.
Kojo Gaborone.
Father Good, good.
Kojo He's a teacher. And then my mother says –
Mother Eat your cake. You're too skinny. Do you hear me?

Kojo's Mother smiles, squeezing his cheeks.

Kojo There'd always be too much to eat.
Brother Can I play football?
Mother It's getting dark.
Brother Just in the yard . . . Just in the yard . . .
Mother Five minutes . . .
Brother Kojo. Two in . . . Two in . . .
Mother Your brother has his homework.

Kojo's Mother and Father exit. Kojo is left sitting, doing his homework.

Brother Hey, Kojo.
Kojo Go away.
Brother Who you going to play for?

Kojo's Brother hits the ball back and forth against a wall.

Kojo Real Madrid.

Kojo looks up from his homework. Kojo's Brother is now gone.

This is how I think of them. When I lie in my bunk at
night, Cheung farting above me. This how I remember
them, the snapshot of my family. Before all this mess . . .
Before I came to this country . . . Before . . . when I
was home . . . With my family . . . With my family at
home.

SCENE EIGHT

The children's refuge.
   Cheung leans down from the bunk-bed above Kojo.

Cheung Hey, new boy.
Kojo Huh?
Cheung You're talking. In your sleep.
Kojo Huh?
Cheung Sleep.
Kojo Sleep.
Cheung *Mian.*
Kojo Huh?
Cheung 'Sleep' in Mandarin. How you get here?
Kojo Huh?
Cheung Me. Lorry. Five months getting here.
Kojo Plane.
Cheung You pay someone? How much did it cost to get
   you here?
Kojo Dunno.
Cheung Where's your family?
Kojo No family.
Cheung How old are you?

   Kojo holds up his fingers, ten then four.

Fourteen?

   Kojo shrugs.

Cheung Me too. (*Seeing look.*) Fourteen. Make sure you
 tell them that. Tomorrow.
Kojo Tomorrow.
Cheung Some of the social workers are thick. And shave.
 Shave your face.
Kojo Huh.
Cheung Don't let them see the hair on your lip.
Kojo OK . . .
Cheung Cool.
Kojo Cool, yeah.
Cheung Yeah, we're cool, man.
Kojo *Mian.*
Cheung *Mian.*

Kojo rolls over and goes to sleep.

Kojo *Sommeil.*
Cheung *Sommeil?* Sleep?
Kojo *Oui.*
Cheung Night.
Kojo Night.
Cheung And Kojo . . . Keep it down a bit . . .
Kojo Yeah . . . Yeah . . .
Cheung No farting in your sleep.

SCENE NINE

The children's refuge.
 *Kojo looks down at his blood-stained T-shirt, pulling
it off.*

Kojo *Fugee.* Slang for refugee of political oppression or
 natural disaster who are usually applying for residency.
 Also used as an adjective. *Fugeed.* Means something
 that has been lived in, soiled, stained, looted or
 otherwise damaged by a lengthy dirty habitation.

'Wow, man, that's a great new plasma TV! Thanks,
I got it cheap from some fugees down the market.'

Kojo holds up the bloody T–shirt, throwing it away.

'Get away with your nasty dirty fugeed T-shirt.'

*The Refuge Manager enters with a Social Worker and
a Translator.*

(*To audience*.) They're actors too. She runs the refuge.
He's a social worker. And a translator. They've given
her glasses . . . to make her look clever. The clever one,
she's going to translate for me.
Social Worker Can you ask him to sit down?
Translator You can sit down, Kojo.

*Kojo obliges by sitting down. The Social Worker faces
him, writing on a clipboard.*

Social Worker How long have you been here?
Translator How long –?
Kojo Two –
Translator Two weeks. He arrived in the UK two weeks
ago.
Social Worker Country of origin?
Translator Where are you from?
Kojo *Côte d'Ivoire.*
Social Worker He can put his shirt back on now.

The Refuge Manager nods to a clean shirt.

Manager You can put it on.
Social Worker He's very developed. For fourteen.
Manager Not particularly.
Social Worker He's got hair. On his face.
Manager A lot of boys his age coming through have.
They're shaving . . . sometimes as young as twelve.
We've had boys who've got papers, ID, that says

they're twelve and they have hair. It doesn't mean
anything if he has hair.

Social Worker Hmm. Can he open his mouth?

The Refuge Manager hesitates, nods to the Translator.

Translator He wants to see your teeth.

Kojo My teeth?

Kojo opens his mouth. The Social Worker peers in.

Manager No . . . This isn't right . . . This is not
procedure . . .

Social Worker He's got back teeth coming through.
Wisdom teeth.

Manager Are you agency? Are you an agency social
worker?

Kojo What's he saying?

Manager You need a doctor. To do a medical. You need
a doctor if you want to do this.

The scene freezes.

(*To audience.*) Sometimes they use agency social workers . . .
They're barely social workers. I read the reports. They
don't even know how to spell half the time.

The scene springs back into life.

Social Worker He's not fourteen.

Kojo What's he saying?

Manager I know when they are lying. This boy is not
lying. He is fourteen. Boys can look older at fourteen –

Social Worker He has family over here?

Translator Is your family here?

Kojo shakes his head.

Social Worker Who paid to get you on the flight?

Translator It was his uncle. He's already said it was his
uncle.

Social Worker Just translate, please.

Translator Did you use an agent, did someone in your family pay to get you over here?

Kojo My uncle.

Translator And you had papers?

Kojo Visa. He told me to destroy it. I flushed it down the toilet on the plane. On a fake visa.

Translator And someone was meant to meet you?

Kojo No.

Translator They just abandoned you here?

Social Worker I have down his story. You can stop now.

The Social Worker starts to write something down on his clipboard. The scene freezes.

Manager (*to audience*) He's writing down 'moustache'. Only he's spelt it . . . 'mustash'. 'The young adult has a light mustach . . . and a deep voice . . .' This is what he'll put in Kojo's notes. They're not all like this . . . But it's the dog arse of jobs . . . No one wants to do social work any more . . . So they draft people in from everywhere . . . And their job is to keep numbers down . . . Their job is to get these kids out of the Home Office's hair as soon as they can . . . It's not his problem if he puts down he thinks this boy is over eighteen . . . The other stuff . . . The other stuff isn't of interest to him . . . The story of this boy's life.

The scene springs back into life.

Translator Your uncle just sent you over with nobody?

Social Worker She can stop now.

Translator Where are your parents?

Kojo I have no parents.

Translator You have no family?

Social Worker He's not fourteen.

Manager (*to audience*) See . . . See . . . He's just a kid . . . He's just a kid.

Kojo What's he saying?
Translator He's saying –
Manager He's age-disputing you.
Kojo What does that mean? What does that mean?
Manager Kojo, you can go now.
Translator He thinks you're not a child, Kojo . . . He
thinks that you're lying . . .

Silence.

Manager Kojo lovey, have some lunch. Go on . . . Go on.

SCENE TEN

Dining room, the children's refuge.
Cheung and Ara sit among three or four other
children, eating their lunch.

Cheung (*to audience*) If you're age-disputed by the social
worker that comes, it means –
Ara (*to audience*) – they don't think you're a kid. If
you're a kid they have to look after you. Give you
food, clothes, bed and stuff. If you're seventeen you're
out of here . . . If you're eighteen, then they don't give
a monkey's about you. They just don't want you as
their problem. So that's why they age-dispute you.

A boy looks up from eating. His name is Hassan.

Hassan (*to audience*) The Home Office gives you eight
weeks to prove you are under eighteen before they
process you as an adult. Some kids end up in hotels.
In Croydon. With other adults . . . They're the worst.
You have to argue . . . You have to fight . . .
Ara Getting here is only the start of the journey . . .
Hassan Legally they have to give you a medical. By a
doctor. If they say you're not the age then they have to

give you a medical. They measure your wrist. Check your teeth. They can tell your age from your wrist and teeth. Like a dog.

Hassan starts barking, making the other kids laugh.

(*To audience.*) I'm Hassan. I'm from Iraq. I'm the good-looking one.

The Girl next to him smirks. Her name is Roza.

Roza Yeah, right.
Hassan She's from Iraq too. (*Looking to her.*) I am. We're all good-looking in Iraq.
Roza (*to audience*) Ignore him. Please. Don't humour him.
Hassan Shut up, Roza. When the living proof is in front of your eyes. You know you want to do it, Roza.
Roza I'd rather fuck a fish, Hassan. (*Eyeing Kojo.*) He's cute.

Kojo slides down next to them, staring at his food.

He doesn't talk much. Hey.
Ara Leave him alone. He's new.
Hassan You getting jealous, girl.

Ara tuts, ignoring Hassan.

Ara (*to audience*) There's nothing to do. Most days we just hang about. Watch TV. Play ping pong. We can't go to school. Not until you get proper refugee status. And that can take months. So we teach one another. We are our own school. That's how we learn things.

Ara holds up her fork, showing it to Kojo.

Fork. Fork.
Kojo Fork.
Ara Knife.
Kojo Knife.

Hassan (*to audience*) Ara thinks she knows everything.
Ara Ketchup.
Hassan Ketchup useful.
Cheung Leave them alone.
Hassan Shut up, Bruce Lee.
Cheung (*to audience*) This is when I kick him with my big toe, send him flying across the table. But the actor playing me, he can't do that . . .
Hassan Fortunately.
Cheung For you.
Hassan Get out my face, man.

Cheung gets up to go. Hassan trips him up. A fight erupting.
The Refuge Manager pulls them apart.

Manager Upstairs.
Cheung Huh. Don't know what you're saying.
Hassan We don't speak English.
Manager Pull the other one, Ant and Dec – upstairs.

Cheung and Hassan are led away by the Refuge Manager.

Ara (*to audience*) There are a lot of fights because no one really understands one another. Everyone's always shouting, trying to be understood. So many languages – Chinese.
Cheung Mandarin, man. There's no such language as Chinese.
Roza (*to audience*) Spanish. The kids from Columbia speak Spanish. French. Serbian. Turkish. If you're from the Congo . . . you might speak –
Ara Bantu.
Roza Kinshasa.
Ara Mande.
Roza Farsi, Arabic. There's a kid from Eritrea. There's nine languages in Eritrea.

Ara Urdu, Hindi, Punjabi . . .
Roza All sounds Dutch to me.

Ara holds up the salt cellar, showing it to Kojo.

Ara Salt.
Kojo Salt.

Ara holds up the pepper pot.

Ara Pepper.
Kojo Pepper.
Roza Cute . . . Very cute.

Ara looks at Roza. Roza smiles.

Roza (*pointing to plate*) Chip.
Kojo Chip.

Roza smiles, eats the chips.

Ara Everyone's always fighting. Everyone's always got
stuff going on in their head . . . Memories . . . Bad
stuff . . . Bad stuff they bring with them.

Kojo smiles, Roza teasing him as he eats.

Roza, stop bothering him.

SCENE ELEVEN

Room, the children's refuge.
Roza sits in a chair, opposite the Refuge Counsellor.

Roza (*to audience*) When you arrive they give you a
counsellor. Someone to talk to, who tries to help you
with your story.

*A Translator comes in, sits down next to the Refuge
Counsellor, smiles at Roza.*

Coming 'to terms' with your story.

Counsellor Can you remember your home?

Translator Roza?

Roza I remember the bombs. We played games trying to work out where they would hit. (*To audience.*) Then she translates. Which takes for ever. And all I can think is why doesn't she shave her legs. Her legs are hairier than a gorilla.

Cheung enters, changes places with Roza. Roza exits.

Counsellor How are you feeling today, Cheung?

Cheung Good. Good.

Counsellor I understand they may have found your aunt.

Cheung She's not even family.

Counsellor I bet she wants you home.

Cheung No. She wants her money. The money my mother borrowed to get us over here. (*To audience.*) My mother died in the lorry we were in on the way over here.

Counsellor But you must miss her.

Cheung (*to audience*) This is where they try and trip you up. No. My mother paid twelve thousand yuan to get us here. Which we owe my aunt who's not my aunt. She's just the woman who arranged the lorry.

Cheung gets up. Hassan takes the seat. Cheung exits.

Translator Your aunt is very concerned. She wants to know how your English is coming along.

Hassan Fish and chips. I like that, baby. Yo, bro. Wicked. Wicked.

The Refuge Counsellor takes notes, bemused.

Good . . . Good . . . English good . . .

Counsellor Good . . .

Hassan flicks his chair with his feet.

Translator Stop doing that with your chair, Hassan.

Hassan Sorry . . . Sorry. (*To audience.*) Sometimes when I'm sitting here, I think what would the Beast do, probably the best of the *X-Men*. Superhuman strength, speed, stamina, agility, reflexes, enhanced senses, ambidexterity with hands and feet, minor pheromone manipulation, felinoid form, blue fur, night vision, claws, wall-climbing. . . It's a wicked movie. You should see it. But this is not about me. Is it? This is Kojo's story –

Hassan gets up to let Kojo sit down. Hassan exits.

Counsellor And how are you settling in here?
Translator Everything OK?
Kojo I have no toothpaste. I have no toothpaste here.
Counsellor The Refuge Manager should sort that for you.

Kojo nods, slumped in his chair.

Counsellor Would you like to tell us a bit about your story, Kojo?

Silence.

Why you came to England?

Silence.

It says here . . .

The Counsellor reads the Social Worker's report in her hand.

You last saw you family on –
Kojo My eleventh . . .
Translator His eleventh –
Kojo Birthday.
Counsellor I see. Would you like to tell me about it, Kojo?

Kojo No.
Counsellor I can't help you if you don't tell me your
story, dear.

Kojo stays silent.

So you're fourteen now . . . It was three years ago.
Kojo Yes.
Counsellor You must miss them very much.

Kojo suddenly scrapes back his chair.

Translator He doesn't want to talk about this.
Counsellor Tomorrow, Kojo. We'll talk again tomorrow.

*Kojo's Brother passes, dribbling a ball. Kojo watching
him.*
   *The Counsellor and Translator follow his gaze,
seeing nothing.*

Kojo?

Kojo nods, sinking back into his chair.

SCENE TWELVE

Kojo stands alone.

Kojo (*to audience*) This is part of my story. Just part of
my story. The story of my eleventh birthday.
   I am walking along the dust track near my home.
I am buying Coca-Cola for my mother.

Kojo's Mother passes, singing.

Mother You see your father yet? Run and meet him.
Don't dawdle. There's chicken for tea. You hear me,
Kojo?

Kojo's Mother holds a hand up to her eyes, squinting into the sun.

The sun's so strong today.

Kojo's Brother passes, dribbling a football.

Brother Hey, Kojo. Kojo, play football with me, eh? Two in . . . Two in . . .
Kojo Later.

The rumble of trucks.

I liked to walk to meet my father. My father is a teacher. I like to walk to meet him when the days are long and the curfews late. And today is special. Today is my birthday. Today my father will say –

Kojo's Father on the approach, carrying schoolbooks under one arm.

Father What's the Capital of Botswana?
Kojo Gaborone.
Father Good, good.
Kojo He'll say –
Father You're getting too big for a birthday cake.
Kojo Then he'll pick me up on his shoulders and carry me home to my mother and brother waiting for me. And my little brother will make us laugh and we'll all blow out candles on a birthday cake.

Kojo suddenly freezes. Two Soldier Boys, guns in hand, passing him.
   They stop, turn, watching Kojo walking away.

Only on that day there is no birthday cake. On that day I don't meet him or on any other day. On that day I don't ever see my mother, brother or father again. On that day I don't get to him. I don't get to my father.

The rumble of trucks going past.

Kojo's eyes watch, as if the truck is passing.

On that day they get to me, instead.

SCENE THIRTEEN

An underground. The scrape of trains passing through.
The Man seen earlier, knifed on the pavement, sitting reading his newspaper on a train.

Man (*to audience*) I'm the man you saw earlier, the one
being knifed. Which hasn't happened yet. Four
minutes before it happened, I was sitting on the train
reading the paper. In the paper it says by the year 2050
there will be over three billion more people on the
planet than there are now. That's a rise of ten million
in London alone. Makes you think about who you are
sitting next to –

The Man turns and looks at the Woman sitting next to
him. They smile.
The Man gets up and exits.

SCENE FOURTEEN

An urban street.
The Man walking along the street.
Two Girls chatting, one on her cellphone sitting on a
bench.
A Market Trader selling fruit, going about his day.
A Street Cleaner emptying bins close by.

Man (*to audience*) I am not thinking about any of these
things as I am walking. I am thinking about how much
work I've got. I'm anxious. I've got a lot on my mind.
I'm late. I want a coffee. And there's some kid in front

of me, dawdling. He's just some kid in a hoodie mucking about with his mate. Just some Chinese kid.

Cheung enters, smiling, sucking on a take-away drink, chewing on his straw, his hoodie pulled up.

I shove him, in a rush, wanting to get past.

Cheung's drink goes flying –

Kojo Get off, man.

Man Excuse me . . .? Excuse me . . .? I don't see the other boy has a knife . . . I don't see anything at first –

Kojo He's staring at me.

Man Oh my God . . . Oh my . . .

Cheung Kojo –

Kojo He just keeps staring at me.

The Man shoves Kojo. Kojo instinctively shoves him back, a knife suddenly in his hand.

Cheung Jesus, man.

Kojo looks down, shocked, blood dripping from the knife.

Girl What's going on?

Two young Girls' mouths gaping in horror, craning their necks to see –
A Woman holds the hand of her Boyfriend.

Woman Is that guy being robbed?

The Man holds out his arms, falling to the pavement.

Kojo (*to audience*) I don't even know I've done it.

The Woman starts screaming.

Girl He's gone, man. Dat man's gone.

The Man drops to the floor, blood pumping from his stomach.

Trader Fuck . . . fuck . . . fuck . . .

The Market Trader is desperately trying to make a call on his cellphone.

Boyfriend Please can someone please get help?

A Street Cleaner looks up from heaving a refuse sack out of a dustbin.

Cleaner Turn him on his side. Turn him on his side. There's stuff coming from his mouth, bro.

The scene suddenly freezes.

Kojo (*to audience*) I want you to know this isn't me. My part is being played by an actor, but this isn't me. I want you to know when you hear this story, that I am not just like all the other stories. I'm not like those other stories you read about . . . I'm not just another kid in a hoodie.

SCENE FIFTEEN

A dusty road. Kojo's Mother stands alone, looking out, clearly waiting.

Mother (*to audience*) When I stand on our road and look straight down . . . the last thing I see is the top of Kojo's head. Just disappearing over the brow of the road . . . It is very hot . . . The further away he walks he looks like he is melting into the road. I think to myself, that Coca-Cola is going to be warm before he ever gets it back to me. I don't know this is the last time I am ever going to see him . . . I don't know that I am looking at the last moments of my life. Memories in a flash, like a flick-flick file, falling from the sky in front of me . . . Kojo . . . kicking when I was making his bones in my belly . . . The sound of Tamba kicking the ball –

The steady slam of a football, back and forth against a wall, somewhere far off.

I don't know that these are the last sounds and smells I will savour. That watching Kojo walk over the brow of the hill, he is leaving me –

A rumble of a truck. A gang of Kids standing in the back of a truck, waving guns.

I don't hear what they are singing . . . But I know I have one son, still playing football with a chance –

Kojo's Mother turns to run.

(*Calling out.*) Tamba!

A Kid with a gun points it at Kojo's Mother.

– and one son who is already lost to me.

Kojo's Mother turns, raising her arms –

(*Shouting out.*) KOJO!

The sound of gunfire.

SCENE SIXTEEN

The children's refuge.

Kojo Maman –

Ara stands in the doorway.

Ara Kojo –

Kojo wakes with a start.

You were crying in your sleep.

Ara comes and sits on the end of Kojo's bed.

Have you been farting?

> *Kojo points upwards. The sound of Cheung snoring.*
> *They laugh.*

Kojo You?
Ara I never sleep. Too quiet.

> *A distant siren. Ara smiles. Kojo smiles.*

It's just too quiet for me. No boom-boom. Kapow . . .
  You?
Kojo Crazy dreams.
Ara Huh?
Kojo Crazy . . . crazy in my head.
Ara Yeah . . .
  Hey, you want something to eat?
  Eat?
Kojo Eat.
Ara Come on . . . Put your clothes on . . . Come on . . .
  We're going to eat.

SCENE SEVENTEEN

A burger bar.
  Ara and Kojo sit eating burgers.

Kojo Good . . .
Ara You've got ketchup –

> *Ara wipes Ketchup off his chin, licking her fingers.*

Kojo They don't ever know?
Ara Huh?
Kojo Out late? No one tell you no?
Ara They don't care. Long as we're there in the morning,
  not bringing back drugs and pimps.

Kojo Huh?

Ara Some of the girls . . . Some, the trafficked ones . . . The traffickers . . . They hang about for them.

Kojo To take them.

Ara Sometimes to take them back. (*Beat.*) Not me. I'd whack them, man.

Kojo laughs.

He does laugh.

Kojo If it's funny. Where are your family?

Ara shrugs.

Ara Boom-boom. Kapow . . .

Silence.

Kojo Just you?

Ara Just me. You want another –?

Ara points to Kojo's drink carton. Kojo shakes his head.

Kojo Too much money. Where you get money?

Ara smiles.

Ara Secret.

Kojo Pimp?

Ara No. Not me . . . Get away. Nasty man.

Kojo laughs. Ara laughs.

Go alright today?

Kojo shakes his head.

You really fourteen?

Kojo nods.

Some of the kids lie. Make up stories. Just to stay here.

Kojo Why?

Ara Where else do we go? No one else wants us here.

The Young Woman wheeling a buggy passes.

They won't let you stay if they don't think you're fourteen.

Kojo and Ara watches through the window.

Kojo I can look after myself. I can.
Ara Good. You're learning. What do you miss? From home?
Kojo *Les arbres.* I miss trees.
Ara Eat your burger.
Kojo Then what?

Ara gets up to go, passing two Girls.

Ara You're coming with me.

SCENE EIGHTEEN

A park.

Kojo Wow.
Ara Wow.
Kojo *Les arbres* . . .
Ara *Les arbres.*

Kojo and Ara run through the dark trees, whooping and shouting –

Ssh . . . Ssh . . . We're not meant to be in here . . . You're not allowed in here at night.
Kojo I want to climb. I want to climb the trees.
Ara You're a nutter. Nut-nut . . .
Kojo *Un fou.*
Ara *Un fou?*
Kojo A crazy.

Ara laughs.

Ara Yeah, you are *un fou.*
Kojo Come on.

Kojo whooping and laughing, running through the trees.

Let's climb the trees.

SCENE NINETEEN

An urban street.
  The scene, frozen –
  The Man walking along the street.
  Two Girls chatting, one on her cellphone sitting on
a bench.
  A Market Trader selling fruit, going about his day.
  A Street Cleaner emptying bins close by.

Kojo (*to audience*) When I replay the moments in my
  life, they are like snapshots –

Cheung, frozen, sucking on a takeaway drink, his hoodie pulled up.

– with all the good bits –

Kojo sucks on the drink, Cheung frozen, unable to complain.

– fighting all the bad.

Cheung's drink goes flying.

Man Oh my God . . . Oh my . . . .

The Man shoves Kojo, Kojo instinctively shoves him back, a knife suddenly in his hand.

Cheung Jesus, man.

Kojo looks down, shocked, blood dripping from the knife.
Two young Girls, mouths gaping in horror, craning their necks to see.

A Woman holds the hand of her Boyfriend.

Woman Is that guy being robbed?

The Man holds out his arms, falling to the pavement.
The scene suddenly freezes –
The man frozen in mid-air.

Kojo Held, suspended in time.

Blackout.

SCENE TWENTY

Kojo, two bottles of Coca-Cola in his hands, breaks into a smile.
Kojo's Father, just visible –

Father Kojo –

The rumble of a truck, passing.
Two Kids with guns, waving them in the air.
Kojo turns, sees at once –

Kojo (*calling out*) Papa.

Kojo starts running, trying to stop him.

No, Papa . . . No . . .

The ricochet of gunfire –
Kojo's Father holds out his arms, falling to the ground.
The scene suddenly freezes –
Kojo's Father, frozen in mid-air.

181

(*To audience.*) In two seconds, the boys . . . The boys
with the guns in the truck will point them at me.

The scene springs back into life.

Kojo's Father falls to the ground, dead.
    The two Kids with guns wave them at Kojo –

One of them is younger than me.

One of the Kids points it at Kojo's head.

Kid One Hey, boy.
Kojo Nine, maybe ten.
Kid Two Don't cry, boy.

The scene freezes, the Kid pointing his gun at Kojo's head.

Kojo They have just killed my mother. They have just
killed my brother. They have just killed my father. Kill
me. Kill me.

Kojo closes his eyes, almost willing it.

But they won't. They will say, 'Welcome brother' . . .
Then they will tell me to get in the back of the truck . . .
In words . . . in words I will not ask the actor who
is playing me to say . . . One of the boys will have a
football . . . my brother's football . . . They will take
me back to their camp . . . their barracks. They will
play football with my brother's football . . . They will
hit me. And beat me . . . And show me how to use a
gun . . . There is always a radio on . . . With music . . .
Rap music and . . . A pipe going around that I learn to
smoke and terrible things happening in the name of
some war . . . that I am now part of . . . I am now
part of . . .

The scene suddenly springs back into life. The Kid
with the gun pulls it away from Kojo's head, smiles.

I am eleven. I am made a soldier, one of their soldiers, on
  my eleventh birthday.

SCENE TWENTY-ONE

*Kojo stands facing the Refuge Manager, a black bin bag
resting on a now-stripped bed.*

Manager I'm really sorry.

  Kojo nods.

You know we tried, Kojo.

  Kojo nods.

I am sure the second assessment will go in your favour . . .
  Anyone can see . . . Anyone can see you're a child . . .
  The hotel's not that far away.

  *Ara stands in the doorway, Cheung close by, Roza and
  Hassan hovering.*

Ara It's a bus and a train and a bus from here.
Manager Ara, you keep out of it.
Cheung He hasn't got any money.
Manager Once they've sorted out all your paperwork . . .
Roza He's a kid. He's younger than me. Anyone can see.
Manager I'm so sorry. Come on, you lot. Downstairs.
Hassan Piss off. Stupid pissing system.
Manager Right, Hassan, that's your first warning. You,
  you don't get to play ping pong today.

  Hassan shakes his head, laughing, crazy.

Hassan Look at my teeth. I've got teeth, wisdom teeth.
  They put down on my form I'm a kid. And you take
  away ping pong . . . Ping pong . . .
Manager What? Talk English . . . Talk English.

Hassan Fuck off.

Manager Second warning.

Kojo It's OK . . . It's OK . . .

Ara Don't . . . Please . . . Don't make him go . . . He's got no money . . .

Kojo It's OK . . . It's OK . . .

The Manager hands him a train ticket and a five-pound note.

Manager That's your travel pass. It'll get you on the bus and the train, and a fiver to get something to eat.

Ara A fiver. And then what? And then what?

The Manager turns, heads out.

Manager You lot, down. Come on. It's bangers and mash for tea.

Ara And then what happens? Will they send him back?

Manager I don't know. He'll be processed and a decision will be taken from there. You'll have a visit. At the hotel. All the men in the hotel looking to stay here in this country get a visit.

Roza He's a kid, man.

Ara Do they know what has happened to him? Tell them your story, Kojo. Tell them . . . Tell them . . .

Ara looks to Kojo, already heaving his bag onto his back pocket.

(*To audience.*) The actor playing me gets really pissed off in this bit. She thinks if he just said here what had happened to him –

He shoves the ticket and fiver into his pocket.

(*To audience.*) – if they just knew that it's hard to stay looking and feeling fourteen when the things you have been asked to do, no one should be asked. When men are boys carrying guns and being a kid . . . being a kid seems like a long time ago . . . She thinks this should be where Kojo speaks up . . . She still believes that if people know, then everyone will look after him . . . Everyone will take care of him . . . And the next bit . . . The next bit won't happen . . . The next bit won't be the end to Kojo's story.

Ara stops him, pleading.

Ara Kojo . . . Kojo . . .

SCENE TWENTY-TWO

A train.
  Kojo, Ara, Cheung, Hassan and Roza seated in the train.

Cheung (*to audience*) We all go with him.

Hassan and Roza peer down the carriage.

Roza He's coming . . . He's coming.

A Ticket Collector moves along the train.

Hassan Just act dumb.
Cheung Easy man. Easy.
Hassan I thought it would be.

Cheung and Hassan go for one another.

Cheung Fuck off, Saddam.
Hassan Fluck off, Chicken Blackbean.

Roza and Ara nudge them apart.

Collector Tickets please.

Kojo holds out his ticket. The Ticket Collector stamps it, moving on.

Ticket.

Hassan Huh?

Collector Ticket please.

Ara No English.

Collector Right. Off at the next stop.

Roza Sorry?

Collector Off . . . Off . . . Now . . . Now . . .

Cheung *Au revoir.*

Ara *Bienvenu.*

Hassan *Adios.*

Roza *Kwa heri.* (*To audience.*) That's Swahili.

> *Kojo waves them goodbye. Kojo is now alone on the train.*
> *He scoops up his black bin bag, staring out blankly.*
> *A Man suddenly appears, sitting down in front of him. He looks up from over his paper.*

Kojo Papa.

> *It is Kojo's Father.*

Father Take your feet off the seat.

> *Kojo takes his feet off the seat.*
> *The train goes through a tunnel. Blackout.*
> *The train comes out of the tunnel.*
> *Kojo looks, the seat in front of him now empty.*

SCENE TWENTY-THREE

The hotel.
> *The slam of the door.*
> *Distant whooping.*
> *Kojo stares down at his bin bag, sinks down on the seat.*
> *He leans over, touches a radiator. It is cold.*
> *Kojo's Mother passes, drinking from a bottle of Coca-Cola.*

Mother Is this where you're going to sleep?
Kojo Yes, *maman*.
Mother Tuck your blanket in tight. Ssh . . . Go to sleep . . .
Go to sleep . . .

*Kojo lies back on the bed. Kojo's Mother pulls the
blanket across Kojo.*

Kojo The radiator's broken.
Mother Ssh. Go to sleep.

SCENE TWENTY-FOUR

An urban street.
A Market Trader selling stuff. Ara and Kojo loiter.

Ara He's very strong. Look.

The Market Trader hesitates, points to a crate.
Kojo lifts it.

Trader Two.

Kojo lifts two.

Four.

Kojo lifts four, nearly crippling him.

Trader Morning five quid.
Ara Six.
Trader You're taking the piss.
Ara That's what you pay me.
Trader You make good coffee. I can't pay you both.
Ara Give it to him. He needs it. He needs the money.
Trader Where you from?
Kojo *Côte d'Ivoire.*
Trader That's a bubble bath, isn't it? Come on, then,
look lively.

Kojo starts to shift crates. The Trader moves Ara on.

Trader Don't you have school to go to?
Ara Nope.
Trader Piss off, then, and go nick something or whatever you do.

A Man passes, slamming into Kojo, a coffee in hand.

You'll get a lot of that.
Kojo Huh?
Trader People like you are invisible to people like him.
Kojo Huh?

Kojo watches the Man already heading to the tube.

Trader The great unwashed. You had a bath?

Kojo hesitates, shrugs.

Look at you. Clean yourself up. Don't want to scare off the customers. Have a wash by tomorrow. You look a bit rough to me.

SCENE TWENTY-FIVE

The hotel.
    Kojo in the bathroom, top off, combing his wet hair.
    A Man banging on the door.

Man Hey, kid . . . Kid, let me in.

Kojo turns, clearly frightened.

Kojo (*to audience*) There are twelve men in the hotel. It's not really a hotel. It's six rooms, with a kettle and a fridge. The heating is broken and there is a man. A strange man. I don't know where he is from, but at night he tries to get into my room.
Man Hey, kid, come on, let me in.

Kojo I'm fourteen. A fourteen-year-old kid shouldn't be
put in a place alone with weirdos and sickos like this.
But there are worse places. There are worse places
I have been. I know what the man wants from me.
There are worse things I could do to him.

*Two Kids pass, carrying guns, waving to Kojo. Kojo
turns, trying to ignore them.*

And I have to remind myself to forget all of that. I have
to remind myself I am safe. I am in the United
Kingdom. I have to remind myself I am just a kid.

*The two Kids smile, swaggering with their guns, past
him.*

Go away.

The two Kids with guns exit.

Go away –

The Man keeps banging on the door.

– or I will kill you.

The banging stops.

SCENE TWENTY-SIX

*Kojo, still drying his hair. Ara holding a tin of tomato
soup and a tin opener.*

Kojo (*to audience*) The good days . . . The good days are
when Ara comes to visit me.
Ara Tomato soup. I nicked it from the refuge kitchen.
No one said anything. You got any bread?

Kojo shakes his head.

Kojo Marmite. Tea bag. Half a bag of crisps.

Ara You're useless.

Ara kisses him, moving on.

Kojo (*to audience*) Ara's in love with me.
Ara (*to audience*) I'm in love with him because –
Kojo Why?
Ara – because you're funny.
Kojo Yeah, right.
Ara Because you laugh like a duck.

Kojo laughs, ducklike.

Because you've the saddest eyes I've ever seen.

Ara touches his face, cupping his face in her hands.

Because of things you don't say. Talk to me.
Kojo About what?
Ara You OK?
Kojo Cool. Cool.

Ara nods, pouring soup into a bowl.

Ara Because there was you and then there was me.
Because you like tomato soup. Because I like tomato
soup.

Ara hands him a bowl of soup.

Because you're my only family.
Ara J'adore. (*Beat.*) J'adore. Say it.

Kojo drinks his soup.

Kojo Nice. (*Beat.*) Creamy.

SCENE TWENTY-SEVEN

The hotel.
  Kojo sitting alone on his bed.

Kojo (*to audience*) Love is like a tight ball, hard just here.

  A Man banging on the door.

The more it grows the tighter it gets.
Man Hey, kid. Hey, kid, let me in.

SCENE TWENTY-EIGHT

The refuge.
  Cheung and Hassan, lost in a game of ping pong.

Cheung (*to audience*) Love is a memory. A smell long
  forgotten.

  Cheung smashes the ball across the table, triumphant
  in a win. Hassan reluctantly concedes.

One day remembered.

  Hassan and Cheung knock fists.

SCENE TWENTY-NINE

The burger bar.
  Roza and Ara sucking on drinks, staring out at the
passing traffic of people.

Ara (*to audience*) Love is him.

  The Woman with her Boyfriend, lost in an argument.

Roza And her.

They kiss and make up.

Love is . . . despite everything . . . still wanting it . . .

Kojo passes carrying crates, the Market Trader shouting at him –

Trader Move it, you lazy shit.

SCENE THIRTY

The park.
Roza, Ara, Kojo, Hassan and Cheung sitting in the top of a tree.

Kojo (*to audience*) Love is sitting in the tallest tree, looking out across the world, and after everything . . .

Ara looks at him.

Ara Not hating it.

Hassan stands up, shakes the branches.

Kojo Don't do that.

Hassan carries on, laughing. Kojo suddenly grabs him, shaking him hard, too hard, shocking them.

Ara Kojo.
Hassan Hey, man, sorry, man.
Kojo Don't do that.
Ara Kojo . . . Kojo . . .

SCENE THIRTY-ONE

The refuge.
Kojo sits opposite the Cousellor, the Translator by his side.

Counsellor I've asked if maybe one of the psychiatrists could see you. But they don't have the paperwork for you, Kojo. You seem to have got a little lost in the system. Can you translate that, please?

Translator She's saying –

Kojo I know what she's saying.

Counsellor I can't see you here. My sessions are for the children living here. You can't keep coming back here. This place is for children. You are not deemed a child, Kojo. It says on your paperwork. It says they think you are eighteen.

Kojo There is a boy in the room next to mine. He is there with his brother. Twelve, maybe thirteen. A little younger than me. He doesn't know how to cook for himself. But it says on his papers, it says he's nearly twenty. I want my father. I want my father.

Kojo turns to the Translator.

Translator He's saying –

Counsellor I'm sorry. I'm sorry.

Kojo You don't care. This country doesn't care. We just get under your feet.

Translator He's saying –

Counsellor Yes . . . I understand. I hear what he says. I'm sorry.

Translator I'm sorry.

Kojo I don't know how to cook. How do I eat if I can't . . .

The distant murmur of a TV – X-Men or the like.

SCENE THIRTY-TWO

The hotel.
Kojo chopping vegetables with a knife.
The banging at the door.

Kojo slams the knife down on the board.
The banging stops. The sound of the Man walking away.
Kojo resumes chopping. Ara enters.

Ara Kojo – why didn't you wait for me?

Kojo ignores her, resuming cooking.

You could have stayed. It's video night. (*Beat.*) I'm going to school. My paperwork came through. I got asylum status. I can go to school.
Kojo That's good. Good for you.
Ara Don't be like that.
Kojo What you going to study?
Ara I don't know. Study something. Get good. Maths. English. Maybe you could one day . . . Maybe you could one day go to school.
Kojo No.
Ara Kojo –
Kojo I'm a grown-up. That's what they say I am. Adult. So that's what I'll be. A grown-up.

Ara goes to touch him. Kojo pulls away, resuming cooking.

Ara Next time come and visit. Eh? Next time you're passing by, come and visit me.

Ara leans over, smells the food.

You make this?
Kojo Who else is going to do it?
Ara Are you alright?
Kojo Huh?
Ara Why you being funny, Kojo? (*Beat.*) Kojo?

Ara exits. Kojo returns to chopping. Kojo stops chopping, the knife in his hand.

SCENE THIRTY-THREE

The hotel.
    Kojo lies in bed asleep.

Kojo At night, my mother sings to me –

    Kojo's Mother passes, singing.

Sometimes I sing along . . . I sing along with her . . .
Mother
    Dodo, l'enfant do.
    L'enfant dormira bien vite,
    Dodo, l'enfant do,
    L'enfant dormira bientôt.

    Kojo sings. Kojo's Mother passes his bed.

Kojo
    Lullaby, child, lullaby
    The child will quickly go to sleep,
    Lullaby, child, lullaby
    Go to sleep, baby.
Mother
    Tout le monde est sage
    Dans le voisinage
    Il est l'heure d'aller dormir
    Le sommeil va bientot venir.
Kojo
    Everybody's good
    In the neighbourhood,
    It's time to go to sleep
    Very soon you'll be asleep.

    Distant voices. Shouting. An argument in another
    room. Kojo's Mother gone.
        A rattling at Kojo's door. The shadowy figure of a
    Man passing, moving on.

Kojo determinedly goes back to sleep.

And that's when the dreams come to me.

SCENE THIRTY-FOUR

The rumble of trucks
  Kojo, standing at its heart, waving a gun in the air.
  Other Kids around him, all waving guns.
  A Man walking, carrying a heavy box on his back.
  The van pulls up.

Kid One Hey, old man . . .
Kid Two Hey, you . . .

  The Man turns. It is Kojo's Father.

Kojo Papa –

  Kid One knocks Kojo's Father to the ground.

Kid One What's inside? What's inside the box?

  *Kid Two kicks the box open, pulling out a birthday
  cake lit with candles. He smiles.*
    Kid Two points to Kojo.

Kid Two Kill him. Kill him. Now.

  Kojo hesitates, pushed on by Kid One.

Father Kojo –

  Kojo takes his gun, aims it at his Father.
    Gunfire.

SCENE THIRTY-FIVE

An urban street.
  Kojo shifts boxes for the Market Trader.
  Cheung loiters, sucking on a takeaway drink. –

Cheung You look like shit.

  The Market Trader passes, on his cellphone.

Ara says you're ignoring her. Talk to me, man.
Kojo Fuck off, Bruce Lee.
Cheung You need to sleep, man. Get some sleep. You look like you haven't slept in a week.

  Two Girls pass. Cheung eyes them up.

Hey, Kojo, nice pussies.

  The scene freezes.

Girl One (*to audience*) It's Saturday. On Saturday, we always do this –

  Girl Two eyes Cheung, frozen, mid-scene.

Girl Two Oh my God, you seen the muscles on him.
Girl One Nah, too small. Not my type. Stop messing, girl.

  Girl Two moves on to Kojo, frozen, mid-scene, holding a crate.

Girl Two He's cute.
Girl One Fuck off.
Girl Two You fuck off.
Girl One Boss-eyed.
Girl Two Nah . . . He's cute . . . How old? . . . Thirteen . . . Fourteen, maybe?
Girl One (*to audience*) So you see it's what we do. We hang. We chill. We just sit about. On Saturdays we sit about, get a milkshake form Maccy D's . . . Eye dem

boys . . . It's what we do. It's what we were doing in . . .
You don't expect . . . You don't expect . . . I hate the
sight of blood . . . And to be honest, I didn't even
notice him. Except . . . except . . . He looked kinda
skanky to me.

*The scene springs into life. The Girls move on, lost in
mucking about.*

Cheung What's happened to you, man?
Kojo Cheung, you know what, brother? Why don't you
stop hanging around me?
Cheung Kojo, man –

Kojo flicks out the kitchen knife, Cheung jumps back.

Kojo –

Kojo looks at him, Kojo looks beyond.
    *A Man in a hurry pushes into Cheung. Sends Cheung's
drink flying.*
    *The Man turns, freezes on seeing the knife in Kojo's
hand.*
    The scene freezes –

Kojo (*to audience*) My name is Kojo. I am fourteen years
old. The person playing me is an actor. I don't exist.
Except in this story. This is my story. I was a boy. Then
a soldier. Then somehow I got here. I'm a kid . . . but
to him . . .

The Man, frozen, mid-step, his arms raised imploringly –

He fears me . . .

*A Street Cleaner passes, a brush in hand, walking into
the frozen scene.*

Cleaner He's a kid. One of those hoodie types. Bloke
didn't stand a chance. He frightened me . . . Just a
kid . . . Just a . . .

Kojo turns, the knife in his hand. The Cleaner freezes, mid-scene.

Kojo (*to audience*) Love is a tight ball in your chest. Hardening every day.

The Man moves, looks to Kojo imploringly.

I choose where it starts. It starts now –

The scene springs back into life. Kojo stabs the Man. A Woman with her Boyfriend, just passing.

Trader Fuck . . . Fuck . . . What the fuck are you doing, lad?

Two young Girls, mouths gaping in horror, craning their necks to see –

Woman Oh my God . . . My God.

The Woman averting her eyes.
  The Man drops to the ground. The Boyfriend pulls off his jacket, covering the bleeding Man.

Trader Fuck . . . fuck . . . fuck . . .

The Market Trader is desperately trying to make a call on his cellphone.

Yeah . . . Ambulance . . . Yeah . . . Yeah . . .

The Woman is screaming.

Girl He's gone, man. Dat man's gone.
Boyfriend Please can someone please get help?
Cleaner Turn him on his side. Turn him on his side. There's stuff coming from his mouth, bro.
Cheung Fuck, bro . . . Run, man . . . just run . . .

Kojo looks down at the bloody knife in his hand. He starts to run.

SCENE THIRTY-SIX

Ara, illuminated in the dark.

Ara In 2005, two thousand, nine hundred and sixty-five unaccompanied minors applied for asylum in the UK.

Cheung, illuminated in the dark.

Cheung Two thousand, four hundred and twenty-five of these were age-disputed.

Hassan, illuminated in the dark.

Hassan In September 2006, local authorties in the UK were supporting five thousand, seven hundred unaccompanied asylum-seeking children in flats and children's homes.

Roza, illuminated in the dark.

Roza One child said: 'They just told me I needed to tell my story and I would be safe. I didn't know what asylum itself was or that what I was doing was called asylum.'

Kojo, illuminated in the dark.

Kojo (*to audience*) It is my birthday.

Kojo's Mother appears, her face illuminated with a birthday cake lit with candles.

All my family are here.

Kojo's Brother and Father enter. Kojo's Brother is dribbling a football.

Everyone is here.

Ara, Cheung, Hassan, Roza, The bleeding Man, the Girl with a buggy, the Market Trader, the Street Cleaner, the Woman and her Boyfriend, the two Girls, the Counsellor, Refuge Manager, Social Worker and Translator, Kid One, Kid Two –

I am eleven. It is my eleventh birthday.

Kojo's Mother smiles, holding out the cake for him to blow.

I am safe. I am home.
All Happy birthday, Kojo.
Mother Blow.

Kojo blows out the candles.
   Blackout.

The End.

Production Notes

MAP EXERCISE

Imagine the stage is a map of the globe.

- Where were you yesterday?
- Where were you born?
- Where was your mother born?
- Where was your father born?
- Where would you like to live in ten years?

The exercise gives a sense of a group's personal history very quickly. In specific relation to this play, it gives us a chance to compare our own journeys with those of the central characters.

THE IMPULSES BEHIND THE PLAY

In researching a television project, Abi Morgan became involved with the world of asylum seekers. She visited a London refugee centre, where children as young as twelve were arriving without parents. All the people were speaking in different languages. Key to the conception of the play was the idea of CHAOS:

1 Physical – in the refugee centre, many young people, speaking different languages, all thrust together.

2 Emotional – all out of their home environment, many suffering trauma, all seeking to find form in their chaos by creating communities and relationships, even though they often could not speak the same language.

The joy of this mixed group, the fun of a group of young people living together, is important to the tone of the play. It is intentionally not sombre or preachy despite being about issues of immigration and trauma.

Three key *adjectives* for approaching the play:

FLUID • FUN • RAW

KEYS TO PRODUCTION APPROACHES

- The playwright's voice should be paramount.
- The play is a bespoke suit, already measured and prepared; the production is the final fitting. The playwright's vision should be at the centre of all decisions regarding the production. This includes the dialogue and the stage directions.
- This is not a 'worthy' play and should be as much fun for audiences as it is for the actors.
- In acting the play, it is vital that the *ball is not dropped*; the energy must be kept high.
- The acting style is stripped back just to delivering the line. Everything each character needs is in their line. It should not be over-emotional.
- Be careful not to give away the play's end at the start.
- This play is radically low-tech. The magic of theatrical simplicity can solve most of the staging issues it presents.
- Asylum is about staying still. The final image of the play is everyone together standing still. It is a specific image, and clearly different from the frenetic nature of the rest of the play. In reality, what would happen to Kojo is bleak; however the final image is a deliberate counterpoint to this.

- The fact that Kojo is not real is fundamental to the play's meaning.

- This is a game. The story is told by actors.

PRACTICAL QUESTIONS

The dialect of the play is very London. Is it OK to adjust it?

Yes. But be sensitive, particularly with speech rhythms.

How would it work with an all-white cast?

Fine. The story is the thing.

My group hasn't got enough boys. Can I change the sex?

It is OK to change the actors' sex, but the characters' sex should stay the same.

WHY TELL THIS STORY?

- To change a stereotypical view of refugees.

- For people who don't have a voice, the play gives them voice and eloquence.

- For a civilised country which treats children in this way.

The performers have to address these issues even though they may come from very different backgrounds.

- Its theatricality creates urgency.

- It addresses a child stabbing an adult – we see a significant increase in youth violence.

The play was written with the understanding that it is not for performance by those who have suffered trauma, but for the large majority of young people in Britain who have not. Its message to these people is that childhood is precious and should be treasured. There is clearly an urgent political story, but the play is not 'agit prop'. By speaking to those who are not immigrants, it puts the story in the hands of those who do have a voice in society.

Despite not being written specifically for those who have suffered trauma, it does still speak to them – it declares: we hear you, we see you, we try to understand you. It is important that the story is told without judgement.

REPETITIONS

Look at the play.

- Where are the repetitions?
- What do they do?
- What happens in them?

The nature of what the play is exploring is imprecise and shifting – it doesn't provide answers. Therefore the approach to repetition should not be over-logical and precise. It is related to the shifting territory of memory.

There is a clear, logical link between what happens to Kojo on the dusty road and the stabbing. There is a series of events – violence leads to violence. The key to justifying the concluding violence dramatically lies in the rhythm of the play that builds to that point.

COMMUNICATION

This is a key theme in the play, both at a technical and thematic level.

What are the issues surrounding communication in the play?

- Its frenetic nature means storytelling must be visual.

- Acting choices need great clarity for the audience to stay with it.

- The frustration of speaking a language that no one understands is an issue the performers must engage with.

- The physical barrier of having a translator challenges what we mean by communication.

The audience is your friend. This is fundamental to communicating the tone of the play. It is not a preaching play. The audience can therefore let their defences down. All these kids want to get love and tell their story.

STAGING THE CHANGES

The play has many swift changes of location. Many worlds can exist on stage at the same time. They can be created without over-illustration.

One completely theatrical and simple solution is to have someone in a scene who then freezes and speaks directly to the audience. This has a simplicity and clarity that can serve this play very well. There are obviously other solutions but the most important thing is that all choices should be precise and specific.

The action of the play should move forward fluidly. The action never ends until the final moment. There is only one blackout in the script and that is at the end.

ACTING STYLE

IMPROVISATION 1 – A group of actors who all know Kojo's story must tell it, otherwise they will be shot. This exercise gives a sense of the need to communicate. They must work together, otherwise they will all lose out. This is a tool to enable the actors to feel confident without the pressure of text.

IMPROVISATION 2 – A group of actors must tell the story, but should play the adults they describe as well. This, again, gives the actors a chance to investigate stylistic choices without the pressure of text.

In order to make these exercises most helpful, all the narrative in them could stay within the world of the play. Here the benefit is both technical and exploratory at the level of content. Both exercises help the actors gain passion for and possession of the play. The style of the play in performance should ultimately be one of organised spontaneity.

From a workshop led by Vicky Featherstone
with notes by Jonathan Humphreys

HE'S TALKING

Nicholas Wright

Nicholas Wright's plays include, at the National, *The Reporter*, *Vincent in Brixton* (Olivier Award for Best New Play) and *Mrs Klein*; *Treetops* and *One Fine Day* at Riverside Studios; *The Gorky Brigade* at the Royal Court; *The Crimes of Vautrin* for Joint Stock; *The Custom of the Country* and *The Desert Air* for the RSC, and *Cressida* for the Almeida. His adaptations include *His Dark Materials*, *Thérèse Raquin*, *Three Sisters* and *John Gabriel Borkman* for the National, and *Naked* and *Lulu* for the Almeida, as well as novels for the screen. His books include *99 Plays* and *Changing Stages*, which was co-written with Richard Eyre.

Author's Note

In the early 1960s, Cape Town, my home town, was shaken by a series of bomb blasts. The targets were all inanimate objects such as electricity pylons, a radio mast and the commuter railway, and the bombers went to great lengths to make sure that no human beings were injured or killed. Their aim was not to harm anyone, but to make a show of resistance to the government's policy of racial separation and oppression: *apartheid*, as it was now being called.

I'd come to London to train as a drama student before the campaign got under way and I'd lost touch with most of the people I'd grown up with, so it was only when the bombing cell was destroyed that I discovered that one of its leaders had been my best friend at school: a clever, funny, charismatic boy with whom I shared a great love of acting.

I've wondered ever since what would have happened if, rather than leaving South Africa and escaping its conflicts in the way that I did, I had stayed in Cape Town and gone to the University along with most of my friends. I would certainly have played some part in politics, even if only a small one; that would have been unavoidable for a young man of my background. But what I still don't know, and will never know, is whether I would have joined my best friend's bombing cell if he had invited me to.

I know that I would have been flattered to be asked. Besides, I hated apartheid and any blow against it would have seemed justifiable. The cloak-and-dagger stuff would

have appealed to me, and I didn't have the political nous
to realise what seems obvious now, that a bombing
campaign carried out by a group of white middle-class
students would be likely to do more harm than good.
And even if I *had* realised it, what was the alternative?
Peaceful resistance was everywhere at that time, and
seemed to have no impact at all. Probably the only thing
that would have stopped me joining, would have been
fear: fear of being found out, fear of horrifying my parents,
fear of prison.

When the group was exposed, some of the bombers
managed to skip the country. Some who stayed were
sentenced to long terms in prison, where they suffered
greatly. There was an appalling epilogue when a loose-
cannon member of a parallel cell in Johannesburg set off
a bomb in a railway waiting room which actually did
result in deaths. For my school friend, the outcome was
disastrous in a different way from his fellow-members:
this is echoed in the play.

I've often wondered what I would have done if, like him,
I had been captured and interrogated. I know that I
would have cracked – almost everyone cracks, sooner or
later – but could I have held out for long enough for the
others to escape? And *when* I cracked, what would that
cracking have led to?

It's this excess of unknowns and 'what-ifs' that prompted
me to write the play in the way I did, with optional
realities being first formed and then contradicted by a
chain of events in the past. I found it impossible to think
of a catastrophe that blighted so many young people's
lives without taking into account the bad choices and the
malign twists of fate that made it happen . . . or the
better choices and the luckier twists of fate that might
have prevented it. I also found myself being convinced

by an argument against violence that wouldn't have occurred to me when I was young: that however muted and symbolic the form you choose, it places you under the power of things that you can't control.

Characters

Tanya

Rosie

Sal

Luke

Deon

Oscar

Skeets

Miles

All the characters are about twenty years old.
They are white except for Skeets, who is black.

The play is set in London in the mid-sixties.

SCENE ONE

A living room in London SW3.
   Evening. Luke, Tanya, Deon, Oscar, Rosie, Sal and Skeets are talking and drinking.
   Tanya calls:

Tanya Can we all settle down, please?

   They start to do so.

More wine, anyone?
Rosie Yes, me.

   To people in general:

Where are we, anyway?
Sal It's Chelsea, isn't it?
Rosie Yes, I know it's Chelsea, but . . .

   To Tanya, who is filling Rosie's glass:

Bit more . . . that's fine . . . whose house is this? Tanya, is
   it yours?
Tanya No, I'm just staying here with my brother. It's our
   mom and dad's house. They keep it on for when
   they're visiting the UK.
Rosie They must be stinking rich.
Tanya Not specially. OK, everyone?

   Everyone is settled.

Welcome to London. I'm sorry about the weather outside,
   but that's December for you. I just wanted to say that
   my time in the group was the most inspiring of my life,
   and it's a big thrill to see us all together again. I'm only
   sorry that it's here and not in Cape Town.

General agreement.

I was eight years old when my brother and I arrived in South Africa and, despite all the negative things, the inequality and oppression and apartheid growing more hateful every day, I grew to love that place like I'll never love anywhere else. That's all, and now it's over to you guys.

Luke Well, thanks for inviting us.

Tanya I couldn't not. It was such a great opportunity, all of us being in London at the same time.

Pause.

Oscar So, Deon, when did, um, when did you arrive?

Deon Just three months ago.

Rosie Did you get out of South Africa OK?

Deon Sure, no problems.

Tanya They were glad to see the back of him.

Sal I bet they were.

Tanya (*to Deon*) Tell them what you're doing now.

Deon I'll tell them later, OK?

Tanya (*to the others*) Deon's landed a job with Anti-Apartheid here in London.

Rosie Well done, hey.

Deon It's only temporary, but I'm hoping to make such a good impression on them that they keep me on.

Tanya Of course they will.

Oscar Where are you staying?

Deon Here with Tanya.

Oscar Here with Tanya, as in . . .?

Deon Here with Tanya.

Sal Wake up, Oscar.

Oscar Oh, right, I see. So did, um, did the two of you get it together here in London, or were you already going out in Cape Town?

Tanya We were already going out.

Rosie While you were still in the group?

Deon Ja, sure.

Rosie I didn't know that. Did anyone else know that?

Luke I did.

Rosie How?

Luke Deon told me. He came and warned me what was –

Rosie Brewing –

Oscar Stewing –

Luke – what was on their minds, and we discussed it.

Deon Luke had qualms about security . . .

Luke I did.

Deon But we decided that it would probably be OK, so long as the rest of the group didn't know about it.

Luke We compromised. Enough about that. We've all got a lot to catch up on, so can I suggest that rather than chat in this scattergun fashion, we go systematically round the room one by one. Everyone agreed?

They are.

Oscar.

Oscar Right, well, I'm, ah, still in Cape Town, still studying medicine at UCT and I do some weekend voluntary work at a clinic on the Cape Flats. Rosie, your go.

Rosie I'm still in Cape Town studying law, and I'm visiting London, as it happens, on the same student jaunt as Oscar. I'm still active on the political scene.

Luke Sal?

Sal I'm not active at all. After that time when Luke was pulled in by the cops . . . I got terribly stressed. I felt they were watching me all the time. I'm sure they weren't, but it wore me down. And I'd finished my drama course, so I decided to come to London to try my luck.

Oscar How's it going?

Sal It's going amazingly. I got an agent, he got me a television series straight off, and I'm going up to Nottingham next week to play Ophelia.

Rosie (*disapprovingly*) You've lost your accent.

Oscar Yes, well, she can't come on for her mad scene, all covered in flowers, and say –

In a comically thick South African accent:

– 'Here's rosemary for remembrance.'

Laughter.

Luke (*crisply*) OK, and Tanya?

Tanya I've been in London since the summer. I'm thinking of doing some full-time study, only I'm still getting used to Deon being here, so I'm in no rush.

Deon Luke, what about you?

Luke I'm still in Cape Town, and I'm active in the struggle.

Deon What brings you to London?

Luke Talks.

Oscar Important talks?

Deon Struggle-connected talks?

Luke I can't discuss it. We still haven't heard from Walter.

Skeets looks up.

I'm sorry, I only know you by your code name.

Skeets My name is Skeets.

Luke Skeets, hi. I'm Luke, that's Rosie, Oscar . . .

Sal Sal.

Deon Deon.

Tanya Tanya.

Luke So tell us, Skeets, how has your life panned out over the last year?

Skeets After the group broke up, I was active on a community level in the townships. I was awarded a grant by a Catholic foundation to study chemistry

in Manchester. That's where I'm living as of this time.
I came to London for this reunion.

Tanya So here we are.

Sal It's nice not using code names.

Oscar Yes, it feels more normal.

Rosie They were bloody farcical anyway.

Oscar Most of us knew each other perfectly well.

Luke We shouldn't have done.

Deon We couldn't help it.

Tanya Small town.

Deon Too many connections.

Rosie We all went on the same marches . . .

Sal We went to the same concerts, we swam at the same
beaches . . .

Tanya We all belonged to the same film club . . .

Oscar In fact, the only member of the group that we
didn't all know was Walter.

Skeets Skeets.

Oscar Sorry, Skeets.

Rosie I knew Skeets.

She smiles at him.

I took my old Chevy in to have the clutch looked at, and
you were there behind the counter with your name on
a badge.

Skeets smiles.

Skeets Sure.

Pause.

Oscar The paradox is that after the group dissolved, all
that casual meeting up just stopped.

Rosie Oscar's right. We had to travel six thousand miles
to London just to sit in the same room –

Oscar – and now we actually had to tell each other what
we've been doing for the last twelve months.

Rosie There's been some mutual avoidance going on.

Oscar It's a revulsion, almost. I haven't just not wanted to see the rest of you. I've wanted to hide when I saw you coming.

Sal There were always tensions in the group.

Rosie Let's be frank. There was a running battle between Deon and Luke.

Luke It wasn't personal.

Deon There was a feeling, which I admit was mainly voiced by me, that violence wasn't the way to go.

Luke It was *selective* violence. No one was injured. No one was killed . . .

Deon Ja, right, because –

Luke – it was the policy of the group.

Deon And if it *hadn't* been our policy, then as a committed Christian, I –

Tanya Deon would never have been involved.

Skeets None of us would.

Oscar May I point out that we're not all Christians?

Deon Sure, but leaving aside our ethical reservations, what had we actually achieved by blowing things up?

Tanya Nothing good.

Oscar We provoked reprisals.

Sal More bannings, more detentions.

Skeets We made a bad situation worse.

Deon Right. So there was Oscar, Skeets, Tanya, Sal and me on the one side . . .

Rosie Me on the other . . .

Deon Five against two. Luke, there was nobody more impressed than me by your commitment and your organisational flair and bla bla bla, but all the time that you were urging bigger and better actions, most of the rest of the group was thinking, 'Hold it!'

Luke Why didn't they say so?

Oscar We were spellbound.

Tanya Right.

Oscar By you.

Sal Then when they pulled you in that day, the spell was broken.

Tanya We saw the incredible risks that we were running.

Deon And for what?

Luke (*shouts*) You know bloody well for what! We were fighting apartheid!

Deon (*shouts*) Yes, we all know that! But –

Rosie Shut up, the two of you. Jesus Christ, you're worse than ever.

Luke OK. But I will say this. The group should never have broken up. And I object to that mistake being pinned on me, as though my experience was any excuse for cowardice all round. Since your imaginations seem to be running riot, let me describe in simple terms what happened. I was raided by the cops. They searched my flat and took me down to Caledon Square. They questioned me. I told them nothing and they let me go. I was shaken. I was frightened, sure. But I got over it. And if *I* got over it, I think the rest of you should have got over it too. I need a drink.

He gets one.

Rosie Great party.

Deon So, Luke.

Luke What?

Deon They pulled you in because . . .

Luke Because, like you, I was a well-known student activist. It was harassment.

Deon Did they suspect that you were connected with the bombings?

Luke No more than anyone else who they had a file on.

Deon So they did?

Luke Up to a point. But they had nothing to go on. My flat was clean and I gave nothing away.

Deon But you could have slipped up . . .

Oscar And that would have led them to the rest of the group. You couldn't have said there *wasn't* a group, because of the railway action –

Deon – because it needed six or seven operators.

Luke Yes, but I lied from Cape to Cairo and I said that . . .

Miles comes in, carrying a sports bag.

Miles Luke! How you doing?

Luke (*awkward*) Hi, Miles.

Miles embraces him.

Tanya Miles, we're having a private meeting.

Miles Yes, you warned me about it. I just came home to shower and change.

To Luke.

Had a great game, by the way.

Luke Miles, I'll call you.

Miles You got the number?

Luke Sure.

Miles How long're you here for?

Tanya Miles! Just go!

Miles Deon, I'll see you later.

Deon (*impatient*) See you later.

Miles (*to the others*) Nice meeting you guys. Have fun.

He goes.

Oscar That's your brother?

Tanya That's my brother.

Deon He was Luke's best friend at school. (*To Luke.*) In fact, that morning they pulled you in –

Luke Leave it out.

Tanya No, this is important. We'd never have known if it wasn't for Miles. (*To Luke.*) The two of you had arranged to go rock-climbing, only you hadn't showed up. So Miles drove over to your place and he saw three

224

police cars parked outside your flat and the cops going in and out. He rang me up. I woke up Deon. Then I rang up Rosie, and she rang around . . .

Rosie Sal and I were sharing a flat, and Oscar's place was across the road, so we all met up in the Gardens.

Oscar Saturday morning in December, height of summer, beautiful cloudless sky, and there's four of us drinking milk shakes in the outdoor café . . .

Rosie Forget the milk shakes. We were terrified.

Sal We couldn't stop wondering, 'What do they know?' 'How long will they keep him?'

Oscar (*to Luke*) And what if you cracked?

Luke I *didn't* crack.

Oscar We didn't *know* that.

Sal We didn't know *what* you were doing.

Tanya It was like our worst fantasies had become real.

Oscar As though some *Boys' Own Magazine* had sprung into life, and the cartoon Nazis were suddenly six foot tall and breaking the door down.

Sal I said to Rosie, I know we can go to prison, but how long for?

Rosie I said, as long as a piece of string. I didn't tell her we could be hanged.

Sal She told me later.

Oscar I knew all the time.

Rosie (*to Deon*) Where were you?

Deon I'd gone into town.

Skeets He came to find me at the automobile repair shop.

Tanya To warn you, right?

Skeets And also to ask if I knew what Luke had done with the new equipment.

Tanya (*suspicious*) What new equipment?

Deon It doesn't matter.

Tanya Deon?

Luke I had told Deon about some new equipment that had arrived from Jo'burg. It seems that, in the turmoil of that anxious summer morning, he decided to look for it.

Deon I wanted to find it before the cops did. Was I wrong about that?

Tanya (*to Deon*) Hang on a minute. Just what was this new equipment?

Luke Four sticks of dynamite from the mines and two detonators.

Tanya (*angry, to Deon*) Why didn't you tell me about it?

Deon I was protecting you.

Tanya Jesus!

She walks away and pours a drink for herself.

Oscar Why were we getting more explosives? I thought we were stopping.

Luke Nothing was decided. Anyway, dynamite isn't cornflakes. You can't just go to the shop and buy it. You have to take it when it's offered.

Tanya (*to Deon*) What happened next?

Deon (*to Skeets*) You tell her.

Skeets Deon asked me if I had seen this new equipment. I said that Luke had given it to me in a suitcase. He'd asked me to connect the other components. I was unwilling but, for reasons of solidarity, I did what he asked and gave it back to him. There was no danger of it exploding. I did not know what Luke had done with it after that.

Oscar So, Luke?

Luke What?

Oscar They let you out of Caledon Square, and you'd hidden a suitcase full of dynamite in some secret place. Did you go to collect it straight away? Or did you wait?

Luke I left it where it was till the heat was off.

Rosie Obviously.

Luke It wasn't so obvious at the time.

SCENE ONE REPLAY (1)

Same place, same time.
  Tanya, Deon, Oscar, Rosie, Sal, Skeets and Miles.

Tanya More wine, anyone?
Miles I'll do it.

  He circulates and pours wine.

Rosie Where are we, anyway?
Sal It's Chelsea, isn't it?
Rosie Yes, I know it's Chelsea, but whose house is this?
  Is it yours, Tanya?
Tanya It's our mom and dad's house. They keep it on for
  when they're visiting the UK. I'm just staying here with
  my brother.
Rosie (*to Miles*) That's you?
Miles Correct.
Rosie What's your name again?
Miles/Tanya Miles.
Rosie Nice to meet you, Miles. Your parents must be
  stinking rich.
Miles I'll say three words. 'Westlake Financial Services.'
Rosie Oh, are you *that* Westlake?
Tanya Shut up, Miles. Can we all settle down please?

  They do or have already.

I just want to say that our time together as a group was
  the most inspiring of my life, and it's a great thrill for
  me to welcome you to London. I'm only sorry that
  there's someone who can't be here.
Deon Let's all think of him for a moment.

  They do. After a few moments, Deon raises his glass.

To Luke.

All To Luke.

Oscar Does anyone know how he is?

Deon I've only heard in a roundabout way via my job at Anti-Apartheid. The good news is that he's adjusting to life in prison and that he's physically well. One of the warders seems to have been a vindictive type, but some of the older politicos banded together and got him moved elsewhere.

Oscar Great.

Deon Luke gets the newspapers, although there's always a lot cut out of them. He can get one letter a month. He wants his parents to have first go at writing to him, but they've agreed to include messages of a –

Tanya – of a hinted kind –

Deon – as long as they're kept short. He gets depressed.

Rosie Ja, well.

Oscar Ten years without parole.

Rosie Bastards.

Pause.

Skeets How was he caught? I only know what I read in the papers up in Manchester.

Deon There'd been a new delivery of equipment.

Skeets Yes, I knew about that but . . .

Rosie Did you? I didn't know.

Oscar Nor me.

Rosie Did anyone else know?

Tanya Deon knew, didn't you, Deon?

Deon (*annoyed*) Leave it, hey? (*To the others.*) It's a bit of a sore point between Tanya and me.

Rosie So cut the squabbling and tell us what happened.

Deon Ja, well, apparently it was like a Hollywood action movie. Luke was driving back to his flat down one of those narrow streets from High Level Road to the Sea Point main drag, when three cop cars appeared from nowhere. Sirens, flashing lights, the lot. They searched the car, and found the dynamite in a suitcase in the boot.

Rosie It can't have been there all along.

Tanya It wasn't.

Deon He was bringing it back from where he'd hidden it.

Rosie Where was that?

Miles It was in my garage.

All except for Deon and Tanya look at him in surprise.

Tanya He didn't know it was there.

Rosie He must have done.

Miles Well, naturally I knew the *suitcase* was there. Luke had asked me to look after it for him. He said it was full of banned books . . . Karl Marx, Lenin, Gramophone-something . . . ?

Oscar Gramsci.

Miles And he wanted it out of the way in case his flat got raided. I said, no problem. The truth is, I was flattered to be asked. He'd never involved me in that side of his life, 'the struggle', as he called it. He probably thought I wasn't clever enough. We'd been best friends at school from Standard Two right up to Matric, and on the rugby pitch, which is where things counted at our school, we were pretty damn even, but he was always the brainy one.

Tanya Suitcase.

Miles Right. So it's a Saturday afternoon, beautiful day, rock climbing cancelled and I'm sitting listening to the cricket when Luke comes in through the patio door. He said the cops had let him go, but he still looked jumpy. He said, 'I've come to collect that suitcase.' I said, 'Relax. Help yourself to a beer, you know where the fridge is.' I went down to the garage . . .

He stops, upset.

Tanya Tell them.

Miles I suddenly didn't trust him. First time ever. I knew
that if I opened it, and it wasn't just books inside, it
would destroy our friendship. But I couldn't stop
myself. I forced the lock, and there were four fat putty-
coloured sticks, wires, a couple of alarm clocks and
some other shit. I looked around and he was standing
behind me. His face was white. I asked him, 'Did
anyone follow you here?' He said, 'Don't worry, I did
every zig-zag in the book, I've shaken them off. Now
give me that, I've got to dispose of it.' I said, 'You do
that. Take it out into the veld, set the timer to zero,
stand close and blow yourself to hell. Now fuck off for
ever.' I never saw him again, so sadly that's how things
stand between us.

He blows his nose.

Sorry about the emotion.

Tanya Miles can't get it into his head that Luke betrayed
him.

Miles He didn't do me any harm.

Tanya Except you had to leave the country.

Miles Well, I obviously couldn't stay. (*To the others*)
I flew to London that same night. My dad found me
a job here and I've never been back.

Deon (*to the others*) We also thought it was wise to
leave.

Tanya We drove to Swaziland. We hung out there till it
all went quiet, and then we came to London.

Sal I also came to London.

Oscar I stayed.

Rosie Me too. I *thought* about getting out. It was such a
nightmare waiting to find out what would happen.

Oscar But nothing did.

Deon It still amazes me that he never talked.

Tanya We wouldn't all be sitting here if he had.

SCENE ONE REPLAY (2)

Same place, same time.
  Oscar, Rosie, Sal, Skeets and Miles.

Miles Glass of wine?

Rosie Ja, thanks. Nice house, by the way. Is it all yours?

Miles It's my parents' house. They keep it on for when they're visiting London. (*To Sal.*) Same for you?

Oscar (*to Sal*) Speak up.

Sal I'll have a small glass.

Oscar I'll have a normal-sized one, if that's OK.

Miles (*to Skeets*) Wine for you?

Skeets Have you got any whisky?

Miles Good idea. I think I'll join you.

Oscar Oh, can I change my mind?

Sal Are you sure about that?

Oscar I'm convinced.

Sal (*to Miles*) Oscar and I got lost on the way here, so we went into a pub to ask directions and he got distracted.

Oscar It was a nice old place. The Chelsea Potter. Full of mad bohemian artists. Only I can't get used to English beer. You think it's flat lemonade that tastes of bark . . .

Sal Yes, well, it's not lemonade.

Miles I can make you a cup of coffee.

Oscar No, whisky will be fine. So Miles, I hope you don't mind that I brought my friends along. Sal is my girlfriend. Rosie is an old comrade from Cape Town, who we met in Trafalgar Square on Sunday. And Walter . . .

Skeets Skeets.

Oscar Sorry. Skeets I didn't know was in London at all.

Rosie I ran into Skeets in the Wimpy Bar in the Earls Court Road, so I said come with.

Miles What are you doing in London, Skeets?

Skeets I'm passing through.

Sal Sounds interesting.

Oscar I'm sure it is.

Rosie (*to Miles*) I've just realised something. Was it you who had the dynamite in your garage?

Miles Yes, that was me. Although I didn't know it was there. Or rather, I thought it was something else.

Sal My ma sends me the papers from home, so I read about that. They were really nasty about you at Luke's trial.

Rosie The prosecutor called you 'Satan's quartermaster'!

Miles Yes, very funny. (*To Oscar.*) The reason I rang you, Oscar . . .

Rosie I used to know your sister, Tanya. Is she still with Deon?

Miles Yes, they're in Swaziland. He's teaching at a Mission School, and she's setting up some kind of, ah, craft initiative aimed at encouraging local skills.

Rosie And they can't get out of Swaziland, isn't that right? Unless they want to get arrested at the border?

Miles Correct. So, Oscar . . .

Oscar has been talking quietly to Sal.

Oscar Hello?

Miles Tanya sent me a couple of possible telephone numbers for you, but it took quite a while for me to track you down . . .

Oscar Why were you tracking me down?

Miles Because I wanted to talk to someone who, how can I say, who knew the background to what happened in Cape Town. Which I gather you do.

Oscar So what's the hold-up?

Miles indicates Rosie, Sal and Skeets.

Miles Can we talk?

Oscar Yes, we can talk.

Skeets All of us here were in the group with Deon and
Tanya.

Rosie So not to alarm you, Miles, but you've got a
roomful of bombers here.

Miles Right.

Rosie We blew up two electrical pylons, a radio mast,
the reservoir in town –

Oscar – and the signal cables on the suburban railway-
line –

Rosie – in three separate places, all at the same time. Big
disruption. Major challenge to the regime. The President
called us 'the faceless foes of white civilisation', and he
wasn't kidding.

Oscar (*to Miles*) So what did you want to talk about?

Miles Have any of you heard any news of Luke?

*At the mention of Luke, it's as though the lights have
gone down or a cloud has passed across the sun.*

Rosie (*suspicious*) How do you know Luke?

Miles He was my best friend at school. I've been
wondering how he's bearing up in prison. I feel a bit
guilty that I've done nothing about him.

Rosie That's your only connection with him?

Miles Yes.

Rosie Except for the suitcase that he planted on you.

Miles Except for that.

Rosie So, to put it bluntly, your best friend landed you in
the shit. And then he talked. And now it's you that's
feeling guilty?

Miles He was caught with the dynamite in the boot of
his car. What was he meant to say, that it didn't exist?
We know what they do. They yell at you. They beat
you up. They force you to stand for hours. Luke held
out for as long as he could. Then he gave three names
and three names only. Tanya, Deon and me. And we
all got away.

233

Rosie And now you can't go back.

Miles I don't want to.

Rosie And your sister is stuck in the bush making batiks, for Christ's sake. What kind of life is that for an intelligent woman?

Miles Luke got seven years in prison.

Rosie He'd have got a lot more if he'd kept his trap shut.

Oscar is at the drinks table.

Oscar I'm helping myself, OK?

Miles (*irritated*) Sure, finish the lot.

Oscar pours himself a whisky.

Oscar The truth is that, except for Luke, it didn't turn out too badly.

Sal It brought Oscar and me together.

Rosie I got a phone call from a school friend who worked at the *Cape Times*. She said, 'I think you ought to know that your friend is naming names.'

Sal She didn't know whose names.

Rosie We were terrified like never before.

Sal I asked myself, if this is my last night of freedom, what's the one thing that I'll always wish I'd done? And there was only one answer. It was to sleep with Oscar. I got dressed and I ran across the street and I knocked on his door.

Oscar She looked a mess. She'd thrown her clothes on in a hurry and her lips were smudgy and her nose was red and shiny from all the crying she'd done. I saw her standing under a light bulb on this crap linoleum, and I tried to think of how to send her away without upsetting her –

Rosie You're upsetting her now.

Oscar – and then I suddenly saw that mess is good. And that our great mistake was to deny that. We were liberals –

Rosie (*with scorn*) Liberals?

Oscar – progressives, young intellectuals, whatever, who'd been driven to despair by the compromises and the feeling of besmirchment – shut up, Rosie – that came from living under an evil system. We hadn't invented the system, we didn't support it, so why did we feel so guilty about it? That I can't answer, we just did. We felt unclean.

Rosie Because we profited by that system.

Oscar Up to a point.

Skeets (*pleasantly*) Not up to a point. You profited pure and simple.

Oscar Sure.

Skeets It's nothing personal.

Oscar Right. You're right. So, Skeets, if I can just go on for a moment . . .? Violence, as we saw it, was the opposite of the muddle we'd learned to hate. It seemed a cleansing flame. That's what attracted us. We chose the purity of violence, and we rejected the mess of life. I looked at Sal, and I realised how stupid that was. So I asked her in.

Rosie That's the biggest load of shit I've ever heard.

Miles looks at his watch.

Miles So look, it's been, um . . .

Rosie Shut up for a minute. (*To Oscar.*) Our whole bloody country is built on violence. I go to my uncle's farm and round the back of a shed I find a labourer who's being flogged for being 'cheeky'. Or a line of prisoners beating a man to pulp. It goes back and back. My forefathers hunted down the bushmen like baboons. They shot them dead for a laugh. South Africa has been violent for three hundred years. It's in our blood.

Oscar Every nation is built on violence.

Rosie You're right. (*She gestures towards Miles.*) My great-grandmother died in one of his British concentration camps, along with thirty thousand other women. That's also violence.

Miles Are you always this hostile?

Rosie It depends who I'm with.

Pause.

Oscar So we got ready to go.

Sal We couldn't believe that it was happening.

Oscar We packed one suitcase each.

Rosie We had one old Chevrolet between us.

Oscar I had lectures planned.

Sal I had rehearsals.

Oscar No pets, thank God.

Sal We got into Rosie's car and we drove to Lesotho.

Rosie We stopped in the bush and walked. Then, when the sun came up, we realised that we'd crossed the border. Now I'm teaching small barbarians in a comprehensive school in Hackney. Oscar, you're at Cambridge, lucky bugger.

Sal I work in a coffee bar there. I'd been hoping to get some acting work, but you can't get an agent if you're not in London.

Oscar We *could* go back.

Rosie We should.

Sal But it's so peaceful here.

SCENE ONE REPLAY (3)

Same place, same time.
Rosie, Skeets and Miles.

Miles (*to Skeets*) What're you doing in London, Skeets?

Skeets I'm passing through.

Miles From where to where?

Skeets Lusaka to Moscow.

Rosie Skeets's with the ANC in Zambia, and he's on his way to the Soviet Union for further education.

Miles Fantastic.

Skeets Rosie, what about you?

Rosie I've done nothing so impressive.

Miles Don't be so modest. Tell him how you got out.

Rosie Ag, no, I'm sick of that story. The only significant part of it is that when we got to the Lesotho border we were stopped by a police patrol that was looking for Sal and Oscar. They got taken back to Cape Town. He got four years. She got three. The irony is that she'd been in love with him for months, and he'd only just noticed her. They'd had one night together. And a snog in the car. (*To Miles.*) It's a shame you never met them. They're beautiful souls.

Skeets So Luke named Tanya, Deon – (*To Miles.*) you, Oscar and Sal.

Rosie Everything he did changed all our futures. He couldn't control it. It's how it was. He only had to open his mouth, and someone else disappeared. Like in that song . . .

Miles 'Ten green bottles.'

Rosie Yes, that one too, but what's the other one?

Miles 'So they all rolled over, and the one fell out, there were nine in the bed . . .'

Rosie That's the one.

Skeets (*to Rosie*) He never named you?

Rosie No.

Skeets Do you know why not?

Rosie I suspect it was random. He must have been approaching the end of the list, and then suddenly, God knows how, he found the strength to stop. There's no other reason I can think of. Why did he leave *you* out?

Skeets I think he really didn't know who I was.

Rosie I was the only one who did. Good luck in Moscow.

It's good to know there's one of us left who's not irrelevant.

Skeets You could be relevant. You could even go back to South Africa. They've got nothing against you there.

Miles Maybe not, but they've got something pretty damn big against me.

Rosie Miles was the man with the bomb in the suitcase.

Miles 'Satan's quartermaster.'

Rosie And there's no way that Miles and me want to put six thousand miles between us.

Miles No way at all.

Skeets I didn't know the two of you were so serious about each other. (*To Rosie.*) You didn't tell me in the Wimpy Bar.

Rosie I'm still getting used to it.

Miles We'd never have met if it wasn't for Luke.

Rosie Miles rang me up just after I got here –

Miles – I got her number from my sister –

Rosie – and he wanted to know if I'd got any news about Luke in prison.

Miles He'd just been sentenced. Four years.

Rosie And Luke, of course, was the last thing I wanted to talk about. I wasn't even all that keen on meeting Miles –

Miles My sister had told her I was thick.

Rosie – but I was lonely, I was teaching at a horrible school, I wanted a free meal and, most of all – and I can't explain this – it felt like Sal would want me to meet him. So I did.

Miles We didn't get on.

Rosie I thought he was like those lumpy boys who pulverise your toes on the dance floor when you're fourteen.

Miles She asked to use the phone and then spent half an hour talking to Cape Town.

Rosie He had Noddy books in the toilet.

Miles She kept ranting on about the Boer War.

Rosie But worst of all, he had this morbid obsession with Luke. I thought, what is this guy, some kind of weird sport-loving closet homosexual?

Miles We sorted that out.

Rosie Not that night.

Miles Soon enough.

Rosie We sorted most things out.

Miles There's just one thing left that we can't agree on.

Rosie It's the group.

Miles We try not to talk about it, but every so often we do, and then we end up shouting at each other. I don't understand how a bunch of intelligent people could think was it a good idea to start letting off bombs.

Rosie No one was injured. No one was killed –

Miles And what a miracle that was. I don't know about Skeets, but I'd bet my bottom dollar that not one of the rest of you knew one end of a bomb from the other.

Rosie So if we'd been explosive experts, you'd be happy about it?

Miles No, because you couldn't rely on that. There'd be some human error, or a bit of bad luck, and suddenly people's lives would be ruined. Violence isn't a straight track. It's a labyrinth.

Rosie Where'd you read that?

Miles It's true. Once you're in, you're gonna get lost. That's why I hate it. (*To Skeets.*) But Rosie thinks that violence is OK.

Rosie I think it's something that has to be.

Miles So what do you think?

Skeets laughs.

What's so funny?

Skeets At any gathering of white liberals that I've ever been to, there's always a moment when someone decides that it's the black man sitting quietly in the corner of the room who's got all the answers.

Miles Well, this is that moment.

Skeets I thought, then, that the group was young white people playing dangerous games. I'm not so harsh about it now, but we did no good. Strategic violence on behalf of the masses is a different matter. I can give you the party line on that. It's just one week old. Peaceful tactics have failed. Violence must be met with violence. I know that policy is correct. But I myself could not be violent to anyone. (*To Rosie.*) So with my brain I agree with you. (*To Miles.*) With my heart I agree with you. (*To both.*) Is that any help?

SCENE ONE REPLAY (4)

Same place. Same time.
Miles alone.

Miles
'So they all rolled over
And the one fell out,
There was one in the bed
And the little one said . . .'

Luke comes in. He's wearing a dark overcoat that looks big on him.

Luke I see you still keep Noddy books in the toilet.

Miles They're ironic.

Luke So you say.

Miles Take off your coat.

Luke I'll keep it on for a minute. I can't get used to this bloody weather. Snow in December, how perverse is that?

Miles Glass of wine?

Luke Ja, thanks. You look well.

Miles I am.

Luke Bit chunkier. Do you have lots of aspiring-executive lunches?

Miles It's just London living.

Luke How long've you been here?

Miles Just a year.

Luke So you left . . .?

Miles I left that night.

Luke That's what I thought.

He looks round.

You've got a very posh house.

Miles It's my parents' house.

Luke Are they here now?

Miles No, they're in Cape Town. They stay there most of the time. Tanya's here.

Luke What, here tonight?

Miles Sure.

Luke I wouldn't have come if I'd known. Where is she now?

Miles I haven't a clue. She said she was going out. Maybe she will. Maybe she's lying down, maybe she's sitting staring at the wall. She's not in a good state. I stay home most evenings trying to talk her out of it. Or waiting for her to come back from whatever dubious haunt she's gone to.

Luke That's your life?

Miles That and the job.

Luke No girlfriend?

Miles No.

Luke Why not?

Miles I don't know. Just hasn't happened. What about you?

Luke Me?

He laughs.

I'd have more chance of a girlfriend if I had leprosy.

Miles That's rubbish. In Cape Town, sure, but nobody here knows anything about you.

Luke People can smell it on me. It's like a disease.

He dangles an imaginary bell.

'Unclean! Unclean!' Why are you smiling?

Miles You reminded me of something.

Luke What?

Miles That movie where Jesus cures some lepers, and you know it's him, but you only see his shadow. We saw it together on your birthday. Then afterwards we went to that tea place with the band, and we spent over a pound and we had a very good time.

Luke *Ben Hur.*

Miles Wasn't it *Quo Vadis?*

Luke Fuck knows.

Pause.

I got your letter. I was shovelling shit on a farm in deepest Yorkshire when it arrived. It'd been halfway round the British Isles. I still don't know why you wrote it.

Miles Then you can't have read it.

Luke I didn't. I took a quick look and it seemed too heavy a trip, so I tore off your address and I threw the rest of it away. But I had to come down to London to fix my visa. I hate being here. I keep thinking I'll run into someone I know from Cape Town. Last time I went to a movie, Sal's mother was sitting two rows in front of me. Boy, did I get out fast.

Miles Who's Sal?

Luke She was in the group. So . . .

He loses his drift for a moment.

. . . so I thought, if I looked you up, at least I'd know what to expect. And now I discover that Tanya's here. Maybe it's all for the best.

Miles Why do you say that?

Luke I can't run away for ever.

He holds out his glass.

Gimme another.

Miles Sure.

He does.

What I said in the letter was that . . .

Luke If I'd wanted to know, I would've read it.

Miles Well, it took me a day to write so you can spend five minutes listening.

Luke I'm listening.

He sits back and closes his eyes.

Miles It doesn't matter to me what anyone else might think about you. You're still my friend and you always will be.

Luke Are you going to go on like this?

Miles Shut up. Whatever you did –

Luke It's not 'whatever'.

Miles I thought you were going to listen.

Luke I'm not gonna to listen to any old crap that you happen to come out with. You say 'whatever' as though what I did is woolly and vague. It's not. It's concrete. It's defined. There's a word for it. 'Betrayal'.

Miles Still making speeches.

Luke At least they're better than yours.

Miles Do you want me to hit you?

Luke Good question.

Miles What's the answer?

Luke Ooh, quick riposte. The answer is 'No.' Get to the point.

Miles I just want to say that I can't condemn you. Because if I'd been in the same position as you, I would probably have done exactly the same thing.

Luke That's just banal. Maybe you would. Maybe lots of people would. But you didn't. I did. That is the fact. If you deny that fact, then you're denying our friendship.

Miles So we do have a friendship?

Luke We have a friendship in distress.

Miles Meaning what?

Luke Meaning, don't bullshit me. I want it straight from the fucking shoulder. And don't pretend that you don't despise me.

Miles I don't.

Luke Then you must have a fucking screw loose. What about when I dumped that suitcase on you?

Miles I didn't mind about that.

Luke No?

Miles No.

Luke Then why did you tell me to fuck off for ever?

Miles I didn't mean it. You'd done the right thing. If you'd stashed it with Tanya or Deon or anyone else who was well known for being political, you'd have put them at risk. I wasn't connected. I wasn't gonna be raided. I was safe and the suitcase was safe.

Luke What about my lying to you about the contents?

Miles You were protecting me. The less I knew, the safer I was.

Luke Till I screwed up.

Miles You didn't mean to screw up. You were just being stupid. Why didn't you leave it in my garage till the heat was off?

Luke I'd come from Caledon Square. I wasn't thinking straight. My head was a mess. I mean, why did I drive it back to my flat? Ridiculous. But hey, it was dynamite, I couldn't think of anything else to do with it. So I drove back home and . . .

He loses his drift for a moment.

Miles And what?

Luke Do you ever get that feeling that you're seeing a
place . . . or you're *in* that place . . . for the last time?
It's some foreshadowing instinct. I was driving round
the side of the mountain with the stuff in the boot,
and I turned a corner and there was the whole of Cape
Town spread out below me like a sea of light. I thought,
I'll never see this again. And I was right. I never have
and I never will. I took a right turn off High Level Road
and I was suddenly starring in a Hollywood action
movie.

He listens.

What's that?

Miles It's Tanya. Stay or go, whatever you want, but
she's gonna give you a bad time.

Luke I'll stay.

Tanya comes in. She pours herself a glass of wine.

Miles I thought you were going out.

Tanya I changed my mind. Is this boys' talk or can I join
you?

Miles Do whatever you want.

She sits. To Luke:

Tanya I've got a question for you.

Luke Ask it.

Tanya Was it a deal? Was it, 'Name the names and we'll
let you walk'? Was that how it worked?

Luke Not at first. Later on, there was a deal. As everyone
knows. But that's not how it started.

Tanya No?

Luke No, it started with me being shit scared.

Tanya At least that's honest.

Miles Give him a break.

Tanya Shut up. (*To Luke.*) Tell me about being shit scared.

Luke I was in the same cell that they'd put me in that morning. I was determined not to talk. I had this fantasy about me pining away in prison and the rest of you saying to each other what a hero I'd been.

Tanya So what was scary about it?

Luke The cops came in with the suitcase. They spread the contents out on the floor. That changed everything. I thought for a moment, I could say that somebody'd planted it in my car. But that would have opened up an even bigger can of worms. The senior guy said, 'Let's not fuck about, we know that it wasn't just you, so give us the names.' I said, 'Whose names are you talking about?' They didn't like that, so they roughed me up.

Miles Badly?

Luke Quite badly, yes. Though plenty of other people have had much worse. The worst thing was realising how much they hated me. They really believed that I was scum, that I was filth. That shook me. So eventually I confessed.

Tanya Confessed what?

Luke I confessed what they knew already. That I was one of a group of bombers.

Tanya What else?

Luke Nothing else. I stuck to the plan. I said I only knew the others by their code names, and that when we met we were unrecognisable to each other because we all wore balaclavas.

Tanya laughs.

Tanya I always knew that plan was rubbish.

Luke Ja, well, they laughed too. Look, I'm not gonna take you through it hour by hour, or day by day, or whatever the hell it was, but when I finally gave them a name, Miles, it was yours.

Tanya (*to Miles*) Did you know?

Miles I think I guessed.

Tanya Why you? You weren't even in the group.

Miles He knew I had a British passport. He knew I could get a plane ticket on Dad's account. He thought I'd probably left already. Which I had.

Luke It wasn't just that. I knew that it wouldn't cause you any pain. South Africa wasn't your country. You had no feeling for it. You were just a rich English brat who happened to go to school there.

Miles Why are you trying to make me angry?

Luke Work it out for yourself.

Tanya Who was next?

Luke Deon.

Tanya Jesus.

Miles There was a reason for that too. He guessed that Deon had already escaped to Swaziland or some such place. And he was right.

Luke Ten out of ten. I named you next, Tanya, because I guessed that Deon would take you with him. I felt quite pleased with myself at that point. I thought, I've given the names of three people who these bastards are never gonna find. I knew I'd be shat on when I got out. If I ever got out. But at least some people would understand. As long as I stopped right there.

Tanya But you didn't stop.

Luke I couldn't. It wasn't possible. That was my big discovery. Once you've let the demon out of the cage, you can't whistle it back. You've lost your chance. Too late, mate.

Tanya So who did you name after me?

Luke Oscar. (*To Miles.*) Medical student. Nice guy. Bit of a joker. Then I faked a nervous breakdown. In fact it wasn't entirely fake. But they assumed that it was and things got nastier. So I named Sal. That was the worst so far.

Tanya For you.

Luke For me. I'm not claiming that my worst compares with anyone else's. (*To Miles.*) Sal's an actress. She's not political. She only got involved because she was Rosie's flatmate. Rosie is Sal's opposite.

Tanya (*to Miles*) You'd have hated her.

Luke She's a bolshie, loudmouth Afrikaner. I loved what she stood for. I saw her as some primitive talisman that I had to protect. I thought, I'm not gonna name her, not if it costs me ten more years. Then the senior cop came in. He said, 'Our backroom boys are saying you couldn't have done that railway job with only five. You're keeping somebody back.' I said, 'So what?' He said, 'So don't forget that you could be hanged.' So I named Rosie.

Tanya (*to Miles*) She was stopped at the border with Oscar and Sal. They were just about to let her go when her name came through on the radio. So they took her too.

Luke (*to Miles*) She got five years.

Tanya (*to Luke*) What about Walter? He got longer than anyone else.

Luke He was nothing to do with me.

Tanya No?

Luke No. The only thing I knew about him was that he worked in a motor repair shop in Long Street. By the time I told them that, he wasn't there any more. The cops told me later that his name was Skeets.

Tanya Who told them that if it wasn't you?

Luke I don't know. I don't want to know.

Miles There's been too much blame already.

Luke There's not been enough. (*To Tanya.*) Tell me about Deon.

She pours herself another drink.

Tanya We got as far as Jo'burg. He went to make a
phone call, and when he came back he had bad news
written all over his face. He said, 'We're in big trouble.
Luke is talking.' He said, 'I can't take this responsibility.
You've got your British passport. You've got money.
I'm putting you on the plane to London.' We said
goodbye at the airport and he drove to Swaziland.
Three months later, he was driving to the Mission
when he was flagged down by a pick-up truck at the
side of the road. He got out of the car to help, and
four Special Branch men jumped out of the truck,
handcuffed him and took him back to South Africa.
The hell with the border. Those guys don't care about
borders. They wanted him. They were so damn furious
about letting you go. So they took Deon instead. He
got the sentence you would have got. Ten years.

Luke I know. I was in the courtroom.

Tanya So what was the deal?

Luke You know what it was.

Tanya I want to hear it from you.

Luke If I testified in court against the rest of the group,
they'd let me walk.

Tanya So here you are.

Luke So here I am.

Tanya Haven't you left something out?

Luke Do you mean my struggle with my conscience? It
wasn't like that. I was lost already. Once you're lost,
there's nothing to catch you. You just keep on falling.

Pause.

I gotta go.

He stands.

If you've done the worst thing you can imagine, then
what you want to do more than anything else is to

apologise. Because that just might lessen the horror. But first you've got to admit what you did. Admit it to yourself, I mean. Admit it fully. And there are so many ways of protecting yourself from that. You think how unfair it is that the rest of your life should be destroyed by one mistake. You tell yourself how unlucky you were. Or that you made one fatal slip. Or that most of the people who look down at you with contempt are arseholes who've never lifted a finger themselves. Or, this is the big one, that the cause is right, that it's a great and noble cause, however crap you were at fighting for it. So your apology dies at birth. It's been excused to death. You could say the words, but they'd be insincere. They'd be worse than a lie. They'd be a blasphemy. Miles, you let me down.

Miles How?

Luke I didn't come here tonight so that the only friend that I've got left could say that what I did wasn't too bad, or that anyone else would have done the same. That's worthless. I want you to look me in the eye and say it was inexcusable. Then I'll know.

Miles It was inexcusable.

Luke That's no good. You're just saying it. You've got to be angry.

Miles I can't be angry for other people.

Luke Then be angry for yourself.

Miles But I'm not.

Luke I don't believe it.

Miles It's true.

Luke You're lying to me. Don't do that. Tell me.

Miles I was pissed off about the suitcase.

Luke What about now?

Miles I'm still pissed off.

Luke Is that the angriest you can get?

Miles Yes, it is.

Luke Try harder.

Miles loses his temper.

Miles It isn't me that's gotta try harder! It's you! Just fucking stop being clever and fucking say it!
Luke I'm sorry about the suitcase.

He thinks about this for a moment, then smiles.

I am. I really am. Thanks for helping me make that small apology. It was the act of a friend.
Miles Any time.

Luke turns to go.

Tanya Luke.
Luke What?
Tanya Maybe small apologies lead to big ones.
Luke Maybe slowly. Good night.

He goes.

End.

Production Notes

He's Talking is based on the experiences of a schoolfriend of Nicholas Wright who became involved in the anti-apartheid movement in Cape Town, South Africa. The friend, who in the play is represented by Luke, belonged to a band of protesters who attacked non-human targets with the intention of causing mass disruption. One of these targets was the railway that runs through the centre of Cape Town, which they successfully bombed.

Nicholas's friend was a well-known student protester and one day the police raided his flat as a scare tactic. They didn't arrest him, but their suspicions were aroused. When the friend panicked as a result of the raid and sent his girlfriend to destroy some hidden explosives, the police followed the girlfriend, and subsequently arrested both her and her friend.

The resistance group had always used code names to protect themselves, although in reality Cape Town is a small place and just about everyone knew the real identities of the other group members; but if caught, it was agreed that they would use the fact that they only knew the code names as an excuse for not identifying the other members of the group. If this was not believed, they were to hold out for at least 48 hours to give the others a chance to escape the country. However, the friend was offered his freedom if he revealed the other members of the group and testified against them in court. He did this.

After his release, the friend was ruined. He believed himself a coward and felt resented by all who knew him.

He left South Africa, and spent many years travelling around labouring. It wasn't until much later in his life that he finally found a place to settle down and make a decent life for himself.

Basing the play on the experiences of this friend, Nicholas wanted to explore how making mistakes when you are young can have a devastating effect on the rest of your life. One decision can send your life in a completely different direction from that which you intended.

The trigger that caused Nicholas to make a play from his friend's story was the increasing number of suicide bombers reported in the news, and the realisation that there are young people who are so driven by their beliefs that they think it is a good idea to set off bombs. He recognised that young people are often very active protesters because they are at a time in their lives when they are actively trying to establish their ideals and their place in the world. This can sometimes drive them to extreme acts which will ultimately end or seriously affect their lives.

The play also examines the idea of forgiveness, and seeks to explore what a person can do to earn forgiveness when they have done something really bad.

THE HISTORICAL BACKGROUND

The events in the play take place during the time of apartheid in South Africa. Apartheid, meaning 'apartness' in Afrikaans, was the name given to the policy that legalised the segregation of people according to their skin colour. It was a system enforced by the ruling National Party in South African between 1948 and 1994; and during this time power and privileges were given to the white people of South Africa, while the black people were

denied many rights and stripped of their citizenship –
only being citizens legally if they lived in the designated
Black Reserves (which were in substantially poorer, less
developed parts of the country). If they didn't want to
live on these reserves and lived in white areas, they were
subject to rigorous segregation. Everything from cinemas
to medical care and education was segregated, with
inferior standards for the black people.

The African National Congress (ANC) was a Black
Nationalist movement banned by the government for its
opposition to the apartheid regime. Nelson Mandela, a
leader of the ANC, was famously imprisoned for 27 years
until 1990, and labelled a terrorist for his association
with the movement. Following the banning of the ANC,
resistance organisations went underground, meeting in
secret and carrying out planned acts of sabotage on key
state structures. If caught, members of the resistance
faced imprisonment, police brutality, and even hanging.
It was such a resistance group that the characters in the
play would have belonged to.

Prior to apartheid, relations between those of English and
Afrikaner origin were not good. However, with its
enforcement the Afrikaner-dominated government called
for a unity of white South Africans, and the ethnic divide
between white and black was intensified and entrenched
in many new laws. The Afrikaners in *He's Talking* (as
represented by Rosie and Deon) were given longer prison
sentences than the English-descended characters because
they were seen as traitors against their own government.

If the actors cannot relate to apartheid, they may find
analogies in their own lives (such as resistance to the Iraq
War) to discover what drives their characters. It is vital
that they connect to their own anger at injustice in order
to fully enter the world of this play.

EXERCISES ON INJUSTICE

- Ask the actors to brainstorm situations or people that anger them and where they see injustice. What would drive *them* to protest, or to carry out an extreme act?

- Think creatively of ways in which you can give them a direct experience of injustice. For example, segregate the group by dividing them into those with brown eyes and those with blue eyes, and give them different rights (e.g. those with blue eyes aren't allowed to sit down).

Some theatre companies will have actors of different racial origins to those in the play, and concerns were raised in the initial workshop about whether it is possible for them to perform this play when one of its themes is race. In response to this, Nicholas Wright said he hopes colour-blind casting is possible. He suggested that as long as the company makes clear decisions as to how they will frame the production and puts clear sign-systems in place to tell the story, it is possible to do this play regardless of the race of the actors.

THE SHAPE OF THE PLAY

He's Talking explores how a life is influenced by the choices we make, and this is dramatised in the form of the play. Each section is the result of a different choice that Luke makes. They are called replays instead of scenes to show it is not a linear play. All the scenes happen as if in parallel universes.

In this play, the action is just behind the words. Very little physical action is needed, and therefore it is strongly recommended that you don't block the play until quite late in the rehearsal process. Allow the actors to find the shape of the exchanges between the characters for themselves.

Rope Exercise

Tie a piece of string/rope around actors' waists and ask them to pull/push away the other actors, depending on their relationship with them at that point.

Tennis Ball Exercise

Introduce a number of tennis balls, and as actors deliver a line, have them decide who the line is for, and throw them the ball.

The actors must think of each section as a new beginning for their character. However, it's important that the director sees the piece as a whole, and the way in which the energy flows through the entire play. Each section has echoes of the last, and these must be recognised.

At the start of the play, the apartment is filled with people. However, with each section, more people are 'subtracted' from the group. Nicholas described how he wanted to show the group getting 'roughed up', and its gradual deterioration should be made very clear.

It is up to the director to decide whether each section should be followed by a blackout, whether we should actually see the characters leaving the stage, or whether the absent characters could be demonstrated in a more abstract way – e.g., by having a light remaining on their empty chairs.

In the final section, the last thing the audience expects is the return of Luke; therefore it is important to protect this moment, and to carry the action on strongly from that point.

THE SETTING

The play takes place in a luxurious apartment in London, owned by Miles and Tanya's parents. From the very beginning of the play it is essential to get across that, even though they are chatting, this is not a social scene. This group is not a social network, but a group of people meeting to discuss their objectives. Just about every time the group has previously met it would have been formal and they would have used code names. This will strongly affect the way they behave with each other in the present. They will find it difficult to change the formal way in which they speak and act. It is also important to note that though the white characters will feel comfortable in this bourgeois apartment, Skeets, the black man will not.

Exercise for the Actor Playing Skeets

Ask the actors to improvise scenes where they are in a situation they don't feel comfortable in (e.g., at the dinner table with their boyfriend of girlfriend's family).

THE CHARACTERS

All characters in the play, apart from Luke, are completely fictitious. During apartheid there was a strong student protest movement, which the group in the play has evolved from. The group is well meaning, but at the same time, naive and amateur.

In this play, the accents are key in demonstrating the different backgrounds of each of the characters, so if possible the actors should try and develop the correct accents for their character: Luke, Oscar and Sal are South Africans of English descent, with soft South African accents; Deon and Rosie are Afrikaans; Miles and Tanya are English. Skeets has a strong African accent.

He's Talking explores how character is not fixed. It can be changed by our actions, and our circumstances. As a result of this, the challenge for the actors is to take each scene as a new play and discover their character afresh for each section.

However, Nicholas has given us a bit of background for each character to help the actors understand what has influenced the formation of each character's beliefs/ideals:

LUKE   South African with an English background. A popular, sporty, intelligent boy at school, Luke is used to being in control. He is driven by the injustices he has witnessed under apartheid, and wants the group to support him in his mission.

MILES   Comes from a rich British family who made their money in South Africa. Born in England, his family moved to Cape Town when he was a child, and he was educated there. He is Tanya's brother, and was Luke's best friend at school. He is not directly involved in the group, and this exclusion affects him. Luke hid the bomb in Miles's garage, but Miles didn't know it was a bomb, and as a result felt let down by Luke, who had lied to him. Miles was the first person that Luke named.

TANYA   Like her brother Miles, Tanya was born in England before moving to Cape Town as a child. She joined the group at university, and met her boyfriend Deon through the group. She is not proud of the way in which her family have made their fortune from South Africa.

DEON   Afrikaans. He comes from a missionary family, and therefore has a strong Christian background. He joined the group at university, and met his girlfriend

Tanya through the group. His principles are rooted in non-violent protest.

ROSIE   Afrikaans. Her involvement in the group is more personal. It's a rebellion against her family and background. She joined the group while studying law at university. Luke sees Rosie as the 'spirit' of the group, the force behind it, so when he names her, the group is destroyed for ever.

OSCAR   He is South African with an English background. An intellectual who reads a lot of serious, political literature, he joined the group when he went to university to study medicine.

SAL   She is South African with an English background. An actress, Sal is not deeply involved in the group, but became involved via her flatmate and friend, Rosie. She is in love with Oscar.

SKEETS   Codenamed *Walter*, he's a black South African who grew up in one of the black townships, and driven by the unjust treatment of his race due to apartheid. He works as a mechanic, but is also politically active on a community level in the townships. He is the only one in the group who knows how to make bombs. Skeets doesn't speak much and remains in his own space. He maintains a silent power through this. It is ironic that, although Skeets represents the cause that the rest of the group is fighting for, they largely ignore him.

CHARACTER DEVELOPMENT EXERCISES

Four Columns Exercise

Ask the actors to go through the whole script and put any information surrounding their character in one of four columns, with page references:

WHAT I SAY ABOUT MYSELF.
WHAT OTHERS SAY ABOUT ME.
WHAT I SAY ABOUT OTHERS.
WORLD VIEWS.

This exercise encourages the actors to put together a complete and thorough collection of all the evidence given about their character.

Timeline

Again, using the four columns, ask each actor to plot the timeline of his or her character's life. Start the timeline at their birth, and plot every year up until Luke's arrest. Then, after the arrest, plot every month up to the meeting in London a year later. In the final twelve months of the timeline (following Luke's arrest) it will be different for each character depending on the replay, therefore they will have to plot five separate timelines.

The ages of each character, and key dates that affected all the characters, were decided on: Miles, 22 years old; Tanya, 20 years old; Rosie, 21 years old; Deon, 21 years old; Oscar, 21 years old; Sal, 21 years old; Luke, 22 years old; Skeets, 23 years old.

KEY DATES

> 1961 Group formed at university.
> 1962–63 Group's protest activities taking place:
>   *Radio Mast on the mountain bombed.*
>   *Reservoir bombed.*
>   *Electricity pylons bombed.*
>   *Railway line bombed.*
> 1963, December Luke's arrest
> 1964, December Meeting in the apartment, London.

When the actors have plotted their own timelines, they must bring them together as a group, and ensure that they all line up against each other (e.g., Luke cannot start a friendship with Miles in 1957 if Miles's family did not move to South Africa until 1958).

This exercise ensures that each individual actor has a clear picture of their own biography but also a shared history with the other characters, allowing them to find cohesion as a group.

IMPROVISATIONS

Once the timeline is complete, the group can isolate some key events on it and improvise scenes around them. For example, the actors playing Luke and Rosie could improvise a scene in which they meet and become friends, then discover that they share a resistance to apartheid.

Title Tableaux

1. Ask the actors to think of a title for each of the five sections that captures the meaning/essence of that scene.

2. In the next session, ask them one at a time to introduce their titles and then arrange the other actors in a tableau to illustrate this title. (Alternatively, once they have given their title, the director could arrange the actors in the tableau, or the actors could arrange themselves.)

3. Once the tableau has been formed, play around with it so it is as strong as possible.

- Do the actors feel right where they are positioned?

- Are the relationships between the characters clear?

- Who has the highest/lowest status in the scene?

Status Exercise

Explore how each character's status changes throughout the play.

- Go through each section with the actors ranking their individual status on a scale from one to ten, where level one is low-status, and level ten is high-status.

SUGGESTED READING FOR ACTORS

Jail Diary of Albie Sachs by David Edgar (useful for the actor playing Luke).

There and Back by Eddie Daniels.

Bandiet: Seven Years in a South African Prison by Hugh Lewin.

From a workshop led by Richard Beecham
with notes by Zenia Bond

IT SNOWS

Bryony Lavery, Steven Hoggett
and Scott Graham

Bryony Lavery's plays include, at the National, the multi-award-winning *Frozen*, and for 'Connections', *More Light*, *Illyria*, *Discontented Winter: House Remix* and *Red Sky*. Other work includes *Stockholm* (with Frantic Assembly), *A Wedding Story*, *Last Easter*, *Her Aching Heart*, *Two Marias* and *Smoke*. Her adaptations for stage and radio include *Behind the Scenes at the Museum*, *The Magic Toyshop*, *Wuthering Heights*, *A High Wind in Jamaica* and *Lady Audley's Secret*.

Scott Graham and Steven Hoggett – the Artistic Directors of Frantic Assembly – create new work that places equal emphasis on movement, design, music and text, in collaboration with a wide variety of artists. Frantic Assembly has toured extensively throughout the UK and abroad since its formation in 1994, building a reputation as one of the country's most exciting companies. Frantic Assembly operates a year-round Creative Learning and Training Programme.

Authors' Note

The coolest period in the middle of the last millennium is referred to as the 'Little Ice Age'. In British terms it ran from medieval times until 1850. Ever since that time our climate has been getting warmer, but even in today's warmer climate snow and ice still cover our highest mountains during the winter months.

Having said that, winter in the UK rarely sets in before December. The coldest months are still usually January and February. There haven't been too many cold winters recently in the UK, and the number of days with snow cover are becoming fewer too. It's getting harder and harder to make a snowman in southern England! Many young children living here are still waiting to see their first white Christmas. If global warming predictions from the Met Office's Hadley Centre are correct, they may never live to see it. The predictions for the next fifty years are that our winters will become milder, wetter and windier. The last white Christmases in London were 1906, 1916, 1927, 1938, 1956, 1964, 1968, 1970, 1976, 1981, 1996 and 1999 . . .

It Snows is about one of those special days. It is about something wonderful and rare falling out of the sky on top of you. It is about a place where the street you walk on suddenly turns into something you can fall on without hurting yourself. Adults, even your turgid parents, *play*. The opposite sex, even the *fit* ones, slide with you!

Everything changes.

Characters

Cameron Huntley
our hero

Caitlin Amoretti
our heroine (pronounced 'Catlin')

The Weird Girl
our mystery

Delisha
Caitlin's best friend

Tamara
Delisha's best friend

Marlee Holmes-Spalding
the poshest, richest girl around

Weird Girl's Brother
another mystery

Then there are various groups:

Everybody
this is everybody: do it all together
or share it out or what seems right to you;
make it real

Lads
these include Mr Trouble, Mr Cool,
Mr Not Cool, Mr Runner, Mr Rubber:
find the name that suits the
physical character you are

Girls
these include Ms Dizzy, Ms Perfect,
Ms Trouble, Ms Big Trouble,
Ms Thing, Ms Glam:
likewise, find the name that suits
the physical character you've made

Mums
ditto

Dads
ditto

Members of the Community
Business Men/Women,
Old-Age Pensioners, Milkmen,
Postmen, Gritters, Sanders, etc.

It Snows is a physical piece.
No videos to be used.
Only Caitlin does mime.

Where Everybody speaks, be amazing
with the sound delivery of the text,
whether speaking together or dividing it up.
It is the language of its streets and should be
both realistic and gorgeous.

ONE – IT'S NOT HAPPENING

*We are in a not-very-beautiful place of buildings and
streets and windows.*
  Cameron is there with a complicated box.

Cameron
  Its finger-freezing-nose-running-bollocking-nut-nipping
  cold.

  It's not Christmas

  It's just after.

  He starts to open the box . . .

  Because my birthday is on Boxing Day every year
  Everybody
  Even my mogging *mum* forgets my birthday
  So because she feels Mega-Guilty
  in the January Sales she always feels she's
  gotta buy me a *Top* gift . . .

  Box is open.

  This year
  It's

  He takes out . . .

  a digital camera.
  (*Very unimpressed.*) Right. That says 'I love you.'

  Drops the box on the ground. Points the camera at us.

  Stay still

  He takes a photograph of us.

269

LAVERY, HOGGETT & GRAHAM

Got it.

Round here though there's not much to make a great picture.

He photographs the box on the ground.

Stay still

Got it.

There's a weird girl living in the building opposite.

The Weird Girl stands with her back to her window.

She mostly looks back into her room. Which is weird. Right?

Sometimes   she looks out of the window

Pause.

Come on . . .

Then she turns to look out.
  Cameron positions his camera.
Stay still

She does.
  He photographs her.

Got it.

She turns back to the room. Vanishes.

Otherwise
There's just streets
Streets
Streets
Buildings
Buildings
Buildings
School

Saturday job.
Streets
Streets
Streets.

The Lads appear. Amazingly.

Oh
And yeah
Some Lads
That like to threaten you on a daily basis.

Lads come and threaten.

Lads
Oi!

And behaviour . . .

Yo!

No!
Cameron
Particularly if you're called Cameron Huntley . . .
Lads
Yo!
Cuntley!
Cameron
Huntley
Cameron Huntley.
Lads
What we said!
Cuntley!

And they threaten a bit more.
They take the box, put it on his head as a nice hat.
They take his camera, photograph him in positions
of pain.

Yo

Yo

Yo

Stick the camera somewhere inaccessible to him.

Yo!

Then turn and vanish.
Cameron takes off his box hat.
Retrieves his inaccessible camera as . . .

Cameron
You get spots.
Your body goes weird on you.
Girls ignore you.
Especially Caitlin Amoretti.

The Girls, including Caitlin Amoretti, prom on.
Cameron points his camera.

Girls
Do What??
Don't Think So!!
Cameron
Stay still
Girls
Cameron Huntley?
Do What??
Don't Think So!!

Get Him!

The Girls do something unspeakable to Cameron.
Caitlin Amoretti watches.

What's in the box, Cameron?

Is it your willy?
Cameron
See?

You wonder if you can vanish.

He tries.

Girls
Go Girlz !!
Say What??
Don't Mess With!!

Coming, Amoretti?
Caitlin
Staying   might   stay

The Girls prom off.

Caitlin
Nothing much happens round here.
School
School
School
You do Theatre Studies.
You learn stuff like   Mime

She does some mime.

Movement

She does some movement.

You learn useful theatrical terms like . . .

'Lights up.' 'Lights down.'
'Blackout.'

The lights may obey her here and throughout . . .

Upstage downstage stage right stage left – wings
Exit right – exit left – find your light.

Possibly, though, the light finds her . . .

You learn acting o-that-this-too-too-solid-flesh-would-
     melt

273

Doesn't count for little butterballs when you come out
and

Lads

Oi!

Yo!

And behaviour . . .

Caitlin

Boys like Cameron Huntley just ignore you . . .

While the others . . .

Lads

Oo!

Yo!

Twatlin Amoretti

Caitlin

Caitlin Amoretti

Lads

What we said

Twatlin.

And they do something unspeakable to Caitlin . . .

Cameron

You discover you're not much of a hero

You go in.

He goes in.

Caitlin

It's so cold your tits are embarrassing in a white school
shirt.

Lads

Look at Caitlin Amoretti's titties!

Caitlin

You use *acting* to protect yourself and hide your all-
enveloping shame

Pointing desperately . . .

Oh No! *Look!*
That's not *the Old Bill* coming this way Is It . . . ?
With *the Drugs-Sniffer Dog?*

Lads magically, speedily, disappear.

It's like whoever's on Weather today's got the dial
   turned up to *Arctic*
It's too cold to be out
You Go In.   Stage Left.

*She does an impressive mime, opening a door,
doorknob. Going in . . .*

We're doing *Marcel Marceau* this term . . .

Shutting it behind her . . .

I'm after an 'A'.

You're *In.*
Cameron
You're *IN.*
Caitlin
Lights up! Reddish Homey filter.

You watch *CSI – Miami*
Cameron
You play Game Boy
Caitlin
You're on FaceBook
Cameron
You're on YouTube
Caitlin
You're on your mum's nerves

*A knot of Mums appear . . .
   And Mums' behaviour as . . .*

Mums

Haven't you got homework to do?

Do you have to be *there*?

You're driving me *up the wall*!!

Cameron

You're on your dad's nerves

A fistful of Dads appear.
And Dads' behaviour as . . .

Dads

Haven't you got coursework to catch up?

Who's finished *the beer*?

When I come home after a hard day's work all I want's
a *bit of peace*!!

Cameron

Your mum and dad row a lot.

Mums

Don't just put your cup down in that sink I've just this
minute / cleaned all the work surfaces . . . cup! No! I
mean it . . .

Dads

I'll do it in a minute can I have just one moment first
with a biscuit and my paper . . .? Moment! Biscuit!
Paper! I mean it . . .

Mums

Ken / Phil / Sanjay / Ronny / Desmond / Luv /
Mustapha / Daddy!!

Dads

Denise! / Audrey! / Amrit! / Jocelyn! / Houdna! /
Mummy!!

Mums

You did you put it in my clean sink you did you did
you did!

Dads
For a couple of minutes for a couple of minutes!!
Caitlin
Lights dim.
Time for bed.
Cameron
Time for bed.
Dads / Mums
For pity's sake – *Go To Bed!!*
Dads
I'm off *out*!!
Mums
GOOD!!
I'm Off To Bed!!

*Mums and Dads disappear magically in opposite
directions . . .*

Caitlin
And you look out
Cameron
And you look out
Caitlin
It's got dark
Cameron
It's got dark
That weird girl's looking out of her window

The Weird Girl looks out.

Stay still

He photographs her.

Got it.

*He turns back into his room so he doesn't see . . .
The Weird Girl bringing up an old threadbare teddy
bear to look through the window.*

She makes the teddy bear look left and right.
The teddy bear sees everything.
It looks up at her.
She looks at the bear.
They both look back out of the window.
Then she disappears it.
Then she disappears.

Caitlin

Then it's like whoever's on Weather *today's* turned the
    dial off *Arctic*
Down to just *cold*
The sky looks heavy
A bit glittery.
You get under *two* duvets
You sleep.

Cameron

Air's full of frost.
You pile *all* your coats
And your bedside sheepskin rug
On top of your duvet
You sleep.

Caitlin

Lights down.

Single small spotlight on the juvenile leading lady.
Rose pink.

You have these dreams.

About flying   and horses
You're on a horse riding away over   the dark green
    hills

Cameron

You have these dreams

You're fighting   with superhuman strength
    superhuman calm

With a superhuman ability to disable but not kill each
   of your dastardly enemies

Not kill   unless you *feel* like killing
Caitlin
   Dream changes!

You're at a Party on a big *yacht* and God you look fit
you can see it in everybody's eyes . . .
Cameron
   Dream changes!

You're at a Party in *Hello* in *GQ* in Heaven where even
fit girls really fit girls treat you with *respect*   and
longing
Caitlin
   You totally *love* dreaming
Cameron
   You're *so* into dreaming!

They sleep.

The Weird Girl appears at her window.
   She is screaming.
   She beats the window with her fists.
   None of us can hear her.
   She disappears.

Cameron
   You wake suddenly / in the middle of the night!
Caitlin
   You wake suddenly in the middle of the night!
Cameron
   What?
Caitlin
   Yes . . .?

They both lie listening.
   The Weird Girl appears at her window with paper
and marker.

She writes a note.
Puts note up at the window.
The words are too small for us to read.
She takes down the note. Turns away.

Cameron

It's weirdly dark

Caitlin

It's weirdly dark   and   *warmer*
You chuck one of your duvets

Joy . . .

You remember it's posh Marlee Holmes-Spalding's
party tomorrow

Cameron

You've woken in a cold sweat
You chuck your sheepskin rug and five of your coats

Horror . . .

You remember
There's the incredible embarrassment factor of posh
    Marlee Holmes-Spalding's party tomorrow

Caitlin

And you're a *great* dancer

Cameron

And you're a *shit* dancer

Caitlin

Please   *Whoever*   Don't let anything happen to
    spoil it.

Cameron

Please   *Anyone* up there   Let something happen
    to spoil it.

The Weird Girl appears with teddy bear and note.
    Fixes the note in among the teddy bear's stuffing via
a split in its chest. Safety-pins the split.
    Tosses teddy bear out through window.

It falls through the air, turning over and over.
It lies on its back in the street below.

Caitlin
End of scene one. Nightlight glow.
Black fading slowly to . . . dawn.

They sleep.

TWO – IT'S HAPPENING

Everybody
Morning
Morning
Morning

Caitlin starts to wake as . . .

You open your eyes
You yawn

Everybody yawns . . .

You look
And you look out
And you look out
And you look out

Everybody, plus Caitlin, looks out.

Caitlin
And the sky today somebody on *Weather's*
breaking off bits of white sky
And the bits the *minute* bits of cloud are falling

Cameron starts to wake up . . .

And
It snows

Everybody

It snows

It snows

Cameron blearily goes to window.

Cameron

Looks . . . goes from zero to wide-awake in a nano-second.

IT'S SNOWING!!

IT'S SNOWING!!

Everybody

Everybody's watching!!

Cameron

Even the girl in the window opposite is watching it snow . . .

Stay still

He photographs her.

Got it.

As he looks away, she looks down, points frantically to her teddy bear on the ground below.

Everybody

It snows

EYES UP!
Everybody watches the snow fall. All the Community.
Everybody catches snowflakes in their mouth.

It's different

Things change

Things happen when
It snows

Its getting thicker!

Its settling!
Its going to be really really deep!!
Brrrrrrrrrrr!!

I NEED TO GET MY SNOW GEAR ON!!!

Everybody starts to get dressed in various qualities of snow gear as . . .

You can't wait to get outside

It's the clothes on the line frozen

It's the possibility of sledging!!

SLEDDDDDDGGGINGGG!!

It's the possibility of the pond freezing over therefore *skaaaaaaaaaaaaaaaating!!*

It's the possibility of   loooooong   sliiiiiiides!!

It's the white
It's the white

The white

The difference

The other

Brrrrrrrr!

Everybody puts on mittens as . . .

It's the clean surface the clean slate you get

It's the car driving through town with the foot of snow
on its roof

It's the hexagonal composition of snow

Hexagonal shape dance.

It's the steamed-up windows

Its how it covers everything up

Even the teddy bear that the weird girl in the window
threw down.

Everything

Gets covered.

*And the teddy bear disappears as the Weird Girl
watches helpless.*

It snows

It's the joy of it
The joy of it
The joy of it.

And everybody is dressed and ready!!

THREE – IT'S HERE!

Everybody ready for the snow . . . ?

Cameron
The world's new.

The space is clean and white.

Nobody was ever here before.
Caitlin
We go MAD!!
Cameron
We go MADMADMADMADMADMADMADMAD!!
Lads
We go Maaaaaaaaaaaaaaaaaaaaaaaaad!!
Girls
Sooooooooooooo Madmadmadmadmad!!!

*OK, this section is 'The Snow Piece'.
People make patterns in the snow.*

Cameron
You start to see the patterns in life

People make Snow Angels.

Caitlin
Centre stage – *wings*!
Caitlin
People walk about with piles of snow on their heads!
Cameron
At the bus stop there's some penguins . . .

*He photographs businessmen looking like penguins
with Styrofoam-cup beaks, etc . . .*

There's some blood in the snow.

He photographs it.

Snow in the tree

*Photographs it.
    Where the teddy bear is under the snow . . .*

Small mysterious pile of snow

Photographs.

Weird girl's window. Empty. But with snow on it.

Photographs.

Caitlin
And still the snow's falling
Its getting deeper and deeper . . .

Horror . . .

I hope Marlee Holmes-Spalding's party's still on!
Cameron
This snow's gonna be too deep for people to find their
    way around!

Joy . . .

Marlee Holmes-Spalding's party's looking problematical!

Everybody
Somebody discovers something . . .
This snow is the sort of snow that makes . . . .

One of the Lads bends down. Discovers the snow is now the sort that makes snowballs!

Lad
Snowballs
Lads
SNOWBALLS!!
Girls
Oh no, not SNOWBALLS!!

People start to make snowballs as . . .

Everybody
Even *THE DADS AND MUMS LIKE SNOW*!!

They ALL come out of the buildings . . . .

Mums and Dads come out of the buildings.

Mums
Snow! Everywhere!
Dads
Best clear some paths!!
Caitlin
The *dads!* Make The Big Snowball!!

Dads make the 'big' snowball which carries all before it.

Dads
Careful!
Careful . . .
CAREFUL!!
Cameron
The mums *watch* the dads make 'The Big Snowball . . .'

Mums watch and smoke. Proud.

Mums
Careful Dad / Ken / Phil / Sanjay / Ronny / Luv / Derek /
   Mustapha . . .
   Careful Careful . . .

   And now . . .
      The Big . . .
      Snowball Fight!
      Not gender versus gender . . . more . . .
      Threatening characters versus wimps.
      Dads' 'Big Snowball' threads through.

Dads
   What d'you say to *that*, Denise / Amrit / Audrey /
   Mummy / Jocelyn . . .?
Mums
   OOOOOOOOOOOH!
   You are *clever*, Dad / Ken / Phil / Sanjay / Desmond . . .!
Cameron (*with perfect snowball*)
   You've never been great at sports
   But
   Just *once* in your loser life . . .
   You have the perfect snowball in your hand
   The right size
   The optimum weight!

   You *have* to throw it!
Caitlin
   You're fit
   You're bendy
   You've dodged every snowball
   Because   you're like that
   Graceful
   Swift . . .

   As she says this, Cameron's snowball flies through the
   air. Hits her square in the mouth.

Cameron

It's suddenly not such a good day.

Caitlin

You've suddenly a gobful of sn . . .

(*To Cameron.*) You *pillock*!

Then you see it's Cameron Huntley . . .

Cameron

You're suddenly a pillock . . .

(*To Caitlin.*) Sorry! Not meant for . . .

Suddenly feels dark

Like the world's ending . . .

Like a familiar pattern's emerging . . .

Mobiles start to go.
Everybody has to find their mobiles in the depth of their snow gear in their mittens.

Everybody

Yes?

Yo?

Oh?

So?

Say what?

Marlee Holmes-Spalding's ringing round saying 'My party's still on!'

I got to get my Best Knock-'Em-Dead Gear On!

Everybody gets into knock-out gear ready for the party.
The Weird Girl is at her window, looking out. She turns back into the room.
There is a boy sitting in a chair. Saying nothing.
She dresses him in warm, warm clothes. He says nothing.

She leads him to the window, shows him the snow.

Weird Girl
It's snow
Come on.

She leads him to a door.
But he won't go through it. He resists.
She leads him back to his chair.
Sits him down.
She goes back to the window and looks out.

Cameron
You're inside.
Snow's got very frosty.
Its *got* to be too slippery for Marlee Holmes-Spalding's party

Caitlin
With her two friends . . . Delisha and Tamara . . .

Lights up.

You're inside Delisha's building with Delisha and Tamara.
You look fabulous, they look fabulous.
You're waiting for your cab to take you to Marlee Holmes-Spalding's party.
It's not coming.

The three make a picture of waiting for a cab.

You're waiting.

They wait. Then . . .
Lights down.

Cameron
Sky with stars

Moon.

He photographs it.

Caitlin
Lights up.

Another configuration of three waiting for the cab.
Desperate.

You're still waiting.

They wait.

Then

Lights down.

Cameron
Weird girl at window
Looking down

Stay still

He photographs her.

Got it.

Caitlin
Lights up.

Another configuration of three waiting. One of them is
on the phone, others listening. More desperate.

Still. Waiting.

They wait. Then . . .

Lights down.

Cameron
You could *not go.*

He considers this . . .

Caitlin
Lights up.

Another waiting configuration . . . very desperate.

Still waiting.

Wait desperately . . . then . . .

Delisha
We could 'not go'

Tamara
We could rethink the plan
We could go up to your bedroom, Delisha, invent a
    dance routine.

Cameron
You prayed for an excuse
You got one.
Snow. Deep snow. Freezing.
Slippery as f—

Delisha
Thinking outside the box, Tamara.
I like it.

Caitlin
But there'll be people at the party you might want
    to *see*

Cameron
But something might *happen*

You might cop off.

Caitlin
You might be like 'Hi, Cameron!
Dance?' 'Sure. Why not?'

Cameron
You might be like 'Oh. Caitlin. What say?
Admirin' my shapes? Join me?' 'Yo! Sure!'

Tamara
We can choose popular upbeat music!
Possibly like a medley   steady beat   go uptempo
Segue into a like *manic* beat cool it into slo-romantic
    vibe . . .
Make it really complex!
Then audition for *Britain's Got Talent*!

Delisha
I'll go to the kitchen get some Tangos and Doritos and some of mi-mum's Pernod!!

Tamara
I'll go clear your bedroom floor, Delisha . . .

Come on, Caitlin . . . Forward Plannning! Fame! Fortune!

They exit . . . where 'fame' awaits them.

Caitlin
You shout up.
(*Really quietly.*) I might just go to the party . . .!
OK

Just *DO IT*!

Even by *bus*!!

Cameron
Just *be A MAN*!!
Get a bus!

And they both leave their buildings.
    Caitlin with an impressive through-the-door mime as always . . . lots of bolts and locks and chains to undo this time . . .

Everybody
Meanwhile
At Marlee Holmes-Spalding's party . . . .

Everybody else is, as if by magic, at the party, very squashed up, doing really really wonderful group dancing!

Among them, very squashed, our hostess Marlee . . .

Marlee
So Many of You! Lovely! Come in!
Coats There! Shoes Off!

No, Seriously Shoes Off!
Drinks in There!
Dips Crisps Eats Stuff in There!
No Going in the Dining Room.
No Going in Dad's Drinks Cabinet!
Come In! Lovely! Welcome!!!

As . . .
   Caitlin and Cameron, on the street, arrive at the same bus stop.

Cameron
   Oh. No. Oh.
Caitlin
   Oh. God. Oh.

They queue.
   They watch for the bus coming.

Meanwhile, the squashed party continues.
   Marlee, squashed within . . .

Marlee
   Don't lean on the walls!
   They've just been redecorated!!
   Who are *You*? Who are *YOU*??
   I don't know *ANYBODY* here!!
   Dad said *twenty* guests! Don't let anybody else in!!
   No Gatecrashers!
   No More! No!!

Back at the bus stop . . .
   Its getting unbearable, and colder . . .
   Cameron points his camera at something very small.

Stay still

Got it.

Caitlin practises mime walking in a very strong wind.

Caitlin
It's *mime*.

Cameron tries to photograph his own face

Cameron
Stay still

Got it.

Caitlin practises being trapped in a mime glass box.
Back at the even more squashed party . . .

Marlee (*even more squashed*)
Put that *Down!!* that's my *dad's twenty-five-year-old malt!*
There's *a scratch* on my mum's *dining-table-for-twelve!*
Don't bring the dips out of the kitchen you'll get it all
over the furniture the paintwork Oh look the carpet!
Why did I say I'd have a party??
I *hate* parties!!
I Hate You!!
I Hate You ALLLL!!

Back at the bus stop, everybody is very very very cold . . .
After what feels to them both like forever . . .

Cameron
Don't think it's coming.
Caitlin
No
Cameron
I'm freezing
Caitlin
Me too.

They sit. This is the journey of the shiver.
They shiver. Apart. In stereo.
Both their teeth chatter for a bit.
Then he, very tentatively, starts to warm her.

And then, they warm one another . . . little bits of
each other's cold extremities, going from freezing and
shaking through everything . . . blowing on one
another . . .
    To warmth.
    To amazing closeness.

Caitlin
Thanks
Cameron
You're . . .
Caitlin
Welcome
Think I might give up on the party
Cameron
Me too.
Gutted to miss dancing, though.

Caitlin
Always.

    She rummages through her snow gear for her mobile . . .
    Finds a dance track on it. They dance.
    Miraculously, Cameron can dance with Caitlin.

Cameron
Er   so   well   um   walk you home?
Caitlin
No!!
Cameron
No. Of Course Not.
Caitlin
Don't walk me
Dance me home.

    And they do.
    Lights: many brilliant bright colours glitterball.
    End of Scene Three.

FOUR – IT'S GOING (SLUSH)

A 'slush damce' . . . as Everybody discovers . . .

Everybody
Snow
Is always followed
By slush

Morning
Morning
You come out
It's all Slush!

Slush!

Slush!

The snow on roofs starts to slide and

Dush!

Trees hurl the snow off their branches

Dush!

The snowman falls over

Dush!

The snow creeps back from the buildings

Dush Dush Dush
White turns to
Soot Grey
Dog-urine-yellow

That blood on the snow   it's gone

Real world starts to re-emerge

It's not pretty

Everything goes back to dull old ordinary old *normal* . . .
Here comes normal . . .

Lads return to threaten.

Lads
   Oi!
   Yo!
   No!

   Girls return to threaten.

Girls
   Say What?
   Don't Think So!
Lads
   Yo . . . *Cuntley?*

   Yo . . . *Twatley?*
Girls
   Oh . . . *Cameron??*

   Hey . . . *Amoretti??*

   But no Huntley or Amoretti.

Lads
   Nobody to threaten!
Girls
   Its sooooo *Boring!*

   Delisha and Tamara appear.

Lads
   Oi!
   Yo!
Girls
   Say What?
Delisha/Tamara
   Don't Think So !

Delisha
Watch this!
Then text *Britain's Got Talent.*

They dance ambitiously.
Lads, Girls watch.

Lads/Girls
Yo!

Impressed, they get out their mobiles.
Start to text . . . then . . .

Lads
ORRRRR . . .
. . . put you on YouTube, yo!
Girls
Build your reputation up *slowly* give you a cool indie feel . . .
Say what?
Tamara
Forward Planning!
Fame!
Fortune!

Everybody films the top dance.
Marlee Holmes-Spalding appears . . .

Lads/Girls
Great Party Marlee!
Marlee
I know!
House? Trashed!
Mummy and Daddy? Ballistic!
Starting next Saturday, I'm grounded for *five years*!

And she joins the dance.

Everybody
Mums return to work.

Mums
 See you tonight!
Everybody
 Dads return to work.
Dads
 See you tonight!
 Darling!
 Sweetheart!
Mums
 You big soft thing!!

 The Weird Girl looks out of her window.
 Cameron looks out of his.
 Caitlin looks out of hers.

Cameron
 Not going out in *this*!

 He watches the street . . .

Caitlin
 I'm not going out in *this*!

 She watches the street.
 After a while, both turn from their windows to their
 mobiles.
 Cameron texts Caitlin.

Cameron
 R U going out in this?

 Caitlin texts back.

Caitlin
 R U?
Cameron
 No.
Caitlin
 Nor Me.

Ponders.
   Texts.

X.
Cameron
X.

Both behave as if they have received a Shakespearean sonnet.

Weird Girl
   Doesn't matter.
   It's all turning to slush anyway.
   Everything's melting.
   Doesn't matter.
Cameron
   Sleep
   I dream
Caitlin
   Night
   Sleep
   I dream
Cameron
   Caitlin – Caitlin Amoretti
Caitlin
   Cameron – Cameron Huntley
   X
Cameron
   X.
Weird Girl
   It's gone.
Cameron
   X   that's *a kiss* that is!
Caitlin
   Lights down   goldish glow   fades slowly.

End of Scene Four.

FIVE — IT'S GONE

Everybody
  Morning.
  Snow's gone.
  Even slush is gone.
  Buildings naked again.
  Streets bare.

  When the snow's gone
  Nobody wants to go out.
  Place is deserted.
Cameron
  With his camera . . .
  The day in's good
  Because
  You spend it fiddling about with your camera
  And
  You discover
  Pillock!
  It has a facility for making
  Short films . . .
Caitlin
  The day in's good
  Because
  You finally work out your three-minute mime routine . . .

  She shows us.
    It is quite complicated, busy with opening and
  closing doors, story and very impressive . . . a journey
  through quite severe weather conditions, etc. . . .
    The Weird Girl appears in her window, looking out.
  Then she turns back to the room.
  Her brother sitting. Suitcase beside him.

Two people come in, gently, professionally, take him out.

Person (*to Girl*)
Would you like to bring his stuff?

Cross fade to . . .

Cameron
You have this idea
Make a short film
Outside
On the street
Say . . . near Caitlin Amoretti's building . . .

Caitlin
You're not *convinced* by what you're doing in your
    showing *cold* mime
You think why not go out *experience* cold
On the street
Say . . . near Cameron Huntley's building . . .

Then

Just opposite his building
You see on the pavement
This teddy bear.

Cameron (*as he does it*) . . .
You're doing a tracking shot from the weird girl's
    window
Through your building
Out of your door . . .
Across the street
And   there's Caitlin Amoretti
With

Caitlin
Look

She picks it up.

This was under the snow.

Cameron
Keep going

He's filming . . .

Caitlin
What?
Improvise?

She does. She picks up the teddy bear tenderly . . .

Poor Teddy   you're soaked through.

Your little jacket   wet through.

Safety pin through your heart.

There's something sticking in your little chest . . .!

Cameron
Keep going . . .

Caitlin
Piece of paper! Could be a *secret* message!

You open it carefully it's really fragile . . .

She opens out the paper. Reads:

'Help.'

They look at each other.
   They look at where the teddy bear was.
   They look up to the window.

Cameron
Knock on the door.

Caitlin knocks on the Weird Girl's door.
   Waits.

If a weird girl answers, say, 'Are you OK?'

Caitlin
OK.

She knocks on the door again.

Waits.

Hell . . . it's windy!!

She does some mime – fighting against an invisible wind.

I'm after an A.

Knocks again.
  Waits.

Nobody.
Cameron
Stop.
Battery's got really low. *Pillock.*

He takes out the batteries. Warms them. Rearranges them . . . as . . .

Caitlin (*mimes as . . .*)
No door can stop you
No locks no bolts
You're *in* . . .

She is, with a mimed but effective Uzi . . . she checks in many possible dangerous rooms . . .

Place is deserted
It's the start of a long, dark, complicated case for
  DSI Caitlin Amoretti . . .

Caitlin props the teddy up somewhere.

Somebody might come back for it.
Cameron
Yes.

This will still do stills.

He photographs the teddy sitting there.

Caitlin
  I might leave here.
  Pursue Acting.
Cameron (*as he photographs the empty window*)
  I might come with you.
Caitlin
  Yes, you might.
Cameron
  I might become a photographer.
  World famous.
Caitlin
  Yes, you might.
  I might become a famous actress.
Cameron
  Yes.
  You might.

  I take a still picture of . . .
  This street
  This building
  My dad
  My mum
  Caitlin Amoretti
  This bare tree against a sky
Caitlin
  I *do* get an A for my mime project.
Cameron
  Obviously!
Caitlin
  That's all.

  They both look up and out at the sky.
    The Weird Girl appears in the empty window.
    She is dressed for leaving.
    She blocks out each of the four window panes with
  her paintings of . . .
    Opposite building in snow . . .

Woods bare . . .
Sun . . .
Field of flowers.
Lights fade slowly   to

Blackout.

And they do.

The End.

Production Notes

THE 'IT SNOWS' TOOLKIT

Bryony, Steven, Scott, Delphine, Nick, Eddie, Vicki, George, Matti, Neil, Matthew and Claudie developed *It Snows* in various rehearsal rooms at the National Theatre in June and October 2007.

We concentrated on making it a movement-led piece. We worked out how the movement pieces could be realised within the text. We've put our ideas in what follows to help you. OK: you want to make a piece of theatre called *It Snows*? Here's your toolkit.

THE TEXT

Read it and re-read it lots of times in lots of different ways. Get to know it really well.

It is divided into five sections . . .

1 It's not happening
2 It's happening
3 It's here
4 It's going (slush)
5 It's gone

. . . which, if you think about it, is the story, the shape of snow . . .

RESEARCH

- Go shopping for the music it suggests to you. Have big fights about your lists.

- We listened to Jon Hopkins, *Contact Note*; Jon Hopkins, *Opalescent*; mum, *finally we are no one*;

mum, *summer make good*; Thomas Newman, *Little Children*; Four Tet, *Rounds*.

- We read *Let It Snow* by David Sedaris.

- We talked about James Joyce's short story, *The Dead*.

- We watched bits from *Together* by Lukas Moodyson.

- We got stuff about everything to do with snow off the internet.

- Sit around and do *all* your stories about things that have happened *in snow*. Make a list. Could be useful.

- This is how *we* started off . . .

ON THE FLOOR

- We threw some shapes, such as trying to form the shape of a snowflake or pulling one another through a blizzard.

- We set up some scenarios, such as: Postman, Milkman and Paperboy all arrive at a garden gate. They only want to leave one set of prints in the virgin snow but all need to deliver to the doorstep.

- We set some physical tasks such as a snow journey that involves a slip, a twist and a slide.

Try them. Or make up your own.

Then we made a text with characters. Within the text are various physical pieces. Here's some ideas how to work on them:

1: IT'S NOT HAPPENING

Weird Girl and window: a restricted space, possibly using height.

Lads: clumped, hooded, also known as the ASBOs. Given to moments of grace and wonder *but* they would have to kill you if they knew you saw them. Maybe they can only exude grace and wonder with their backs to you! As soon as they see you they will return to menace.

Girls: prom-like and strong on stance, though both Girls and Boys should only be still when they want to. They are strategic as to where they are and are strangers to tableaux.

Mums: like one big Mum with lots of mouths.

Dads: like one big Dad with lots of arms and shoulders.

Dreams: not an excuse for wafting or ephemera. Dreams here are vivid and pacy, with hypercolours, and the thrilling and supernatural.

Falling Teddy: A choice here as to whether it is about the falling of the object or the response of watching the Teddy fall.

2: IT'S HAPPENING

- *Watching snow*
- *Snowing*
- *Snow-catching*

None of the above need be too naturalistic, though should start or be rooted in the real quality of movement they instil. All should be spectacular, with ingenious use of choreographed chaos and/or unison.

- *Getting dressed for snow*
- *Mittens!*

Both of these have a natural energy and construct that is there to be explored and exploded.

3: IT'S HERE

1. *All the snow stuff* Angels should start with the principles of the genuine act: creation. Then stand up/back to witness the creation – and expand on it.

2. *The big snowball* Avoiding mime might be the best decision ever made here.

3. *Penguins* As it says . . . but it is a transformation. The Businessmen become Penguins over time – 5 to 10 seconds? 1 minute? Let briefcases become precious eggs being protected from the frozen floor. Let coffee cups become beaks. Let them huddle for warmth.

4. *Snowball fight* Find the structure in the genuine event and then opportunities for an ever-expanding unison response with different characters and responses to the same event. Dodging snowballs is always exhilarating but not always successful or funny for those involved.

5. *Life in mittens!* Start with a company-compiled list, 'Things That Are Hard To Do With Mittens On'.

5. *Lights up/lights down. Play . . . Party crush* Make it more of a creative moment than 'the bit where we dance'. If you've been so creative thus far, don't treat this as the easy bit. Look at opportunities for creating tasks, playing proximity and shifting the relationship between dancers and audience. It should look like

more than an 'eyes-front, lined-up, in-formation' pop video moment. This is housebound and increasingly out of control . . .

6. *Journey of the shiver /warming up* Start a shiver in the smallest place possible and experiment with where it travels and how the body responds. Warm a partner up in the smallest places where they themselves cannot get to or in a place where no one would bother normally to care about.

4: IT'S GOING

Slush dance It's all about the 'dush' . . .

5: IT'S GONE

This section should be the accumulation of everything that has gone before but also the start of something brand new. It is not a coda to the piece and should not decelerate in terms of rhythm and pace.

IN GENERAL

We encourage you to put text with movement wherever possible and appropriate, but in doing so ensure that you do not render the language suddenly strange in rhythm and inflection.

We also heartily suggest that no one, at any time, is made to resemble a piece of furniture to be sat on or propped against . . .

We ask you to remember that the characters are regular people, not ex-circus performers.

Ensure that music choices truly support the scenes. If the natural rhythm of a scene is uplifting, then an ambient or soft music track is only useful if there is a genuine need to counterpoint something within the scene. Performers should not feel restrained by a music track, but nor should they get themselves lost in it, particularly if the track uses a slow tempo. Music choices should never be there just because the track itself is well liked. Appropriate choices will always be subjective but stay true to the essence of the scene and ensure that the music track is truly supporting the action onstage.

There are a lot of images in *It Snows*. Let none of them outstay their welcome. Keep it moving.

Your audience should be applauding you within forty minutes of kicking off.

Above all, we absolutely insist that your imaginations and bodies and voices treat themselves to a riot in creating your version of *It Snows*.

Bryony Lavery, Scott Graham and Steven Hoggett

MY FACE

Nigel Williams

Nigel Williams's novels include *The Wimbledon Poisoner*, and his writing for the stage includes *Class Enemy*, *Country Dancing* and *Lord of the Flies*, adapted from William Golding's book. He wrote the Emmy award-winning screenplay *Elizabeth I*, starring Helen Mirren.

Characters

Susie

Mark

Lou

Dave

Sam

Emma

Pete

Dave

Aisha

Susie is standing centre stage – a bare stage with lecterns that stand for computer screens. Characters can carry them on or off as needed. Susie – a nice but bossy girl – is standing a little away from her computer as she addresses the audience.

Susie London is the biggest centre of My Face users in the world. Everyone I know is on My Face. I mean, I know other people but they don't count. All of my real friends are on My Face. I have eight real friends. Here they are.

Mark steps forward. He is a very clever but paranoid Jewish guy.

Mark My Face is a social utility founded by a Harvard dropout called Zuckerberg. He is not a dropout now. He has, reportedly, turned down a one billion dollar offer for the company for the site.

Mark shrugs.

Zuckerberg, huh. My name is Finkielkraut and about the one thing I have in common with Mr Zuckerberg is that, judging from his picture on the web, I am even more Jewish-looking than he is. I am sorry to raise this fact so early in the conversation. I know that your race and your religion is not supposed to count any more than your sexual orientation these days. I just thought I would get it out of the way. I am Jewish and I am called Finkielkraut and – though it pains me to say it – I conform to a great many Jewish stereotypes. I am paranoid, I am very clever and also extremely

317

confrontational – especially about the fact that I am Jewish.I go on about being Jewish all the time. This is just the beginning. OK? Alright? Got that?

Susie Mark – are you going to write something on my wall?

Mark She can't hear what I'm saying. Unless I write it on her wall. Or if I want privacy – email it to her. I mean – I suppose I could go round to her house and actually say it to her. But nobody does that any more. As a result of which – privacy is almost extinct. Because – whatever anyone may say – email is not a private form of communication.

Susie Mark! Are you going to write something on my wall? Do write something on my wall!

Mark pulls his lectern towards him. Looks at it.

Alright, Mark! I am going to send you a terrapin for your aquarium!

Mark Oh! Lovely! A terrapin! (*To audience.*) What the fuck is a terrapin? Are Jews allowed terrapins?

He speaks to his computer.

Really looking forward to my terrapin!

Susie talks to the audience.

Susie So – that's me and Mark. We are really good friends. And I just sent him a terrapin. And all my friends know I sent him a terrapin. So they know we are good friends and do things like that. Mark is a lovely boy but will probably never have a boyfriend as he is . . . like . . . quite ugly. But lovely with it. This is my next friend. She is called Lou.

Enter Lou. She is dressed as a gorilla.

Her picture on my My Face friends is of a gorilla. Isn't that wild?

Mark Susie and Lou have known each other for ever. Susie bosses Lou around something shocking. But then – she bosses everyone around. I think Lou put a picture of a gorilla up on My Face because she is so amazingly hot that she would be stalked unmercifully if her real picture got out there.

Lou Hi Susie!

Susie Hi Lou!

Lou How are you, Susie?

Susie I'm good, Lou. How are you?

Lou I'm good.

She takes off the gorilla costume and addresses the audience.

I'm not actually good. I'm really really depressed. Because I'm fat.

As she takes off the suit we see she is in fact amazingly thin.

I hate how I look. Which is why I put the gorilla picture up on My Face.

She holds out the mask in front of her.

That is so much better-looking than me.

Mark God, Lou is hot!

Lou Susie is my best friend. We talk about everything. About how my mum said I was fat. And . . . everything really.

Susie I made Lou realise she was so in love with Sam.

Lou And Susie also told me that Mark was keen on her. But she didn't fancy him. I mean he is very sweet and her best friend and so on but . . . you know . . .

Confidential voice, as she clicks on an image on her computer and – at the same moment Dave comes in . . .

This is the boy she is in love with. He is a friend of Mark's.

And though she has never met him she has been sending him really hot emails.

Dave – for this is he – is indeed a very handsome chap. He speaks with amazing suavity.

Dave Hi! I'm Dave! I'm a friend of . . . like . . . Mark's! I think Mark is . . . like . . . cool! But check me out too, babe!

Susie jumps up and down.

Susie Oh my God! It's Dave! It's Dave! (*To Lou.*) It's Dave, Lou! Jump up and down!
Lou It's Dave!

And, obedient to her friend, she jumps up and down.

Susie Oh my God! Dave!
Lou Dave! My God!
Dave Hi! Write on my wall!

Susie types, laboriously.

Susie You . . . are . . . amazing!

Lou types laboriously.

Lou You are . . . incredible!

Dave preens himself.

Dave My wall is . . . like . . . full of compliments . . .
Susie What is your favourite colour?

This, like many of these interchanges, should be typed – though not so as to interrupt the flow.

Dave What is *your* favourite colour?
Susie You see? He is so sensitive.
Lou Do you like the Sugababes?
Dave I used to like them. But now . . .
Susie You see? He is so intelligent!

Dave I like Boot Boy Seven!

Lou and Susie jump up and down.

Susie/Lou Boot Boy Seven! Yeaahh!

Susie talks to the audience.

I sent him flowers for his garden. I bit him three times using the werewolf application. And I have his email address. And my emails are really hot! Like . . .

She types.

If you're ever in West London – let's meet up!

Mark There is no danger that Dave will respond to Susie's 'hot emails'. Dave, I am afraid, does not exist.

Dave Woah there, dude! Steady! I do . . . like . . . exist!

Mark Oh, there is a Dave. Or rather a David. And it is his photograph I put on Susie's My Face profile. But the Dave on Susie's My Face profile has a completely different identity to the real Dave. The real Dave has never heard of Boot Boy Seven.

Dave That is so . . . like . . . uncool!

Mark The real Dave. Or David. Is actually my cousin. He lives in Leeds and he does not even own a computer so there is no danger of him logging on to My Face and finding out that Susie has sent him a tench for his aquarium or whatever.

Dave The real Dave sounds a real drag. I am so glad to be . . . like . . . the virtual Dave!

Mark You are the perfect teenager. I invented you. And don't ever forget that. Or get big ideas about having your own identity.

Dave OK, dude!

Mark (*to audience*) You may wonder why I created an imaginary friend for Susie. Well – if you want to know, I have been in love with Susie since we were in primary school. Ever since I saw her as the Virgin Mary in the

school Nativity play. Being a Jew I have always had
the hots for the Virgin Mary. I mean – what a woman!
The blue hood! The donkey! The stable! The yellow
haze round her head! And – have you noticed this –
she never looks Jewish! The mother of the most famous
Jew in history and she looks like a fucking Nazi! Well –
Susie, in my view, is a bit of a Nazi. Which is exactly
why I like her. And when she was playing the mother
of Jesus at the age of nine I had real trouble keeping
my dick in my trousers. I was a Roman soldier – in
keeping with the unracial stereotypical casting of my
primary school. But she never looked at me.

Shrugs.

So – enter Dave!

Dave Hi! It's me!

Mark The weird thing about my cousin Dave is that,
although he looks like the kind of guy Hitler would
have invited to the nineteen thirty-six Olympics, he is
actually even more Jewish than me.

Dave How do you work that out, dude?

Mark Shut it. The real Dave is actually an ultra-serious
religious Jew who, as he lives in the middle of an
almost entirely Islamic district of Leeds – never goes
out.

Dave Woah, guys! That sounds . . . like . . . dull!

Mark Whereas this . . . *schlemiel* is the perfect neutral
internet character. No racial or religious flavour to him
at all. Designed to ingratiate himself to young women.
Look at him. Doesn't he make you sick?

Dave preens some more.

Dave Hi! I met Mark Finkielkraut because we hooked
up. I don't get up to London much. But it is great to be
one of your friends, Susie. I'm taking fourteen A levels

and have just had a trial for Chelsea, but I don't want
to talk about me. I want to talk about you. And Mark.

Mark Virtual Dave is my best spokesman. He makes
Cyrano de Bergerac look inarticulate. He whispers
virtual honey into Susie's virtual ear. And it is paving
the way for my big move.

Dave Mark is . . . like . . . the hottest guy on the planet.

Susie You think?

Dave I know.

Susie Dave is devoted to Mark – which is so sweet. He is
always trying to get me off with him. I mean, I am very
fond of Mark.

Lou As a friend.

Susie Did I say that, Lou?

Lou No. But . . . er . . . you do sometimes say it . . .

Susie Don't tell me what I do and don't say, Lou. Please.

Lou Sorry. Am I fat?

Susie No. You are not fat.

Dave Mark is very dynamic sexually.

*Susie absorbs this briefly, and very quickly gets on with
business.*

Susie Anyway – this is my next friend – who is called
Sam.

Sam comes on with his lectern/computer.

Sam Hi!

Susie Sam is . . . like . . . a friend of Lou's.

Sam Hi!

Susie And when I say 'friend', I mean . . . you know . . .
'friend'.

She winks broadly.

They are so in love with each other it is amazing. Lou
and Sam are just head over heels. But they are both

too shy to acknowledge it. At the moment Sam is
having a fight with Lou on My Face. Which is something
you can do. You can drop-kick or head-butt your
friends. Sam has just punched Lou.

Mark I am supporting you, Sam. In your fight against
Lou.

Lou You punched me, Sam.

Sam I did.

Lou So I suppose I better . . . you know . . .

Sam Punch me back.

Lou I suppose.

Susie I have to be very careful about what I say. Some
people think I am a bit bossy. So I try and be really
subtle about it. But I am hoping to bring Sam and Lou
together.

She types.

Hey Lou! Did you see what I wrote on your wall?

Lou Did you write on my wall?

Susie Yeah. I supported you in your fight against Sam.
And I said –

Lou reads.

Lou Fighting is often a way of saying 'I love you!' Oh my
God!

Susie Oh my God!

Lou Do you think I love Sam?!

Susie I think you do!

Lou Oh my God! My God! I love Sam!

Susie I think you do! (*To audience.*) You see. If you are
really subtle about it you can usually get people to
understand their true needs.

Mark As you can see, Susie's My Face friends profile is a
hotbed of lust and intrigue. She does the intrigue and
I do the lusting.

All this time Sam has been typing, very laboriously.

Sam Er . . . Lou . . .
Lou It's amazing, Susie. I never realised it before. I mean, like, Sam is not at all like me. He is very quiet.
Susie He is.
Lou And shy.
Susie He is.
Lou And I am not shy.
Susie You are not.
Lou I am fat but I am not shy.
Susie Lou – you are not shy and you are not fat.
Lou You are a really good friend . . .
Sam Er . . . Lou . . .
Lou It's so good to have you as a friend, Susie!
Sam I punched you back.

Both girls ignore this.

Lou I mean, sometimes in relationships you don't realise until ages have passed, like with Kiera Bennett and Mr D'Arcy . . .
Susie And then you suddenly realise –
Lou My God!
Sam I punched you back, Lou.

Lou suddenly catches on. Jumps up and down.

Lou My God! Sam punched me back! My God!

Both girls jump up and down and generally go wild. As Emma comes in from the back, they stop.

Susie Ssshhh!
Lou What's up?
Susie I think Emma has come online.

Emma is typing in her My Face password and email on her lectern. Susie talks only to Lou.

Why did I accept her as my friend?

Lou You didn't.

Susie Didn't I?

Lou No. You did not accept her as your friend.

Susie Then why is she on my My Face list of friends?

Lou Because you accepted her as your friend.

Susie Lou – you cannot have this both ways. I cannot have rejected her and accepted her as my My Face friend.

Lou You did. You rejected her nine times and then you accepted her.

Susie Why did I do that?

Lou Because you felt sorry for her.

Susie She only wants to be my friend so as she can talk to Pete. (*To audience.*) I'll introduce you to Pete in a minute.

Lou I know.

Susie Now she is fat.

Lou Do you think?

Susie Hugely fat. And boring. And shy. My God! Why is she my My Face friend?

Lou Because you accepted her.

Susie And we must be kind to the afflicted. We are fortunate.

Lou We are.

Susie And we have to be kind to people like Emma . . .

Emma Hello!

Susie Hi!

Lou Hi!

Susie Although God knows it is hard sometimes!

Emma has glasses and speaks in a rather nasal voice.

Emma My aquarium is empty.

Silence.

No one has given me a fish for my aquarium.

Lou Your Dad's so rich, why don't you buy one!

Lou and Susie giggle. Emma looks sad. Susie types.

Susie I am sure Pete will send you something for your aquarium. He is such a kind person.

Emma He is wonderful. He is the most wonderful person I have ever met in my life. I will never meet such an amazing person.

Lou She hasn't really met him, actually. She has like . . . seen him at the other end of the lunch queue is all.

Susie But she would like to meet him.

Lou Everyone would like to meet Pete.

Emma looks sad. She talks to audience.

Emma I wish I didn't wear glasses. And the only thing I am really interested in is the music of the Early Renaissance. But I daren't admit to that. People would laugh.

Susie Thank God you don't fancy Pete, Lou.

Lou Don't I?

Susie No. You don't. You fancy Sam.

Lou Oh. So I do.

She jumps up and down. Both girls squeal.

Susie/Lou Oh my God!

Sam has been typing very slowly all this time. He raises his hand like a kid in class,

Sam Er . . . Lou . . . I . . . er . . . bit you using the werewolf application!

Both girls continue to jump up and down and ignore him totally. He looks very sad and hopeless.

Susie And this is my last My Face friend. And my most important – apart from Dave, of course, because I am in love with Dave. But I haven't actually met Dave.

Yet. Though I will meet him and I know it will be amazing.

Pete enters at the back. He wears Wolverhampton Wanderers football strip.

This is Pete. And I have lived all of my life with him. He is my big brother. And he is the kindest and most gentle and most super big brother anyone could ever wish for and I love him to bits.

Lou That is so nice!

Susie Thank God you don't fancy him is all I can say!

Lou Thank God I do not! That would be so weird if I fancied your brother!

Pete Hi!

Susie Hi!

Lou Hi!

Sam Hi Pete!

Emma Hi!

Pete Hi Emma! I sent you a whole troop of dolphins for your aquarium!

Emma Oh Pete!

Mark Did you see that? An extra effort to be nice to Emma because she is a total dweeb and no one likes her and she was rejected for his sister's My Face list nine times. Pete is one of those professionally nice *goyim*. You know the ones?

Pete Hi Mark! Can I borrow your essay on the Renaissance?

Mark Sure thing!

To audience.

You have to be nice to Pete – as he is gigantic and very good at all forms of sport. I suppose, if I am being objective about it, I would have to admit that he is . . . nice. But what's nice? You know? He is also Susie's brother so I crawl to him shamefully in an effort to

get him on my side. I don't think he even really realises
I am crawling to him. He is as thick as two short
planks. He supports Wolverhampton Wanderers, for
God's sake!

Pete Really nice to see you all, you guys!

Susie speaks to the audience.

Susie Well, now you've met all my friends on My Face!
Say hello to them!

*She should get the audience to say 'Hello' and the
friends should all say 'Hello' back. Then she whispers:*

I have a surprise for them.

She types. Very fast.

Here is some really exciting news going to all you people.
For the first time ever I am going to get all my My Face
friends for a real live party. I am going to ask Lou!

Lou jumps up and down.

Lou I'll come!

Susie And Sam!

Sam Er . . . I bit Lou using the werewolf application.

Susie Sam'll come. I know he will. And I've asked Emma,
which I think is really nice of me.

Emma You are so kind, Susie. You are so good and kind
and sweet.

Susie I have also asked Pete, of course . . .

Pete Of course!

Susie Because he is my brother and I love him!

Pete That's about the size of it.

Susie And I've asked Mark.

Mark I'll be there.

Susie And I've asked Dave.

Dave looks at Mark.

Mark I'm afraid Dave will not be able to come. Will you, Dave?

Dave looks helpless.

Dave Like . . . er . . . dude . . .

Mark I have already answered for you, Dave. And I am afraid you are not coming to Susie's My Face party. You are a virtual, as opposed to a real, person. And since in real life you are an Orthodox Jew who is not allowed out and thinks the internet is the work of the Devil, I do not think you will be quarrelling with my decision.

Dave I would . . . like . . . love to come, Susie. And hang with you and all my other My Face friends.

Mark You what?

Dave It will be so cool.

Mark This is not allowed!

Dave Really looking forward to it.

Susie Oh, so am I, Dave! I am so looking forward to meeting you! I am so excited! And all my friends are excited for me! Aren't you, friends?

Lou Oohh! Yeess!!

Susie Friends?

Emma Oh. Yes. Really. Yes. It is awfully nice of you to ask me.

Pete Hear, hear!

Sam Er . . . Lou . . . I bit you using the werewolf application . . .

Susie Sam is really excited about coming! And so is Mark!

Silence.

Aren't you, Mark?

Mark Really thrilled.

Susie Will you be coming with your friend Dave?

Dave Oh yah. He prob'ly will.

Mark addresses audience.

Mark How can I come to a party with someone who does not exist? What is happening here ? How am I going to survive this? Is this the beginning of a pogrom? Who is behind it? What am I going to do?

Dave You are going to . . . like . . . go with the flow, dude.

Blackout.

Lights up on a bare stage.
  No lecterns anywhere.

  Mark comes on.

Mark How did this happen? How did an entirely virtual person start accepting invitations on my behalf? This is what comes of the internet. Why can't we go back to dropping cards on each other and actually talking face to face. How did it happen? Did I press the wrong key? Was I asleep at the wheel or what?

He sits on the stage. In despair.

I didn't get Susie's invitation to her My Face party until two or three days after it was sent. And, when I logged on to my My Face account – or rather 'Dave's' My Face account – and went into his sent messages I found he had been in strong communication with the girl of my dreams. This entirely imaginary person had sent her five emails, all saying he was really looking forward to coming to her party. Someone must have been hacking into my account. After I had changed my password I tried to work out who it could possibly be. It had to be someone even smarter and more twisted than me. And it had to be someone on Susie's My Face friends. Someone in our immediate circle. And I had to find out who. Before he or she did me any more damage.

He shivers.

Which is why I am standing on a cold pavement on the other side of the street from Susie's party waiting for my Orthodox cousin from Leeds. And believe you me – to get him to come here I have had to lie big time.

On the other side of the stage Susie and Lou come on. Highly excited.

Susie Oohh! I am so excited!
Lou I am excited too!
Susie I am more excited than you!
Lou No! I am more excited than you!

They jump up and down.

Lou Actually –
Susie What?
Lou I wish I had worn the gorilla costume.
Susie Lou – you do not need the gorilla costume.
Lou I do. I am fat.
Susie You are not fat.
Lou You are so good to me.
Susie/Lou Oooohhh!

They jump up and down.

Susie And Sam will be here soon!
Lou Oh my God! Sam!
Susie You are in love with Sam!
Lou I am! I am totally in love with Sam!
Susie Oh my God! Here comes Sam!
Lou Sam! My God! Sam!

They jump up and down.

Susie And Emma!
Lou Sam and Emma!
Susie My God!

They do not jump up and down.

What is Emma doing here?
Lou You invited her.
Susie Why in God's name did I do that?
Lou Because you were . . . like . . . being kind to people.
Susie Oh. Yes. So I was.

Emma and and Sam are deep in conversation.

My God! She has no shame though.
Lou No?
Susie No no no. She is . . . like . . . so chatting up your
    boyfriend . . .
Lou Is he my boyfriend?
Susie Almost.
Lou Ooohh! It is so exciting!
Susie That is really rich of her. I ask her to my My Face
    party and she chats up your boyfriend.
Lou My almost boyfriend.
Susie Almost boyfriend.
Lou I wonder what they are chatting about?

*Sam and Emma have come past Mark on the street
and are waiting at the front door.*

Sam Shall we wait a moment?
Emma If you like.
Sam I just . . .
Emma Are you shy?
Sam I'm a bit shy at parties.
Emma Me too.
Sam I don't know . . . Susie's lovely and Lou is . . .
Emma Lou is gorgeous.
Sam She is. Too gorgeous for me.
Emma No one is too gorgeous for you, Sam.
Sam Oh, thanks, Emma. But . . . I mean . . .

333

Silence.

I bit her using the werewolf application.
Emma That's great.

Sam reaches for the knocker.

Can't quite face the My Face party?
Sam I don't know. I think I would probably rather be
   sitting at home and listening to some Joachim du
   Fontenoy. Or anything really from the early Renaissance
   really – preferably involving viols of some kind.
Emma Do you really like the music of the early
   Renaissance?
Sam Can't get enough of it. Shall we go in?

They step in and Susie and Lou jump up and down.

Susie Sam! It's Lou!
Lou Hi Sam! It's me!
Susie Hi Lou!
Lou Hi Sam!
Susie/Lou Oooohhh!

They jump up and down.

Emma Hello!
Susie Oh! Hi! (*She whispers to Emma.*) So keep your
   hands off Lou's boyfriend. Or you are one dead girl.
Lou And Dave will be here soon!
Susie Dave! My God! Dave!
Lou Dave! My God! Where is Dave?

*They jump up and down and peer out of the window
into the street. Where Mark is pacing up and down
looking paranoid.*

Mark Indeed! Dave! My God! Indeed! (*To audience.*)
   Where is Dave? It wasn't easy to get him to come
   down here. He is scared of London. He is scared of

everything. I had to get Susie to change the date of her My Face party. My God! She was going to have it on Friday night! Jesus! He doesn't move on Friday night. He is . . . like . . . strapped down with a towel on his head, worrying about what happened to the Jews over the last two thousand years. That's a lot of worrying. (*Confidential.*) In the end, I told him it was a charity event raising funds for the Israeli army. I also told him that prayers would be said in Hebrew and that all the food would be kosher. I told him there would be no alcohol and only Jewish traditional dances approved by the Chief Rabbi would be allowed. All men would be in *yarmulkes*.

He takes out his yarmulke.

You may think this is a crazy scheme. How long can I fool them that 'Dave' is not an insane religious bigot? I tell you this. It does not really matter. All I need to see is their faces when I bring him in. I will know at once who tried to stitch me up. All I have to do then is get him away as soon as possible and whoever the person is who hacked into my email will be utterly and totally crushed.

Silence.

Unless of course, it is Susie who is pretending to be Dave. And it is Susie who has rumbled me. The thought is unbearable. But I do not think Susie is bright enough to do anything of the kind. She is almost as thick as her brother. Why do I fancy her? I do not know – any more than I know why I have asked my cousin to an event he thinks is a fund-raiser for the Israeli army.

He paces.

Dave? Where are you, Dave? Surely you are not going to let the Israeli army down?

Meanwhile, inside the house Susie has approached Emma, who is talking to Sam.

Emma Hi Susie!
Susie Hi Emma!

This is very tense and falsely polite.

Still enjoying talking to Sam?
Emma Er . . . yes . . .
Susie And what are we talking about, I wonder?
Sam The role of the madrigal in the downfall of the Ottoman Empire.
Susie Mmm! Interesting! (*Hissing to Emma.*) Keep your hands off him. He belongs to Lou, OK?
Sam Are you interested in early Renaissance music, Susie?
Susie Can't get enough of it!
Emma Sam and I found out we were both fans!
Susie Super. (*She hisses.*) Hands off, bitch! (*Brightly, to Emma.*) So. How many friends do you have on your My Face profile, Emma?
Emma One, Susie. You.
Susie Well. Let us hope that friend stays loyal, Emma. Or you will have . . . like . . . no friends on your My Face personal profile. Which would be very sad indeed. You would belong to no networks whatsoever.
Lou Oh my God!
Emma It's funny. I never thought I would ever meet anyone who felt the same way about two-part canzonetti as I did. I mean Schintzlerhuder is -
Sam My God! You like Schintzlerhuder! I didn't know anyone else in the world had even heard of Schintzlerhuder!
Susie How amazing! I thought everyone had heard of Schintzlerhuder! I mean, he runs a great restaurant, doesn't he?

Lou I wonder where Pete has got to?

Susie I can't think, Lou. Although I don't expect you are really interested in my brother, are you? That would be weird.

Lou It would be totally weird!

Susie But try not to be too upset that Emma is . . . like . . . totally monopolising Sam and forcing him to talk about Schintlastrudel or whatever!

Lou Look! There's Pete! Now!

Susie Is he?

Lou He's there, Susie!

Susie Big deal!

Flouncing.

I really cannot understand why everyone at my My Face party is just so obsessed with themselves. When the man I love has not even turned up!

Lou is waving from window.

Lou Hi Pete!

Susie He is only my brother, Lou! He's no big deal! Though he is mine! All of him!

Peter, still in Wolverhampton Wanderers strip, is greeting Mark in the street outside.

Pete Hi Mark!

Mark Hi Pete!

Pete So! My Face party!

Mark So!

Pete Meet the man of my sister's dreams!

Mark Indeed! (*To audience.*) Suspicious. It is the first thing he mentions. Is he the one who hacked into my email? I don't think so somehow. Pete couldn't hack into a pile of wet grass. (*To Pete.*) Pete – can I ask you, why do you always wear Wolverhampton Wanderers football strip?

337

Pete It's like . . . a bet. I have sworn not to take it off until they get into the Premier League.

Mark My God! They will bury you in it!

Pete If that is what it takes.

Pete talks to the audience.

Mark thinks I'm boring. And stupid. Because I play football. And because he fancies my sister. I'm not actually stupid. It's just something he wants me to be.

Mark So – how is the beautiful game?

Pete Beautiful.

Mark Well. That's . . . beautiful.

Pete You coming in to the party?

Mark I'm just waiting for . . . you know . . .

Pete No . . .

Mark Dave. Susie's friend.

Pete Ah. My little sister's . . .

Mark Passion.

Pete Of the moment.

He shakes his head.

She's a good kid basically. But she needs her bottom smacked. She is such a bossy little cow. See you in there.

And he goes in. Mark turns to audience.

Mark Can you beat this guy? He lives in the same house as the hottest woman on the planet and all he can say is, 'She is a bossy little cow.' My God! He probably uses the same toilet as her! Jesus! I can't think of it without going all hot! And I suppose if he knew some Jew called Finkielkraut wanted to bone her he would have me disembowelled by other practitioners of the 'beautiful game'. Jesus! If ever there was a misnomer. Isn't football the most grotesque and pointless piece of bollocks you have ever seen?

He paces, frustrated.

Where are you. Dave? Have you disappeared back into cyberspace? Am I a figment of your imagination rather than the other way round? How else am I going to find out who else is impersonating you apart from me? And how am I going to do it anyway? Even if you do turn up!

Banging his head with his fists.

This is a punishment for being born Jewish.

Dave has appeared behind him on the stage. The real David, this time. Although played by the same actor as his virtual counterpart, he is very different in manner. Much less Jewish-seeming than Mark. In the conventional sense of that term, anyway. This guy speaks with the quiet and terrifying confidence of the leader of a Mossad hit squad.

Dave Hi!

Mark Dave! You came!

Dave Of course I came.

Mark I'm amazed. You came.

Dave Anything to help the state of Israel.

Mark Indeed.

Dave The Palestinians want to destroy us.

Mark Indeed.

Dave People are saying we should not have nuclear weapons.

Mark It's appalling.

Dave We need nuclear weapons. And lots of them.

Mark My God! We do!

Dave How else are we going to stop the Palestinians?

Mark Indeed. Although we seem to be making a fairly determined effort in that direction with . . . you know . . . guns and stuff.

Dave We need more than guns.

Mark Indeed.

Dave We need nuclear weapons. And lots of them.

Mark Of course.

Dave It is the only thing the Palestinians will understand.

Mark I am sure.

Dave So. Tell me about tonight's event . . .

Mark Oh, it's . . . fairly low key . . .

Dave Yes?

Mark I mean there may even be some . . .

Light laugh.

Some non-Jews there.

Dave Non-Jews? Are you crazy? How can we trust these people?

Mark Oh, they are . . . you know . . . almost-Jews.

Dave How do you mean?

Mark They want to convert. A lot of them.

Dave I see.

Silence.

I am not sure I approve of that.

Mark Look. We need more Jews. Everyone agrees that. How else are we going to repopulate the West Bank when we have dropped nuclear weapons on Gaza City?

Dave You may have a point there.

Mark I mean, I know these people are scum. We will give them a really hard time. But at the end we will have . . . you know . . . more Jews.

Dave I see this.

Mark Second-class Jews. That we can order about. And get to do the rubbish disposal and so on.

Dave Rubbish disposal!

Mark Exactly.

Dave Getting rid of the Arabs.

After a while Mark realises this is supposed to be a joke. And manages a bout of forced hearty laughter. Then – to the audience.

Mark This guy is sick! He doesn't even look like a Jew! He looks like Anton Diffring in *The Great Escape*! And he has a rather similar outlook on life!

Sam emerges from the party.

Sam! Was it him hacked into my emails? He's clever enough. But he is really shy and timid. I can't see him –
Sam Hi Mark!
Mark Hi Sam!

Dave whispers.

Dave Is he one of these converts?
Mark God no. One-hundred-per-cent Jewish.
Dave That's good.
Mark I just need to have a quick word with him.
Dave Fine.

Mark crosses to Sam.

Mark How is it in there?
Sam Terrible. Just absolutely terrible.
Mark What's up?
Sam Well. You know I've always fancied Emma. Well, tonight I find out she is interested in early Renaissance music.
Mark God, that is so sad, Sam.
Sam But . . . like . . . Susie seems to think I fancy Lou. And I think Lou thinks I fancy her.
Mark You have to fancy Lou. Everyone fancies Lou. She is hot hot hot.
Sam I don't. I fancy Emma.
Mark But she is a spectacled dweeb, Sam. Who likes early Renaissance music.

Sam I know. And so am I. (*Quietly.*) People in glasses should always fall in love with other people in glasses, Mark. We shouldn't try and punch above our weight. We don't have the right to get to jump the bones of beautiful people. It would upset the balance of nature. I just love Emma. But I don't know what to do about it. (*Whispers.*) Is that your friend Dave? The one Susie is in love with? Can I meet him?

Mark Indeed. Before you do . . . I just need to tell you a few things . . .

Inside the house Pete is talking to Emma and Lou and Susie.

Pete What is up with Sam, little sister? Why did he go out?

Susie I think he was upset. Because Emma was hitting on him.

Pete Really?

Susie Really. And he really loves Lou.

Pete He does?

Lou He does!

Susie And she loves him!

Lou She does! Oh my God!

They both jump up and down. Pete looks a little put out.

Pete Well, Lou – you are a very . . . beautiful girl . . .

Lou You are so kind, Pete. But we both know I am fat.

Pete You are what?

Lou I am grossly overweight.

Pete Lou – you are not overweight!

Lou I know you are a kind person, Pete. As well as amazingly good looking! My God! If you weren't Susie's brother I would probably be madly in love with you!

Pete Why would it be weird if I were in love with you?

Lou It would be totally weird.

Pete Would it?

Susie You are my brother, Pete! It would be weird!

Lou It would be totally weird!

Emma And I have totally ruined it by hitting on Sam.
And talking about early Renaissance music with him.

Susie You are forgiven, Emma . . .

Pete Can I just say that I still do not see why it would be
totally weird if I was in love with Lou. Or Lou was in
love with me.

Susie My God, big brother! You can be weird sometimes!
You are . . . like . . . my brother!

Lou It's true. You are her brother.

Emma That is true, actually.

Pete I really do not understand women sometimes. I have
a good mind to get Sam back in here and ask him
whether it would be weird if I was in love with Lou.

Susie My God! Typical man! That would be so insensitive!

Lou My God!

Susie My God!

They both jump up and down.

Pete Would you both stop jumping up and down!

Susie Oh my God!

Lou Oh my God!

Pete Why would it be insensitive to ask Sam whether it
would be weird if I was in love with Lou?

Emma Because Sam is in love with Lou.

Susie And Lou is in love with Sam.

Lou Only Sam is too shy to express himself.

Susie/Lou Oh my God!

*They jump up and down. Emma tries, unsuccessfully,
to jump up and down.*

Pete I do not understand women.

Susie You so do not.

Pete I am going outside to talk to the blokes.

Susie Go on then, bruv. Go on. Ignore my My Face
party. Go on.

Pete goes to the window. Looks out.

Pete I think that bloke you fancy has arrived, Susie.

All the girls squeal and run to the window.

Susie It's him!
Lou It's Dave!
Emma It's amazing Dave!
Pete Jesus! (*To audience.*) Wait till they find out what
that little tosser Mark Finkielkraut has been up to.
(*To the girls.*) I don't know why Mark is keeping him
out there. I'll bring him on in and you girls can check
him out.

*Pete goes to the door. Outside in the street Mark is
trying to prepare Sam for his cousin.*

Mark The thing is – I don't think my friend . . . er . . .
Dave . . . has fully revealed himself on My Face.
Sam No?
Mark You know . . . it's a social networking site and
people are . . .
Sam Cautious.
Mark Exactly.
Sam They keep things . . .
Mark Neutral.
Sam Exactly.
Mark Which is great. And I mean Susie is mad about
Dave.
Sam Indeed.
Mark And I really wanted her to meet Dave.
Sam That is really nice of you.
Mark Well . . . you know . . . I know him really well.
And Dave is . . . he has very strong political views.
Sam Yeah?

Mark He is very pro-Israel.

Sam Is he?

Mark He is. I mean very, very pro-Israel. And at first he was very doubtful about coming to this party.

Sam He was?

Mark He was. He is really one hundred per cent on the Israel thing and . . .

Sam And what?

Mark So I . . . er . . . told him it was a fund-raising event for the Israeli army.

Sam My God! Why did you do that?

Mark It was . . . like . . . the only way to get him to come.

Sam I see.

Mark So . . . you know . . . for the moment . . . if you could go along with that.

Sam How do you mean?

Mark Well – for a start it would help if you pretended to be Jewish.

Sam Why do I have to do that?

Mark Because he is not really very keen on people who aren't Jews.

Sam Well, he's a narrow-minded bastard then, isn't he?

Mark Sam – I am not asking you to do this for me.

Sam Who are you asking me to do it for?

Mark For Susie.

Sam How will this help Susie?

Mark He might come in to the party if he thinks there are Jews there.

Sam Is Susie Jewish?

Mark I've never thought about that. If she isn't, she may have to convert. Tonight. If she wants him to talk to her.

Sam I am not sure about this, Mark.

Mark Susie has been dying to meet him for months. I really don't want to disappoint her. It won't be for long.

Sam But what happens when he finds out this is a My Face party and not a fund-raising event for the Israeli army?

Mark I'll deal with that. Look – we may even deal with his prejudices. Talk about them frankly. Try and broaden his outlook.

Looks at Dave.

Though I must say that could be difficult.

Sam Alright, Mark. As it's you. And for Susie. I mean, who else would imagine that Lou would ever go for a guy like me. She is mental, that girl. I love her.

He crosses to Dave.

Shalom.

Dave *Shalom.*

Sam Good to see you.

Dave Good to see you.

Sam Already.

Dave Sorry?

Sam Good to see you already.

Dave Indeed.

Sam *Oi vey!* Whatever that means!

Dave Sorry?

Sam I am sorry not be wearing my . . . you know . . . hat!

Dave It is good to wear it.

Sam It must have dropped off. In the synagogue. When I was . . . you know . . . banging the old head on the floor . . .

Dave turns to Mark.

Dave This guy is really weird.

Mark I know. But he is on our side.

Sam Do you know *Havanah Gilah*?

Dave I have heard it. A few times.

346

Sam Shall we sing it?
Dave Now?
Sam Why not already?

Sam starts to sing Havanah Gilah. *Pete, who has been watching this from the house, crosses to Mark.*

Pete Why is Sam singing *Havanah Gilah*, Mark?
Mark He is pretending to be Jewish.
Pete Why is he doing that?
Mark I told him to do it.
Pete Why are you such a berk, Finkielkraut?
Mark I don't know. Tell me.
Pete The only person at all worried about you being Jewish in all of our acquaintance – is you.
Mark Someone has to worry about these things. My God!
Pete If you must know – just to confound your stereotype of me – as a matter of fact, I'm Jewish.
Mark My God! They get everywhere!
Pete My name may be Cholmely-Furness-le Grange. But my mother was Jewish. So I suppose that makes me Jewish.
Mark And your sister too! My God!
Pete I repeat – why make a big deal out of your race or your religion?
Mark Why not?
Pete If you fancy my sister, why don't you just tell her? Instead of inventing a friend who can chat her up? Where did you get that picture of 'Dave'? Out of a magazine?
Mark Actually, he's my cousin and he's over there and –

Stops.

It was you hacked into my system.
Pete So what?

Mark How did you do it? Did you use the *Machine Code Handbook*?

Pete No.

Mark The Hellenbaum algorithm?

Pete No.

Mark Did you reprogramme my MS-DOS receptors?

Pete No. I went into your room one day when we were round at yours. And you had your email up. So I had a look at your conversation with my sister via 'Dave'. And then I looked next to your screen and you had your password written down in large capital letters in case you forgot it.

Mark I do forget things.

Pete So I took it from there. So who is this guy? Your cousin? How come he is so much better looking than you? Is he going to get off with my sister?

Mark How dare you infiltrate my private emails?

Pete How dare you impersonate your cousin in order to seduce my sister?

Mark Bastard!

Pete Bastard!

Mark What do we do now?

Pete Hit each other.

Mark Right.

He hits Pete. They start to fight. Dave watches, appalled. Turns to Sam.

Dave What's going on?

Sam I should be so lucky to know already.

Dave This is not right. Why are they doing this?

Sam We should not be such . . . er . . . *schnorrers.*

Dave We are all Jews. We should unite against the common enemy.

Sam *Lachaim*!

Dave Syria, Iran, Iraq, Jordan, Kuwait, United Arab Emirates, Oman, Jordan, Saudi Arabia, Indonesia,

Yemen, Libya, Dubai, Pakistan, the Sudan, the
Lebanon, Turkey, Albania, Chechnya, the United
States –

Sam I thought America was on our side?

Dave What kind of Jew are you?

Sam A . . . singing Jew . . .

Dave America has sold us out to the Arabs!

They watch as Mark and Pete continue to fight. Inside the house Lou, Susie and Emma have been watching intently.

Susie This is awful!

Lou I had a fight with Sam on My Face.

Susie You did.

Lou But this isn't like that.

Susie It isn't.

Lou It's like . . . a real fight.

Emma Not a virtual fight!

Susie Why are you always trying to be so clever, Emma?

Lou It is awful!

Susie It is!

Lou Oh my God!

Susie Oh my God!

They jump up and down.

Lou Poor Peter!

Susie My God!

Lou My God!

Emma My God!

Susie I don't know why you are making a fuss, Emma.
It's not as if you are interested in either of them.

Emma Aren't I?

Susie Duh!

Lou Poor Peter!

Susie And poor Mark!

Lou Oh poor Mark, yes!

Susie I mean . . . he is . . . like, getting the worst of it!

Lou He just hit poor Peter! Oh my God!

Susie Why are you always going on about my brother, Lou?

Lou I am just worried for him. He just got hit. By Mark. Oh my God!

She jumps up and down. Susie does not jump up and down.

Susie I mean, my brother is my concern, Lou.

Lou Oh my God!

Susie I will worry about my brother, thank you very much.

Lou Oh Pete! Oh my God! Pete!

She is totally absorbed in the fight as Mark is gaining ground. Ignoring Susie, she jumps up and down on her own.

Susie Do you fancy my brother or what, Lou?

Lou So what if I do, Susie?

Susie 'So what if I do'? 'So what if I do'? My God! This is my brother, Lou! My God!

Lou I know! Pete! My God!

Susie Stop this at once, you stupid cow!

Emma Don't argue!

Susie You keep out of this!

Lou Yeah! You keep out of this!

Susie Why should she keep out of this? He's my brother!

Lou So what if he's your brother? You don't own your brother. Do you think you own your brother?

She jumps up and down.

Oh my God! Pete! Oh my God!

Susie This is my party, you know.

Lou Never said it wasn't.

Susie It is my party.
Lou So what if it's your party? Pete! Bash him! Pete!

Susie grabs her sleeve.

Let go of me. Bossy cow!
Susie What did you say?
Lou You heard me! Pe–ete!
Susie Bossy cow?
Lou Bossy cow!
Emma Please don't fight!
Susie/Lou Shut it!
Lou Bossy cow!

*And Lou and Susie start a real cat fight. Emma looks
on in distress.*
    *Meanwhile, out in the street, Mark, who has been
getting the worst of it, staggers over, his face bloody,
to Dave and Sam.*

Dave What is going on?
Mark I hate that fucker!
Dave Mark – we have to stick together. These people in
Gaza are practically in Tel Aviv. They are melting
down their houses to make bullets. We have to melt
down their houses before they have the chance to
make bullets out of them. This guy is a fellow Jew.
Mark He is not.
Dave Then what is he doing at a fund-raiser for the
Israeli Army at which prayers in Hebrew will be said?
Mark A good question. Maybe he works for Hezbollah.
Dave Hezbollah! My God!
Mark My God! Hezbollah!
Sam Hezbollah! My God!

Silence.

Who are Hezbollah?

They look at him.

The bad guys? Right?
Dave Right!
Mark Right!

They both charge Pete.

Sam Guys! Two against one! Is this fair?

Pete fights Mark and Dave.

Pete Who the fuck is this guy, Mark?
Dave Hezbollah!
Pete Your cousin! Right?
Dave Hezbollah!
Pete Get him off me! He is crazy!
Dave Hezbollah!

They grapple on the floor. Mark aims a few kicks at Pete.

Why are you pretending to be a Jew?
Pete I am not pretending to be a Jew. I am a Jew.
Dave You are a Jew.
Pete Yes, I am a Jew.
Dave And you support the Israeli army actions in Lebanon?
Pete No.
Dave Bastard.

He attacks him furiously.

Sam Listen! Dave! I know about you and Susie!
Dave Who?
Sam Susie. And he is not pretending to be a Jew. I am pretending to be a Jew.
Dave My God! I thought there was something funny about you!
Sam There's something pretty bloody funny about you!

Dave Exactly what do you mean by that?

Sam I only pretended to be a Jew so as you would come to the party and Susie could get to meet you because she fancies you.

Dave Susie who?

Sam But you are such an extreme Zionist I don't really think she should even give you the time of day. You guys are just as bad as Osama bin Laden!

Dave Osama bin Laden?

Sam Osama bin Laden!

Dave Osama bin Laden?

Sam Osama bin Laden!

Dave runs at Sam and attacks him. They fight.
Inside the house Lou and Susie are still fighting.
Emma is watching from the window as Dave attacks
Sam.

Emma My God!

Susie What?

Emma Dave is attacking Sam!

Susie My God!

She stops fighting Lou. To Lou:

Dave is attacking Sam!

Lou So?

Susie What do you mean, 'So'? You fancy Sam.

Lou I do not fancy Sam.

Susie Oh for God's sake! We have been through this!

Lou I do not fancy Sam. I fancy your brother!

Susie Oh my God!

Lou Oh my Go–od!

Emma I fancy Sam!

Susie Don't be stupid!

Emma Sam! Fight back! Sam!

Susie How dare you?

Emma Oh shut up, Susie!

Susie Shut up?

Emma Yes! Shut up!

Susie Did you hear what she said? She said shut up!

Emma Yes. I said shut up!

Susie Shut up!

Lou Yes! Shut up!

Susie Exactly! Shut up!

Lou No. I mean, shut up!

Susie What?

Lou I mean you shut up!

Susie Shut up?

Lou Yes, you! Shut up!

Emma You are always bossing us all around!

Out of window:

Sam! Bash him! Sam!

Susie Do you know who you are talking about?

Emma I know who I am talking about.

Susie That is Dave. That is the boy I love.

Lou How can it be the boy you love? You've never even met him.

Susie I've seen his picture on the internet.

Emma That is not the same as meeting him, you stupid, bossy, vulgar little girl.

Susie How dare you?

Emma I dare!

Susie goes to window.

Susie Dave! Bash him!

Emma Sam! Bash him!

Susie Cow!

Emma Cow!

Emma and Susie fight.

Susie Lou – defend me!

Lou Why?

Susie Lou!

Lou Shut up!

Susie Lou!

Lou Stop telling me what to do all the time!

Susie Lou!

Lou attacks Susie. Lou and Emma fight Susie. Susie defends herself furiously.

Meanwhile, on the street Dave is making mincemeat of Sam.

Pete That's enough.

Dave What do you mean, 'enough'?

Pete Leave him alone!

Dave Why should I leave him alone?

Pete Violence doesn't achieve anything.

Dave No? I can see you've never read a history book.

Pete And I am sure you never read one that disagreed with you.

Dave Do you want some?

Pete Look – if you really want me to, I will smash you into very small pieces. I am bigger than you and with Sam on my side I could spread you all over the road. A bit like you think you are going to do with Hezbollah.

Dave Hezbollah! My God! Hezbollah!

He goes for Pete. Sam holds him from behind.

Pete Listen. Your cousin used your picture on My Face to try and get off with my sister.

Dave He what? What's My Face?

Pete A social networking site. You talk to your friends and play games and have fun.

Dave How does this help the Israeli army in their struggle against the Arabs?

Pete It doesn't.

Dave goes for him. Sam restrains him.

355

This is not a fund-raising event for the Israeli army at which prayers will be said in Hebrew. It is a social occasion at which young people of all religions and races meet to drink alcohol, play loud music and try to get off with each other.

Dave My God! This is appalling! (*To Mark.*) Is what he says true?

Mark It is. I'm afraid.

Dave What kind of a Jew do you think you are?

Mark A clever one. Who is desperate to shag Pete's sister.

Dave How could you do this to me?

Mark It is not the end of the world, Dave. You certainly needed to get out more.

Dave What do you mean by that?

Mark I mean – Sam's right in a way – you are incredibly narrow-minded.

Dave I cannot believe I am hearing this. You are saying you . . . impersonated me . . . on a . . . website . . .

Mark Look. You are a very good-looking bloke, Dave.

Dave Am I?

Mark You are.

Pete Your only problem is with your mind. If you were slightly more flexible in your opinions you would probably get laid seven nights a week.

Dave You think?

Mark And probably with his sister.

Dave This is all very confusing.

Mark Life is confusing.

Dave I've never been laid.

Pete Never?

Dave Never.

Sam That makes two of us.

Mark You should have been laid, Dave.

Sam I mean . . . I have glasses . . . and I like early Renaissance music.

Dave Jesus! You sad character!

Silence. Dave considers his position.

I suppose I haven't had the time, really.
Mark No?
Dave It's been . . . you know . . .
Mark Full-time Zionism.
Dave Exactly.

He shakes his head.

This is really strange
Mark Maybe it was good in a way.
Dave What was?
Mark Me lying to you about this being a fund-raiser for
the Israeli army and pretending to be you on My Face
so as I could impress his sister and . . .
Dave And what?
Mark I mean . . . you got to get to a party. Your first-
ever party. And to listen to different points of view.

*Inside the house Lou and Susie are still fighting. Emma
has broken away and gone to look out into the street.*

Emma They've stopped.
Susie Stopped what?
Emma Stopped fighting.
Lou Get off me, can't you?
Susie You get off me!
Lou No. You get off me!
Emma They have stopped fighting! Look!

Lou and Susie stop fighting, go over to the window.

Susie My God!
Lou My God!
Susie You're right!
Lou You're right!
Emma I mean – why don't we go out there? And join
them. As they don't seem very keen on coming in.

357

Susie You think?
Lou I'm sure Dave needs you.
Susie You're right. I've never met Dave.
Lou Oh Susie –
Susie I'm a bossy cow. I've never met Dave.
Lou Susie –
Susie Sam doesn't fancy you. He fancies Emma . . .
Lou Susie . . .
Susie They both like early Renaissance music.
Emma That is true.

Susie bursts into tears.

Lou Oh Susie . . .
Emma Don't cry, Susie . . .
Susie I'm a cow. And a bitch. And a slag. And a slapper.
Lou Oh God!
Susie I am! Oh my God!
Lou Oh my God!
Susie I am!
Lou You are!
Susie I am?

She is in danger of getting aggressive.

Well . . .
Susie I know.
Lou I know.
Emma I know.
Susie Do you, though?
Emma I do.

Silence.

Susie Let's go out there.

She dresses herself down.

I'm all nervous.
Emma Don't be nervous.

Lou Why are you nervous?
Susie Because of Dave. Oh God!
Lou Oh God!
Susie Dave! Oh my God!
Emma Dave! Oh my God!

They all jump up and down. Then they go out into the street.

Susie Hi!
Mark Hi!
Dave Er . . . hi!
Susie Hi!
Lou Hi Pete!
Pete Hi!
Emma Hi Sam!
Sam Hi Emma!
Mark Well. Here we are.

A gorilla comes up the street.

Lou God!
Susie My God!
Emma It's a gorilla!
Gorilla Hi!
Lou Hi!

They all look at the gorilla.
Blackout.

Lights up on the stage set with lecterns/computers.
Everyone is at his or her lectern. Susie, Lou, Mark, Emma, Sam, Pete, Dave and the Gorilla.

Gorilla My name is Aisha. I had been turned down eleven times for Susie's My Face party and I knew one of her friends – Lou that is – had put a picture of a gorilla up as her picture on My Face. So I had the crazy idea that if I went as a gorilla I would get in without me having to say who I was.

359

Susie is typing.

Susie Who was that . . . like . . . gorilla at my party?

Lou I don't know. It ran away.

Aisha Well, if I had gone as me I wouldn't have stood a chance. None of them like me. Just because I stand up for the Islamic faith and the Holy Koran. And I say that all these terrorist things in the world happen for a reason. My father is a very strict Moslem and I have only just been allowed out and I want to make friends but it is really hard. So that is why I dressed as a gorilla. I am just about to see if Susie will accept me as her friend on My Face.

Dave I have only just got a computer. And it has changed my life. I have discovered for example that the state of Israel was not founded in 300 BC. As I had previously thought. And that not all Palestinians are terrorists. It has been a bit of a revelation. But the real thing that obsesses me is – that gorilla. The moment that gorilla walked up the street I knew I was head over heels in love.

Lou My life has changed too. I discovered that I really loved Pete – not Sam, and a few days after Susie's My Face party I started going out with him.We went to hear Boot Boy Seven. And they were amazing. We don't spend nearly so much time on the computer now. We are usually up on the common or having a drink in the pub. Pete tries to take off my bra. I have not let him yet – although he has . . . like . . . explored my breasts thoroughly. And, by the way, I no longer think I am fat.

She walks away from her lectern and down to the front of the stage.

Pete I am going out with Lou, big time. And it is amazing. I have not really got into the sexual thing with her yet.

I mean I haven't even taken off her bra yet – though this will only be a matter of time. The weird thing about her was – she seemed to think she was fat. Which is . . . like . . . insane. We talked about anorexia and all that stuff but I came to the conclusion that this was really to do with my sister. Susie is not really a total bitch – but she does very often behave like one, and I do not think she had been very good for Lou. And so neither of us click on as Susie's friends much any more.

He walks from his lectern and down to the front of the stage. He kisses Lou passionately. He tries to take off her bra. She resists tactfully. This continues to go on while the rest of the dialogue continues.

Sam Susie's My Face party was a revelation to me. Not only did I realise that Susie and Lou had been totally winding me up, I also understood that it is sometimes necessary to fight for what you believe. And that I loved Emma – and always had loved Emma – whether she wore glasses and was a posho or not.

Aisha It is really hard to type in a gorilla costume. But I have taken to wearing this whenever I am alone. It kind of makes me feel secure. And if my father or my brothers get heavy with me, I can beat my chest and say 'Piss off! I am an Islamic woman! I run my own life!'

She continues to type her My Face application to be Susie's friend.

Sam We go out most nights to a concert of early Renaissance Music. But we are broadening our horizons. Last week we checked out a recital of some motets by William Byrd – and in the weeks to come we may get even more daring. Emma has said she would like to look into the early work of Johann Nepomuk Hummel and I have found myself casting longing looks in the direction of the odd Handel oratorio. I don't spend nearly so much time on the computer as I used to.

He goes down front of stage.

Emma Neither do I. In fact, I am so busy going to concerts with Sam that I don't really see any of those people in that group. Besides, Sam and I are both learning the theorbo, which is quite a commitment. Most evenings – it's summer now – we end up in a quiet part of the common just sitting on the grass and holding hands and staring up at the sky and talking about Monteverdi. I rather hope that soon Sam will attempt to take off my bra but he has not yet done so. He is very shy.

The two of them sit at the front of the stage, holding hands.

Aisha My God! I do hope Susie accepts my friend application!

She continues to type in the gorilla costume.

Susie I have had a terrible time since my My Face party. It wasn't only that Lou got off with my brother – which I still think is disgusting – but everyone seems to be avoiding me. I can't imagine why. Sam and Emma are all over each other and never even talk to me at all, and about the only person I can talk to is Mark, who did that disgusting thing of putting a picture of his mad cousin on My Face. Prayers in Hebrew! I ask you! My mum was Jewish and she always used to say that the best view of a synagogue was through the rear window of a taxi on its way to a damned good restaurant. I have been emailing Dave actually, and trying to change his extreme views on the subject of Arabs and Palestinians. And I must say since he got a computer he has mellowed a lot. But I don't really fancy him, I'm afraid. So I am stuck with hanging around with Mark. Or rather sitting in my room and emailing him – since Mark is a brainiac and never goes anywhere.

She types.

Mark – what are you doing?

Mark You know what I'm doing. I'm sending you more fish for your aquarium.

Susie Mark – I cannot move for fish in my aquarium. They are seriously overcrowded.

Mark I'm sending you more flowers for your garden.

Susie My garden is like . . . loaded with your flowers, Mark.

Mark I love you, Susie. I just love you. I have always loved you.

Susie I'm sorry. For me you will always be the boy who pretended my My Face party was a fund-raising event for the Israeli army.

Mark It might have been more fun if it had been.

Susie Thank you for nothing.

Mark I just made a joke. That was all.

Susie I have no friends left. On or off My Face. All thanks to you . . . hang on . . .

She bounces up and down in her seat.

Susie I have a friend request coming!

Mark Oh my God!

Susie A friend request!

Mark Oh my God! A friend request!

Susie Mark – don't pretend to be excited! I know you are not really excited!

Mark I am! My God! I am! I am jumping up and down in my seat!

Susie Liar!

Mark Who is it from?

Aisha Hi! This is Aisha! Guess what?

Susie looks bored.

Susie What? (*To Mark.*) It's only Aisha. Miss Koran 2006.
   Jesus! She is so boring! And so . . . Islamic!
Mark Don't be so intolerant!
Susie Well – they are intolerant!
Mark It doesn't mean you have to be.
Susie Look who's all sweetness and light these days.
Mark I have been rethinking my life since your party.
   I think I have been a self-hating Jew.
Susie No you haven't, Mark. It is other people who hate
   you. You are rather pleased with yourself.

Mark talks to audience.

Mark My God! This girl is bright!
Aisha I have a secret to tell you, Susie. The gorilla who
   turned up to your My Face party was me.
Susie You?
Aisha Me.
Susie You?
Aisha Me.
Susie Oh my God!
Aisha Oh my God!
Susie That is amazing!
Aisha But you won't tell anyone, will you?
Susie Of course I won't!

She types.

Hey Mark! The Islamic Wonderwoman has asked to be
   my friend on My Face. And – guess what – she was the
   gorilla at my party.

Dave has been typing furiously.

Dave I have not told anyone about the fact that I am in
   love with a gorilla. I mean – it is not the sort of thing

you own up to in my community. My parents do not
approve of my having a computer or of my being on it
all the time, but I said I would leave home if I didn't
have one. Anyway – the atmosphere round here is not
exactly pro-Jewish, so staying in is probably a good idea.
The good news is that we are moving to Hendon –
which my dad says is a bit like Las Vegas. But I need
to tell someone about my obsession. And I think it will
have to be Susie. We email each other a lot and she has
really changed my mind about a lot of things.

He types.

Hey Susie – would you think I was mad if I told you
   I was in love with that gorilla who turned up at your
   My Face party?
Susie Oh my God!
Mark Susie? Are you there?
Aisha Susie – will you accept me as your friend on My
   Face?
Susie Mark – Dave is in love with Aisha. And it was
   inside that gorilla costume at my party.
Mark My God!
Susie My God!
Mark My God!
Susie What do I do?
Mark Well, if Aisha wants to be your friend . . . you
   accept her as your friend. And you put her in touch
   with Dave. And they can get it together.
Susie You are so annoying, Mark.
Mark I know. I'm a Jew. I'm annoying.
Susie I'm a Jew and I'm not annoying.
Mark You are incredibly annoying.
Susie You think?
Mark I know.
Susie How can you say that?

Mark We would be the perfect Jewish couple. We could annoy each other for ever and ever and ever.

Aisha Susie – can I be your friend on My Face?

Susie My finger is poised over the ACCEPT button on my computer. Should I accept Aisha as my friend?

Mark Of course you should.

Susie Should I?

Sam Yes!

Emma Yes!

Lou Yes!

Pete Yes!

Susie turns to audience.

Susie Should I accept Aisha as my friend on My Face?

The rest of the cast encourage the audience to shout 'Yes'.

Should I tell Dave that she was the person inside the gorilla suit?

The rest of the cast encourage the audience to shout 'Yes'.

Aisha Will you be my My Face friend, Susie?

Susie Yes! Yes I will! And I have something else to tell you!

Aisha After Susie told me she would be my friend and that a friend of hers called Dave really fancied me – I thought it was the happiest day of my life. It was only later that she told me the person called Dave was an Orthodox Jew that I began to realise there might be a few problems. And I won't pretend it was easy.

Dave Susie was absolutely brilliant. The very things that sometimes make her absolutely infuriating are what make her absolutely wonderful when she has decided to be on your side. I won't bore you with all the details, but eventually Aisha and I met and started to go out. I'm afraid that neither of our parents were very understanding. But that is their problem. It seems to me that parents should let their children love who they want to love – provided they are not serial killers or something.

Mark What's wrong with serial killers? They have rights!

During all this, Aisha and Dave move away from their lecterns and down front stage. They lie together with their arms round each other.

Aisha Mark! He is something! We got quite good friends with him and Susie, and when me and Dave both moved out of home they were both really supportive. But we don't see so much of them now. We got ourselves a little flat. I am not going to tell you where it is – but I will say it is a long way from Hendon.

Dave Most nights we stay in quietly, reading and talking. And Aisha turns out to be a fantastic cook. Oh, and we shag an amazing amount. I don't think anyone in the world has ever shagged quite as much as me and Aisha. Well – she says that the communities from which we both come are both so full of hatred for each other that it is going to take an awful lot of sex to wipe it out.

Aisha Dave is very good round the house. And we don't really feel we need anyone else these days. Although I shall always be grateful to the people who brought us together. And I know I shall always love Dave – until the day I die. On special occasions, I get out the gorilla costume and he shags me in that. It is amazing!

Now Susie and Mark are the only ones at lecterns.

Mark It's a bit lonely now.

Susie Mark is the only one of my My Face friends who writes to me.

Mark And I write to her a lot.

Susie He keeps telling me he loves me.

Mark I do, Susie. I've always loved you.

Susie I don't know . . .

Mark Just come out with me. Once . . .

Susie I don't know. Will we be right for each other?

Mark I don't know. Will we?

Susie We are so similar.

Mark That's good, isn't it?

Shrugs.

Susie Am I clever enough for you?

Mark Oh, you are clever alright. You just pretend to be
  stupid.

Susie Do I? Oh my God!

Mark There you go again . . .

*He gets up and leaves his lectern. Susie is alone at hers.
He holds out his hand.*

Please, Susie. Please.

Susie I just . . .

Mark We'll have a great time.

Susie Will we?

Mark There's only us left, babe.

Susie Alright then. Alright.

She gets up and goes down front. They kiss. Slow fade.

The End.

Production Notes

STRUCTURE

The play is split into three parts, with the characters

- on their computers;
- at the party;
- during the aftermath.

As with all good comedy, any production of this play should be fast-paced.

FORMS OF ADDRESS

Companies producing this play may want to go through the text methodically, working out when the characters are addressing the audience, when they are addressing each other and when they are speaking to their computers.

The play starts with Susie and Mark directly addressing the audience. They 'say' what's coming out of their fingers. They then meet face to face.

Consider: if characters are on stage at the same time as other characters, are they able to hear each other? The convention seems to be that they are in their own bubble, speaking to each other, but can't hear each other. But it is often more dramatic if you have a firm convention and then break it. Bear this in mind in Part One, when Mark is monitoring the effect that Dave has on Susie. Here, it is crucial as to where they direct their comments. It is vital to the drama that Mark knows what reactions he's getting from Susie. After all, he is the hacker.

Perhaps Susie can talk to the audience and to the other characters. Or are they battling for who gets to tell the story? Maybe there is no private sphere after all. It could be that the real humour lies in criss-crossing the conventions – for example, allowing one character to 'overhear' another as they go past on their computer-mobile and make a comment.

INTERNET ETIQUETTE

In social networking sites such as the one in this play, e-messages are not always private. Perhaps this public exhibition is what makes the social pressures even more acute for Susie. Like Jane Austen's Emma, she is a middle-woman, caught up in her friends' lives, who spends her time matchmaking for those around her.

Characters here seem to have two identities: behind the computer and face to face. There are many young people who rarely talk in real life and yet on the internet are very vocal. The element of anonymity protects them, liberates their expression and allows them to experiment with their personality.

This anonymity can give new confidence and make a shy person articulate, so that they in turn, become more confident in real life. Things that are hard to say face to face become easier online. It's more possible to find people with feelings and interests in common. People tend to experiment with life more over the internet than in reality.

There is an internet language which uses acronyms and abbreviations like 'LOL' ('laugh out loud') that frequently go further than people's actual feelings. This leaves them open to misinterpretation, and one can become neurotic trying to interpret the semiotics.

INTERNET GAMES

There are hundreds of virtual games such as *The Sims* and *Furkadia* where you can create a virtual self in an online world and connect with other people. Perhaps this is a human tendency enhanced by the internet. Some people feel the same with celebrities. They think they love Pete Doherty although they have never met him.

In the play the only example of a split personality is Mark, who has invented a friend and rival for himself.

CHARACTERS

As far as age is concerned, all the teenage characters in the play are past sexual maturity. Aisha and Dave are the oldest. Apart from Dave, they all go to the same school.

Who is the least likeable person in the play? Is it the invented character of Dave, the cardboard cut-out, stereotypical 'cool' guy?

In rehearsal, actors sometimes want to know about their characters as if they are fixed tightly in to their roles, which they are not. Characters are fluid and change depending on who they are with.

So what does that say about Susie, who's fallen for this artificial Dave? You could dislike Susie the most, as she's the kind of person who labels people very quickly and decides who is cool and who is not.

Is Lou really insecure about her looks, or is she just fishing for compliments? Is it social pressure? Is the gorilla suit attention-seeking? Nigel wrote her to be genuinely insecure. Whoever plays Lou has to decide this, before they can properly play the character.

Is Sam really made to believe that he and Lou are an item? He is flattered and excited by the proposition, as well as a little confused.

Is Pete as nice as he seems? At what point does Pete stop pretending to be thick and start to become his real self?

Some of these questions may not *need* an answer, because the characters themselves don't know it! Remember, the characters drive the plot in this play.

STAGING

STAGING PART I

THE LECTERNS   A lectern has a ritualistic, symbolic element. It reminds one of public speaking, as in church. However, the idea of the lectern as very public is at odds with the point about the internet, which is that these kids are in the privacy of their bedrooms. The lecterns also imply that the characters are standing rather than sitting, as they might do in their own rooms.

When creating the play, Nigel felt the lecterns were a halfway house, a theatrical representation. They had to be symbolic rather than realistic and also free up the actors to move about. So the lecterns are not necessary. They *represent* the fact that the characters are at their computers.

Another option is to set out each character's own space naturalistically. However, as they each inhabit a virtual world, the characters can be in close proximity; their space does not necessarily need to be private.

STAGING DAVE Ask the question, how do we tell the difference between the phoney Dave and the others? Possibly he walks around freely while they have computers.

Or perhaps one could use light to differentiate between the characters. Dave could be like a puppet, miming, while Mark types. Or Mark doesn't type and Dave just speaks. He could be a voice-over instead. How could Dave be made physical? Perhaps he could float on. Perhaps the virtual Dave could be projected onto a screen, so we can only see his face.

STAGING PART 2

THE PARTY   Part One of the play presents us with the problem of creating the virtual world, but in Part Two, the characters meet face to face at the party. Here, the difficulty is in staging near-simultaneous action in the house and on the street. There are many options, all dependent on the configuration chosen for your production:

- The areas could be two sides of the stage, or upstage and downstage.
- The street scenes could be filmed and played back on a screen.
- One area could be higher than the other.

STAGING PART 3

THE AFTERMATH   The third part is a movement away from the computer. The relationships and body language change again when we see the couples that have formed.

SPEAKING/TYPING CONVENTIONS

Characters speak what they type. Does this suggest that, instead of saying the lines as they would if talking to each other, it is more like dictation?

Try the same piece of text as:

- Normal conversation.
- Speech with a flattened-out pitch and slower, as if they were typing at the same time.

The slower speed quickly became monotonous, but it did open up some possibilities of dramatic pauses, as if the characters are thinking of the next word to type, or a variety of styles.

Nigel envisages the dialogue as normal speech. He didn't imagine anything specific to typing when he was writing the play.

PROBLEM SOLVING

When the actors directly address the audience (e.g., when Susie asks the audience: 'Should I accept Aisha as my friend on My Face?') it breaks the fourth wall, which is a different form of communication. It makes the audience complicit with the characters' thought processes and makes the actors' jobs easier. It is up to the cast to give the right energy. If the audience is awkward it's so much the better, as it opens up all the conventions for examination. Maybe all the characters have to be involved in engaging the audience.

At the big moment where the virtual Dave speaks back, what to do with Pete? We don't want to give the game away – that he's the one behind it. Perhaps Pete could speak at the same time as the imaginary Dave, once he has taken over control. The moment where the virtual character becomes real is perhaps enough to deal with – you don't want to over-complicate it by also showing Pete taking over the reins. However, provided it is clear and the story keeps moving, you can do it any way you like. This will become clear in the rehearsal room.

JUMPING UP AND DOWN   This is a repeated action, and has the potential to be hilarious. It is important to make a choice – does the humour lie in the fact that it is always exactly the same? Or is it funnier if there's a progression, and it builds from small to energetic?

FIGHT SEQUENCE   This could be continuous, in real time or slow motion – or the characters could even freeze in between. Mostly the young people do not want to be fighting, so there is potential for physical comedy in the characters who portray violence with reluctance.

MAIN THEMES

Nigel explores social engineering and the ways that computers narrow people's choices. For example, you can only choose to accept or reject a friend, there is no in-between. Internet exchange in this play is based on a kind of controlled politeness, with no interruptions.

By the end of the play, all the characters have moved away from their computers. Susie has the biggest problem with this, but Mark helps her to move into the real world.

From a workshop led by Bill Alexander
with notes by Sophie Lifschutz

THE PEACH CHILD

Anna Furse

Anna Furse, Artistic Director of Athletes of the Heart, was also Artistic Director of Paines Plough in the early 1990s and of Bloodgroup in the 1980s. She is an award-winning director and writer of over fifty productions that have toured internationally, including *Augustine* (*Big Hysteria*) (Time Out Award for Writing and Directing) and *Gorgeous*. *The Peach Child* was originally written and directed for the Little Angel Theatre (Japan Festival and the National Children's Theatre Festival 2001). She wrote and directed *My Glass Body* for BBC Radio 3 in 2007, and her current productions include *Don Juan, Who?* (with Mladinsko, Ljubljana, touring the UK in association with FeEAST) and DUST, being researched in India on an ArtsAdmin Bursary.

Author's Note

I wrote this play as a love letter to my daughter who was four years old at the time. I had taken her to the Little Angel Theatre and fallen in love with the place. Soon after, I was commissioned by them to develop, write and direct *The Peach Child*, which we premiered in 2001 for the National Children's Theatre Festival and Japan Festival. The project was part of a series of performances I have created from my experience of infertility and the IVF treatment from which my daughter was born when I was forty-two years old – a miracle birth at the time with a three per cent prognosis. Some of these projects have been 'sci-art' – multi-media theatre for adults and young audiences – and I have also created a performance installation that was commissioned by a hospital (*Glass Body*, 2006). Then BBC Radio commissioned me to write and direct *My Glass Body* for Radio 3 in 2007. All in all, *The Peach Child* has been part of a journey, of making sense of infertility, emotionally, physically, medically, scientifically and ethically. The National Theatre 'Connections' brings everything full circle, to where I began exploring involuntary childlessness.

The play is actually an adaptation of a very ancient Japanese tale: *Momotaro, or The Peach Boy*. I was given this as part of an anthology when I was a child and, of all the stories, for some reason – perhaps premonition – *The Peach Child* had always remained with me. It was therefore extraordinary to discover, when my production had been featured in the national Japanese press, that not only is the story as famous in Japan as, for example,

Cinderella might be to us, but that the figure of Momotaro even has a cult in Japan, dedicated to the spiritual/life-positive values he represents. I have dined with such devotees in London and have *Peach Child* memorabilia from them to prove it.

The play and production were originally an experiment on several levels: on how to explore *bunraku* (Japanese stick and rod) puppetry in 3-D (i.e., not using the convention of the play board and puppeteers behind), and from this also an exploration of how to mingle live performance with puppeteering. I was a novice, venturing into an unfamiliar world with the kind of shameless 'what if' optimism that comes with total ignorance. I survived the whole experiment by the enthusiastic support and advice of my cast, including the ever-resourceful and brilliant Sue Dacre, who worked on the 'Connections' workshops. As we discovered in Scarborough, puppeteering isn't all strings or rods. We can animate even a piece of paper and make it somehow come to life as a suggested human or animal form.

My play was written for very young audiences (four- to seven-year-olds), though many adults came to the show (even without children!). My fervent aim was to stretch these audiences' sense of the power of a visual image (seasons changing to just the fall of blossoms, leaves, snow for example) and to 'de-Disneyfy' the story. I tried to avoid anything cute or sweet, but grapple with some of the tenderness of the tale as well as the darker and ominous material of the unknown Ogre's land of hell and destruction. Environmental issues suggested to me the old folk's justification for the magic size of the fruit and also the havoc that the Ogres had created on earth. I gender-bent the spirit guides from the original story to create female characters who inspire Momotaro to overcome his natural and very human fear of the huge and dangerous adventure he feels fated to undertake. The humour for these characters is definitely that of a five-year-old, as it was my daughter who worked at the time as script editor and joke consultant.

I wrote this play to direct it myself and never imagined anyone else would want to stage it. With 'Connections', I wanted to offer up the piece for adaptation as well as interpretation, since it has also been produced by mixed ability groups. I wouldn't wish to impose any ideas on how others might wish to stage it. Only an important point: the original story is Japanese. But it is, like all good old stories, universal. Neither *bunraku* nor Japanese references are absolutely essential, and I would be happy to hear from anyone who wished to transpose the work into other cultural contexts. We at the Little Angel certainly never played it 'Japanese', but set the story in an ancient, non-time-specific Japan-like world – a poor, close-knit peasant community living with a lot of hardship, where being childless would mean being both different and special. I wanted to evoke the story as I had read and remembered it over so many decades, and hope that rather than culturally appropriate this, by retelling it with the play's contemporary references and very free approach to geographical or ethnic detail, we might all find some identification with its themes.

Characters

(in order of appearance)

Old Man

Old Woman

Party Guests and Children

Peach Child
as a baby

Momotaro
aged fifteen

Lady Dog

Lady Monkey

Lady Pheasant

Chief Ogre

Essential Props
Lanterns, broom, peach, bread knife,
laundry basket and laundry, rice bowl,
chopsticks, feather, sword, boots, bed,
rice cakes, raft, ogre's box, prayer mat

Essential Scenographic Ingedients
Interior (with screens optional).
Exterior: mountains, ogre/volcano,
ocean, moon, stars, river

Video as used in the original production is optional

Notes on Staging

A visual/puppetry/animation play for six performers (with doubling) to be played with or without an interval.

Inspired by an ancient Japanese tale, this piece deals with issues of childlessness, adoption, parenting and letting go. It also deals with friendship, collaboration, courage and struggle. Working on an epic storytelling canvas but with the simplest of means, it contrasts the domestic/family/social world with the wider world of magic, nature, danger, good and evil.

The story has four phases:

1 (miracle) birth;
2 growing up: the journey/quest;
3 the battle of good over evil;
4 victory and homecoming.

Whilst set in an imaginary ancient rural Japan, the piece might actually be adapted to other cultural contexts without changing the text and dialogue, except perhaps for some names (to be negotiated with the writer).

The play offers an opportunity to experiment with visual approaches to solve some of its several challenges for storytelling. Scale can be played with, for instance, to create both a sense of landscape and of the small warrior versus the gigantesque enemy. Interiors and exteriors are sometimes played simultaneously.

The audience is, at times, to be given different points of view on the same location. Overall, simplicity is advised. The piece should not be rushed but instead unfold patiently and seamlessly.

For Nina

Act One

PRESET

*As audience enter, a very peaceful atmosphere. A huge
glowing moon. Stars. Dark blue light. Old Man and
Old Woman sit facing the moon with their backs to the
audience. Sounds of bubbling stream, nightingale.
Incense burns.*

SCENE ONE

*Slow fade up on crowd of people carrying lanterns and
whispering to each other to be quiet. They are going to
surprise the Old Couple with a party! They creep up on
them and shout . . . .*

All (*improvised*) Happy Birthday! Surprise! (*Etc.*)

> *A party ensues. Sounds of merry-making, music and
> song, a feeling of a large crowd. Ringing above this,
> the sound of Children telling jokes. Much laughter.
> A clock chimes eleven.*

Voice One Time to go!

Voice Two Come on, kids!

Children's Voices Why? We're having fun! I don't want
to go home! I don't want to go to bed. (*Etc.*)

Voice Two You know the rules. We have to get back
before midnight or the Ogres might come –

Child One Steal our toys!

Child Two The cake!

Child Three The wishes you made when you cut it!

Child Four Our shoes even!

Old Woman and Man Hurry along now! Thank you so much. It was wonderful. Really lovely! You're angels! Thanks. Bye! Bye! (*Etc.*)

The crowd leaves. In the distance we see them (e.g., lanterns in miniature) moving up the side of a distant hillside. The Old Man and Old Woman turn slowly to audience.

Interior: They slide the paper screen doors shut. Old Woman starts to pick up a broom and sweep. She suddenly stops, melancholy . . .

Old Woman Did you hear what Yoko said?

Old Man You mean about swimming like a fish under water and being able to do handstands holding her breath?

Old Woman Yes. And the joke Fumio told about the tortoise without legs . . .

Old Man Where do you find a tortoise without any legs?

Old Woman Where you left it!

Old Man Where you left it!!

They both laugh together, but this mutates into a sad laughter.

Old Woman Beautiful children . . .

Old Man Beautiful! Happy birthday . . .

Lights dim on the shadow image of Old Man and Old Woman embracing. Old Woman cries.

Old Man If we haven't been blessed with children in this life, maybe in the next . . . it must be because Buddha wanted it this way . . . in the next . . .

Old Woman Yes . . . yes . . . in the next life . . .

Old Man sits eating out of his rice bowl, Old Woman exits.

SCENE TWO

The River. Winter.
   *Film of water, peach and hands for close-ups and play
with scale, or live: Old Woman is singing the lullaby as
she washes kimonos in a stream. The water is clearly
freezing. The Old Woman keeps blowing on her hands
after they have been in the water. Eerie music: an
unnaturally enormous blushing peach appears, bobbing
towards her on the water. Old Woman's hands reach
out to it tenderly. It keeps slipping out of her grasp, till
at last she gets to hold it.*

Old Woman There! See? Even my gnarled old bones
   were too fast for you! Buddha only knows what you
   could be doing in my bit of river in the middle of
   winter, but my husband happens to love peaches and
   cream and I can't wait to take you to him! He'll never
   believe his eyes!

She bundles the peach up in her laundry.

SCENE THREE

Interior.
   *Old Man is eating from a simple bowl. He is alone,
and cold. Rubs his hands together.*
   *Old Woman appears carrying her laundry basket with
the enormous peach wrapped hidden inside. She is clearly
exhausted and cold.*

Old Man What took you so long? I was starving. I had
   to get my own rice and light the fire and set the table
   and and and . . .
Old Woman And?

Old Man And wash up this morning's dishes!

Old Woman And?

Old Man And keep the fire lit and stir the rice, wipe the table before setting it, and and and . . .

Old Woman And??

Old Man (*suddenly tender*) And I thought you'd drowned . . .

Old Woman And?

Old Man And you're all I have in the world . . .

Old Woman Well, now you have me.

She unwraps the peach and presents it to him.

And this! So stop moaning and go and get yourself a knife. I'm afraid there's no cream, but this peach looks really sweet and juicy. Perhaps I should scrape some fresh ginger onto it . . .

The Old Man is astounded . . . As the Old Woman busies herself unpacking her laundry, washing her hands, etc., he obediently goes to fetch a knife, stumbling as he goes, for his eyes remained transfixed on the peach, which glows luminescent. By the time they both meet at the table again the peach is glowing as brightly as a yellow moon. The Old Man raises his knife and plunges the blade into the flesh of the peach. Eerie music as before.

SCENE FOUR

The peach splits open to reveal a naked baby: Peach Child. Old Man and Old Woman gasp, clutching each other. Peach Child begins to crawl. He reaches for the knife, fascinated. Old Man and Old Woman both instinctively reach out to stop him, tutting at him. He looks at them fascinated, questioning.

Old Man No! The knife is sharp. See?

He runs his finger along the blade and pretends to be very hurt.

Old Woman Knives are dangerous. They're very very sharp. They can kill you. Here . . .

She reaches into her kimono and pulls out a feather.

Play with this. See? It's from a bird. It's part of its wing. A bird flies with its wings. Like this!

A dance/game ensues with the Peach Child and the Old Woman, very playful, much mirth. At the end of this, the Peach Child farts and falls into her arms, snuggles into her. Old Man looks on.

Old Man Buddha has heard our prayers.
Old Woman Yes, What a beautiful child . . .
Old Man Beautiful . . .
Old Woman Let's call him Momotaro: Peach Child!
Old Man Of course! Our perfect little Momotaro. Our peach. Our miracle.

Momotaro has fallen asleep in his new mother's arms. She sings her lullaby to him. Lights fade as the moon glows big and silver in an indigo blue sky, studded with stars.

SCENE FIVE

Momotaro, grown up.
A series of images follow which show the baby growing into a child, then a bigger child. These images disappear.
Beautiful pure music. Time is passing: blossoms fall, then green leaves, then golden ones, then (in silence) snow.

SCENE SIX

*A shadow-play birthday party, exactly as in the Prologue.
Everyone sings 'Happy Birthday' to Momotaro. There
is much laughter. Momotaro is now aged fifteen years,
a young and handsome warrior. The Old Man and
Old Woman, looking much older and frailer now,
ceremoniously present him with a gift. He unwraps it.
It's a long sword. He's delighted and begins playing with
it, childlike again, teasing the old folk with his lunges and
manoeuvres. Laughter. The clock chimes eleven exactly
as before and, as before, everyone talks about needing to
leave before the Ogres come out. The party begins to
disintegrate as people begin to leave.*

SCENE SEVEN

*Old Man and Old Woman with their backs to the audience
as before, waving goodbye to the diminishing group
carrying their lanterns up the hillside . . . They are waving
out to the audience, bidding the last guests farewell.
Momotaro watches them, carefully choosing his moment
to speak.*

Momotaro Mother. Father. You've been the best parents
a child could possibly want . . .
And I love you both more than the sun and the moon and
the stars . . .

*A sudden change of atmosphere. The Old Woman
bows her head in pain . . .*

*The old couple reluctantly turn downstage to
Momotaro, sensing what he's going to say.*

Please don't cry. Don't be unhappy. We all knew that one

day the time would come for me to leave home. Well,
now it's here.

*The Old Woman weeps. The Old Man goes to comfort
her, as yet a little confused by the portentous atmosphere.*

You've taught me everything I know, and one thing you
have certainly taught me is how to try to be strong
when things are frightening or sad, or when you can't
have what you want. Well, it's time for me to use these
skills and go out into the world beyond the edge of our
mountain and see what's there . . .

Old Woman But there's evil there! Bad things! Ogres!!
Ogres who stole people's love of nature . . . and . . .
and powers of healing . . . and beautiful things . . . so
we find it so hard to do good, live well now. We can't
even grow healthy food any more . All the monsters
and bad spirits. It's dangerous. You could get hurt.
They could kill you . . .

Momotaro Or I could kill *them*!

Old Woman But nobody who's tried before has won yet,
and you're hardly grown up yet!

Momotaro How old do you have to be before you can
tell good from bad, hmm?

Didn't you both teach me this from the moment I could
talk? To love all the good in the world and fight all
that's bad. Well now it's time to act on it. That's all.
You will have to let me go. Please . . .

Old Woman No! It's dangerous!!

Momotaro MUST!

*The Old Man and Old Woman are dumbfounded. They
slowly, reluctantly relent as they see how determined
Momotaro is.*

Old Man You'll need proper footwear . . .

Old Woman And food . . .

Momotaro Thank you!

Old Man I'll go and dig out my old fighting boots. Warm socks. A compass. Erm, let me see, maps, binoculars, jerrycan, matches . . .

Old Woman And I'll go and make some rice cakes and some of my special medicine. And you'll need a toothbrush and a change of clothes. Your pillow and duvet. Some books. A torch. Some postcards and pens so you can write to us . . .

Momotaro The sword and the rice cakes will do fine. It's really all I need. I mean, you can't fight all the evil in the world with everything but the kitchen sink on your back!

Old Man/Old Woman BUT . . . !

Momotaro Look . . . sword. Boots. A bit of food. Great!

Old Man/Old Woman As you wish . . .

SCENE EIGHT

Old Man fetches his boots and Old Woman a bundle of cakes. Momotaro puts the cakes in his bag, puts the boots on and slides his sword into its sheath. He embraces his parents. The Old Woman is crying. The embraces are repeated several times. The three then bow deeply to each other and say their last farewells. Momotaro exits.

A miniature version of him is seen climbing the hillside in the distance upstage.

Act Two

SCENE NINE

Darkness. On top of the mountain in the middle of the night. Mist. Wolves howl. Owls hoot. The wind blows. Momotaro is sitting by a small fire he has made. He is very lonely and frightened. He unwraps his bundle of rice cakes and nibbles on one. He then takes his sword out of its sheath and examines it. A sudden noise startles him and he reflexes into an attack position with his sword. Silence. When he is confident that the noise isn't sinister, he sits down and begins to sob.

Momotaro Oh . . . I'm scared and I'm lonely and I don't really know if I want to go to the other side of the mountain to fight all the evil in the world after all. I want my own bed. I want a hot dinner. And I want . . . I want . . . my mum and dad . . .

There's a sudden barking very close to Momotaro which makes him leap to his feet brandishing his sword. Lady Dog appears. A flurry of dogginess.
    After barking and growling a bit to frighten Momotaro, she stops and begins preening herself.

Lady Dog Oh, put that thing away, it's only me! Thank Buddha I found you. I've been looking all over the crest of this mountain and couldn't see a sausage. Then I heard crying and whimpering and thought to myself, 'There's my boy! That'll be him, Momotaro, the peach child with a mission! Mmhm!' And, well, I was right.

Lady Dog helps herself to a rice cake and settles in next to the fire. Momotaro is speechless.

Lady Dog (*mouth full of rice cake*) Of course, what
you need to understand is that you aren't the first
or the last young man to try his hand at ridding the
world of evil, and it certainly isn't a piece of cake
(these are very good by the way). But you're special.
And you've got me and I'm very very brave and
fearless and courageous and I'm not frightened of
anything or anyone and I'm going to help you. I've
decided I'm sticking with you till we get all those nasty
evil horrible ogres and give them what they deserve.
Oh yes! You and me as a team will be invincible, oh
yes! They won't know what's hit 'em! Trust me. Now
let's get some beauty sleep so we're fit for action in the
morning, OK?

Momotaro Er, yes, er . . . of course, erm . . . Excuse
me, but I don't even know your name or who you are!
I mean, you can't just barge in on my big heroic quest.
We've never met. How can I trust you?

Lady Dog My apologies. (*She offers a paw.*) Lady. This
whole area is my domain. I am extremely interested in
your desire to kill all the monsters the other side of
this mountain. (*She waits for a response.*) I expect you
want to know why?

Momotaro Er . . . why?

Lady Dog Because they devastated my land and killed my
family. So I suppose you could say I am very personally
motivated in helping your cause . . . Besides which,
I have very very sharp teeth with which to snap the
monster's heads off and if you don't let me come with
you as a fighting companion, your mission will fail.
Why? Because I control all this territory which you
need to cross, to get to the other side of the mountain.
Nighty night. Sweet dreams. Make sure the bugs don't
bite . . . if they . . . do . . . squeeze them tight . . . then
they won't . . . to . . . morrow . . . night . . .

Lady Dog curls up to sleep. Momotaro decides to do the same . . . Lady Dog snores.

Fade to black. The sound of the night intensifies and plump stars twinkle.

SCENE TEN

Morning. Lady Dog and Momotaro are asleep. Suddenly there's a big screeching commotion. Lady Monkey appears, swinging from the branches above their dozing heads. They suddenly wake. Lady Monkey screams as they cry out:

Momotaro Get off! Hey!

Lady Dog What the . . . Who do you think you are?! This is my domain, huh!? And I am Momotaro's retainer and I'm all he needs right now, thank you, and so . . .

Lady Monkey At your service, folks!

Lady Dog This whole area is my domain! And I am this young man Momotaro's special retainer and I'm all he needs right now, so . . .

Momotaro and Lady Monkey are staring each other in the face . . .

As I said, Momotaro and I have got it all worked out. The approach. Attack. Who's going to carry what back to the other side of the mountain after the victory, etc., etc. . . .

Momotaro and Lady Monkey are still sizing each other up.

Momotaro Lady Dog, don't lie! You know as well as I do that we'll need all the help we can get to fight all the evil in the world, the other side of this mountain. There's dangerous and difficult work ahead of us. We must welcome, er –

Lady Monkey Lady Monkey, but you can call me 'Mo'. Everyone does.

Momotaro – er, Mo, as second retainer, and be grateful
for her support and courage in assisting our mission.
Give her a rice cake, please, and let's all be friends.
Alright?

*Lady Dog (reluctant and proud) and Lady Monkey
(enthusiastic) shake hands.*
Then the three pack their bags and head off.

Momotaro Let's go!

The trio head off on their long journey.
*The following sequence needs to find a theatrical
device – use of space, lighting, music, exits and
entrances, etc., to convey this. Lady Monkey's joke is
supposed to be being told throughout, so that we pick
up only sections of what we must imagine has been
told, in between times.*

Lady Monkey Hey, does anyone know the joke about the
wide-mouthed frog?

Momotaro/Lady Dog (*unenthusiastically*) Nope. Can't
say I do. No.

Lady Monkey Well, you see, there's this wide-mouthed
frog who wants to change his diet cos he's bored of
eating what he eats. So he goes on a long long looonng
journey to ask all the animals from far and wide what
they like to eat, to see if he'd like to eat it too . . .

The journey moves to another phase.

Lady Dog Are you scared?

Momotaro Me scared? Hrm. Of course not. Well. I mean.
I've got you, haven't I?

Lady Monkey Then he gets to Africa . . .

We see a miniature of the trio climbing in the distance.
Lady Monkey chattering away.

Lady Monkey So he says, 'Hello, Mr Elephant, I'm the
Wide-Mouthed Frog and I'm bored of what I eat and

wonder if what you eat might be more interesting, would you mind telling me what you eat please?' And the elephant says, 'Well, Mr Wide-Mounthed Frog, I like to eat bananas from the tops of trees . . . (and tops of trees for that matter) and iced buns,' and the Wide-Mouthed Frog says, 'Well, that's very interesting, but buns and treetops and bananas aren't really my thing, but thanks anyways, it was a pleasure talking to you.' And so the Wide-Mouthed Frog continues on his journey . . .

SCENE ELEVEN

The mountainside is reversed now. The trio, life-size, are descending the other side.

Lady Monkey And the snake hisses, 'Well I like birdsss . . . and micccce . . . and I'm very partial to wide-mouthed frogsssss.' And the Wide-Mouthed Frog quickly pulls his lips very very very tight like this and says, 'Ooooooh, you don't see many of those around these days, do you?'

Suddenly, a squawking commotion as Lady Pheasant appears from a bush. Lady Dog instantly runs forward barking.

Lady Dog Off with her head! Off with her head!

Lady Pheasant, undaunted, swoops through the air in a big circle and begins to attack Lady Dog. Momotaro watches, fascinated.

Momotaro What a clever bird! I must invite her to join us in our mission to rid the world of the ogres' evil. She'll be such a help attacking from the air. Brilliant. Hey! Lady Dog, whoah!

Momotaro swipes Lady Dog's backside. He turns to Lady Pheasant.

How dare you molest my personal retainer? We are
bound on a most personal mission and we haven't a
minute to lose. So please stop holding us up with all
your screeching and pecking . . .

*Lady Pheasant suddenly kneels and bows elaborately
and coquettishly.*

Lady Pheasant I'm soooo sorry. I don't mean to be rude.
It's just my nature. I just had to come and help the
famous miracle peach child Momotaro, about whom
all the birds have heard. Lady Pheas.

She offers a wing and bows deeply.

I am absolutely and wholeheartedly and passionately
behind your mission to conquer evil. Pleeeease may
I join your retinue? It would be an honour to serve
under your leadership and help in any way – terrestrial
or aerial – that I can. Do I smell cakes?

*Lady Dog snarls jealously in the corner as Momotaro
insists on sharing a rice cake between all three animal-
spirit guides.*

Well, ladies, thank you. I feel a lot braver now I've got
you to help. With our brains, and my sword, with your
teeth (*to Dog*) and your tail (*to Monkey*) and your
wings (*to Bird*) I reckon we're pretty invincible, don't
you? Well, time we got a move on. Mo? Lady? Lady
Pheas? Ready to fight some ogres?

They all respond affirmatively.

Then let's go!

*Lady Pheasant circles in the air above the trio as they
set off, with a confident spring in their step.*
Time passes.

Lady Monkey What did the policeman say to his chest,
anyone?

No one responds. They are tired now.

You're under a vest!

Time passes. The quartet suddenly come to the sea, staring out to the horizon, over the audience.

Momotaro See the ocean? We'll sleep here tonight and in the morning we'll build a raft and search for the ogres' island, OK?

Lady Pheasant OK!

Lady Dog OK . . .

Lady Monkey I always think, it isn't the destination that counts, but the journey. Know what I mean . . .?

Fade to black. Sound of the sea swells.

SCENE TWELVE

Dawn. Lights fade up on the quartet putting the final touches to a makeshift raft.
Momotaro folds himself in prayer on to the ground.

Momotaro May the spirit of water, which brought me to life, now bring us to victory. Howmmmmmmm . . .

They embark and set sail. Momotaro sings the lullaby the Old Woman sang when she found him. The others join in:

Mori mo ii agaru,
Bon kara sak n ya,
Yuki mo chira tsukushi,
Ko mo naku shi.

[*In the original production, this was sung in Japanese. Translation: 'The babysitter hates the time after the Bon Festival. The snow will fall. The child will cry.'*]

401

*The ocean swells. The sun turns gold and red and the
moon rises.*
   Blackout.

SCENE THIRTEEN

The next morning. Raft on a calm sea.
All concentrating on the horizon. Tension.

Lady Monkey Hey, anybody, what's the most musical
fish?

No response.

Tuna!!

All groan.
   Suddenly Lady Pheasant flies in, very agitated.

Lady Pheasant Land ahead! Land ahead! I can see the
island! It's far but not too far. If you row hard we'll be
there before nightfall. I'll direct you.
Momotaro Fly ahead and see what you can see.

Lady Pheasant flies away.

Lady Monkey Why do birds fly south in winter?
Lady Dog/Momotaro Don't know. / Why do birds fly
south in winter? / No idea.
Lady Monkey Cos it's too far to walk!!

SCENE FOURTEEN

*Suddenly the ocean swells and a violent storm smashes
the raft and shipwrecks the quartet, who land in disarray,
hanging from a tree on shore.*

Dusk. A very ominous atmosphere. In the distance, a large grey volcano: the ogres' fortification. Gothic, heavy doors, iron railings, barbed wire, etc. The sky is a livid red. Black vultures wing in circles. Sulphurous green smoke rises. A quiet menacing roaring sound. The volcano is heaving, snoring. Momotaro and his retainers are terrified, awed.

Momotaro (*whispering*) We must think very carefully about this attack. We must wait till nightfall when all the ogres will be sleeping. We must each use our particular skills: Lady Pheasant – your powers of flight and the cry you know that sounds like an earthquake; Lady Dog – your speed and your very sharp teeth; Mo – your fantastic agility and climbing; and me – I'll . . . use my sword. We'll work as a team. We'll keep going until all the evil ogres have been totally destroyed. And we shall, Buddha willing, all survive to tell the tale.

The foursome perform a ritual pledge of allegiance: each puts a wing, paw or hand into a circle.

Momotaro Now we must wait our moment. Lady Pheasant – go! Good luck!

The moon glows. An owl cries. The sound of the volcano/Ogre's snoring fills the air. A tongue suddenly falls out of the Ogre's mouth like a dropped drawbridge. All are terrified.

SCENE FIFTEEN

Lady Pheasant, in the distance now, circles high above and lands on the highest turret. All is still. Suddenly she screams out her terrible cry:

Lady Pheasant KAIEE KAIEE KAIEE KAIEE!!

*There is total commotion as the slow and sleepy Ogre
wakes. The battle ensues. Lady Monkey attacks by
jumping and swinging, Lady Dog bites off limbs,
Momotaro thrusts his sword, and Lady Pheasant
pecks. Limbs fly. Lights flash. Thunder claps. The sky
seems to be aflame. Suddenly the whole volcano
explodes and morphs into the chief Ogre. All scream.*

SCENE SIXTEEN

Simultaneous time. Interior.
*Old Woman and Old Man in bed . . . As if she has
heard the scream in her dreams, Old Woman suddenly
sits bolt upright, screaming. Old Man wakes and
comforts her.*

Old Man He'll be alright, you'll see . . . because he's
special, and very brave . . . you'll see. Sleep now, sleep . . .

They disappear.

SCENE SEVENTEEN

*Dawn. Smoke rises off the ground, which is littered with
corpses. Momotaro and his companions are exhausted.
The chief Ogre alone has survived. He appears, slowly
staggering forward to survey his defeat. He has no weapon.
He is carrying a box. He breaks off his horns as a ritual
sign of his failure and hands them to Momotaro, who
appears tiny by comparison. The Ogre opens the box
and takes out some keys that he hands to Momotaro. He
bows down low.*

Chief Ogre Take these keys, they are yours now. They
will open the storehouse where everything good we

ogres stole from you and your people has been kept all these years. You will find the precious stone with which the seas can be cleaned, and the magic needle and thread with which to sew up the hole in the sky so no more storms ravage the earth. You will find the endless source of water with which to feed the dry earth in hot countries where children have no food. You will find the silver scales with which to balance everything just right. And you will find the special secret that will tell you how to look after nature so she can look after you. You will find precious gems, and perfumes, and books of wisdom which teach you how to live well and generously. Take them, I don't want them. I never used them anyway. Besides, it would seem that your people really need them . . .

Momotaro takes the keys.

SCENE EIGHTEEN

Interior.
   Downstage, Old Man and Old Woman are kneeling, praying, bent over their knees. A chime suddenly makes them startle in unison as if sharing a premonition.

SCENE NINETEEN

Action, interior and exterior simultaneously.
   Sunset, the hillside.
   Momotaro and his companions in the distance, making their way towards the Old Man and Old Woman's village.
   They are singing the Old Woman's lullaby.
   Interior: the Old Man embraces the Old Woman.

Old Man See? I told you he'd be alright! He'd come back!

Old Woman Yes! Goodness, he'll be hungry . . . he'll
need a hot bath . . . clean clothes . . .

They start moving about to prepare for his arrival.

Old Man We were right to let him go, see? He came back!
He came back!

Chime. They both suddenly stop still in their tracks.

Old Woman Can you feel it?
Old Man Yes, I can feel it.
Old Woman It's changing, isn't it? It feels warmer . . .
Old Man Yes, yes . . . it is . . . it's as if . . .
Old Woman As if everything good was coming back to
us . . .

She goes to look out for Momotaro.

Do you see what I see?

Old Man joins her.

Old Man I can see that you suddenly look young again . . .
Old Woman No, there, look!
Old Man My eyes aren't that strong, you'll have to tell
me . . .
Old Woman He isn't alone . . . ohhhh . . .

*They embrace as Momotaro and his companions enter,
carrying the box of goodness that the Ogre gave them.
Colour and warmth fill the stage.*

The lights fade slowly as the lullaby crescendos.

The End.

Production Notes

THE STORY

The Peach Child was written by Anna Furse and inspired by the ancient Japanese folk tale *Momotaro*. The play has been written with the intention that a variety of puppet forms and visual approaches can be used in its staging.

Anna wrote *The Peach Child* after personal experience of infertility. *Momotaro* is a well-known tale in Japan and deals with issues of childlessness and parenting. It doesn't have to have a Japanese 'look'; the story is universal and will sit comfortably in any setting. The piece was written with many visual ideas in mind, as Anna Furse was attempting a fairy tale without the Disney factor. Simple devices can work best.

CHARACTERS

If you change genders in casting, consider carefully how the text will work.

OLD MAN–OLD WOMAN   The piece shouldn't be at all sentimental; avoiding this hinges mainly on how you deal with their relationship. It's a simple relationship which is tired and tender. Perhaps approach it in terms of atmosphere in the first instance. What happens in the space they occupy when they aren't talking – e.g., her sweeping, him eating?

THE OGRE   He is open to interpretation. Who is he? He is humans at their worst, thematically speaking, because he is the force of destruction on the planet and within communities. So he doesn't have to be fairy-tale evil, but he needs to suggest something dark yet human. His monologue is unsentimental. It is the dignity of the vanquished speaking. He is simply explaining what he was made of and what must now take his place.

MOMOTARO   He feels the weight of destiny on his shoulders. He is braver on the outside than on the inside. He learns his courage with the help of the animals.

DOG/PHEASANT/MONKEY   are a trio and will work best when their individual 'tics' are found. Monkey is the joker, Dog is a bit of a bossy-boots, and Pheasant slightly above everyone else. Momotaro galvanises them into a team as the first step in becoming mature and able to face life and the battle ahead.

THE PEACH   itself should suggest something wrong in the land (e.g., GM crops or radiation) that makes it larger and brighter than natural (as in the script). You might not want to use an object at all (mime) but it seems appropriate as it would be great to find a way of it being split open with a knife from which the miracle emerges.

ISOLATION EXERCISES

There are an many options in terms of puppetry that can be used in telling the story in your production. It is very important in puppetry to be able to split your focus so that you are able to do one thing with one hand and something else with the other hand, as well as move around the performance space using only your peripheral vision. Here are some exercises which puppeteers use to develop these skills:

- Hands out in front. Palms down. Move little finger out to the side on its own, then back in. Next move the little finger out to the side again, but this time joined by the second finger. Each time the fingers move back they pick up the next finger. And so on. Then do the reverse, until the little finger is once again moving on its own.

- Pat head. Rub stomach. Easy as something to touch. Try this. Make left hand into a fist. Hold out fist in front of the body – make it do an up-and-over arc, as if drawing a hill. The right hand out in front of the body is flat and moves round and round as if washing a window. Start to do both at the same time, slowly at first, then speeding up. Once you get into a rhythm and relax it gets easier.

- Working in pairs, one partner holds arms out in front and crosses arms at the wrist. Then locks hands together interlacing the fingers. Then turns arms inside out towards themselves. The other partner points (without touching!) to one of the interlaced fingers which has to be moved independently. Are you better at moving some fingers independently more than others?

- Puppet hand show. Each hand (just the naked hand!) is a puppet. Find the different ways each hand moves. Find a different sound that each 'character'-puppet has. Try to make the characters very different and defined. Act out a little scenario with your puppets. One hand wakes up the other hand. Remember to keep each hand alive all the time, at the same time. Your puppet performance can take place on a chair, the floor, wall or table.

This hand-puppet exercise illustrates some fundamental principles of puppetry:

- Absolute belief in what you are doing is essential, as that is part of the audience's belief.
- Rhythm of movement: contrasts of characters evolve from this.
- A sense of the puppet having breath.
- Keeping it simple: i.e., choose a couple of things that the puppet does really well.

EXERCISE FOR MULTI-FOCUS

In groups of four, sit at compass points. Person 1 is in the hot seat and is only allowed to look at Person 2 opposite them. Person 2 does movements which Person 1 has to mirror. Person 3 asks Person 1 questions which they must answer without hesitation. Person 4 asks Person 1 simple maths questions which they must answer without hesitation.

This exercise is very good for puppeteers as the focus has to be in many places at once.

STICK EXERCISE

In pairs, in silence, each actor holds a bamboo stick in one hand. One person leads the slow movement of the tip of their stick. The other person must follow with the tip of their stick, always keeping one ping-pong ball apart. Pairs can move around the space, i.e., not be static. Don't make it *too* interesting: keep it simple. *We should not be able to tell who is leading the movement.*

Add another stick (i.e., each have two sticks now). One person concentrates on following the movement of one stick and the other person the movement of the other stick – i.e., you are only focused on the end of one stick.

Now the workshop leader changes focus of ends of sticks to another group, so eventually the entire group is linked in movement by sticks to the rest of the group.

It is hard work to keep the focus so intently on one thing. The temptation is to look around at other stuff that is going on. Puppeteers must keep all their focus on the puppet they are operating.

BRINGING A COAT/JACKET/JUMPER TO LIFE

Button or zip up your coat. Lay it down in front of you. Head away from you, close your eyes and just concentrate on your own breath. Which we rarely do.

Put your hand about three-quarters inside your coat. Keep a sense of your own breath, but let that movement extend to the movement of your hand. See that the coat starts to 'breathe'. Keep it very much connected to your own breath – just the hand, not the whole arm breathing. Now amplify the sound of your breath.

Slowly keeping the breath, raise up the coat, but don't leave contact with the ground. Have a look around now at the other coats. You will see that by giving them breath there is already a sense of life around the coats.

With hand still inside coat, bring it upright and scrunch head area and hold a sleeve. Choose three points of focus and explore those with your creature/puppet. If it's interested it might use its arm to move towards it. Keep it very specific. Stillness is also very important. Only have the three points of focus, and make it a very distinct turn of focus. Remember your focus as puppeteer is the puppet, not what the puppet is looking at.

Does your puppet have a voice/sound?

Don't try to do too much at the same time – i.e., do the head movement, then arm, then another movement, not all at the same time. Have real clarity of focus and intention in what you are doing.

Introduce your puppet to the puppet next to you. Your focus is your puppet, don't forget. How do they feel about meeting each other? Don't forget the sense of breath – i.e., you are always giving some sense of life to your creature.

Now you have met the puppet next to you, have a dance together!

GROUP SCENE WORK

Exercise One
Get into groups of five. Each group is given one type of material and asked to develop a short piece depicting the first scene of the play. Each group has twenty minutes to devise the piece.

The object of this exercise is to force the groups to explore all the different possibilities their material possesses for puppetry, animation and visual storytelling. It also illustrates how simple, effective and powerful such storytelling techniques can be.

You could experiment with objects like: polystyrene balls, fabric, bamboo sticks, paper. One person in each group should be an outside eye/director as this can prove particularly important, especially when working with puppetry and object animation.

Exercise Two
Working in groups of five, use a variety of materials to create a short piece depicting a transformation as part of

the story. The object of this exercise is to explore the integration of a variety of materials as well as puppetry and visual techniques for storytelling. These could inform the whole production.

Puppetry devices can be used to great effect in the exploration of scale. In *The Peach Child* there are many opportunities to work with scale – e.g., the small warrior versus the giant.

SHADOWS

Many possibilities for storytelling can be realised using shadow work/puppetry. All that is needed is a large white screen, a stretched sheet, with an overhead projector behind it. Try the following:

- A person walking behind the screen. This works particularly well in profile and if the person moves with slow, deliberate movements. You can also work with scale. As the person walks towards the light they get bigger on the screen and vice versa. Add another person and you can perform the warrior meeting the giant.

- Try putting things on top of the projector – e.g., acetate colours and cut-out shapes can create locations and landscapes. Hands and objects can become creatures. Cut-out characters can defy gravity and go on a journey through 360 degrees. With all these techniques you will be working with the reverse mirror image.

- Water in a glass tray on top of the overhead projector can create wonderful backdrops and underwater effects. Ripple the water. Create bubbles. Add food colour and oil to get swirly colours.

- Sand in a tray is slightly different, since it reveals paths of light by just drawing a finger through it.

- Instead of using the fixed light of the projector to light the shadow-screen, try hand-held lights, such as a halogen bulb on a stick or torches with coloured gels over the tops. Experiment with all the different effects you can get as the light sources move and/or your subject moves. Maybe try two or three hand-held light sources. This technique can be very good for dream and time sequences.

THE LITTLE ANGEL THEATRE

The Peach Child was developed by the Little Angel Theatre in Islington, London, a puppet theatre opened by puppet-master John Wright in 1961 whuch has become known as 'The Home of British Puppetry'. The theatre was specially designed for children and for the presentation of marionette shows. It is the only puppet theatre in the UK that has a double bridge for marionette work. Productions at the Little Angel have used every type of puppet and have drawn their themes, styles and stories from a wide range of cultural traditions. In addition to the Little Angel's own productions, visiting companies from all over the world perform there, giving audiences the opportunity to experience the diversity of this art form. The Little Angel also houses a workshop space for puppet-making and has a large education and participation programme.

USEFUL BOOKS AND DVDS

Dictionary of Puppetry, A. R. Philpott (Macdonald/Plays Inc).

Worlds of Shadows: Teaching with Shadow Puppetry, David Wisniewski and Donna Wisniewski (Teacher Ideas Press, Greenwood).

The Puppetry Handbook, Anita Sinclair (Richard Lee).

Puppetry and Puppets: An Illustrated World Survey, Eileen Blumenthal (Thames and Hudson).

Wolfgang Amadeus Mozart, *Bastien und Bastienn/Der Schauspieldirektor*, Salzburger Marionettentheater, staged and designed by Thomas Reichert (Deutsche Grammophon, 4400734244).

USEFUL WEBSITES

www.sagecraft.com/puppetry

www.theworldthroughwoodeneyes.co.uk

www.amoros-augustin.com/accueil.html
   (an inspirational shadow puppet company)

www.youtube.com/watch?v=2Mow_6C-7Y4
   (large and very well-operated street puppets

www.puppeteersuk.com

www.puppetcentre.org.uk

*From a workshop led by Peter Glanville,
Artistic Director, Little Angel Theatre,
and puppeteers Susan Dacre and Nigel Luck
with notes by Leonie Dodd*

SCENES FROM FAMILY LIFE

Mark Ravenhill

Mark Ravenhill's plays include *Shopping and Fucking*, *Faust is Dead*, *Handbag*, *Some Explicit Polaroids* and, at the National, *Mother Clap's Molly House*, and, for 'Connections', *Totally Over You* and *Citizenship*. Recent plays include *The Cut* at the Donmar Warehouse, *pool (no water)* for Frantic Assembly, and *Dick Whittington and His Cat*, the Barbican's first pantomime. His seventeen-play cycle *Shoot, Get Treasure, Repeat* was given readings at the Edinburgh Festival in August 2007 and full productions in London in 2008.

Author's Note

I wanted to write a play about teenagers wanting to have babies and their desire to do so, rather than it being a play about unwanted teenage pregnancy. I began to understand that for many young people today the desire to have children and a family was overwhelming. As Lisa in the play says: 'I've wanted to have this baby since I was thirteen.'

As with many of the characters in the play, we notice from an early age that they're trying to create a structure to their lives. This is something I feel is a natural response to the world we live in – a world that has become too chaotic and has lost a sense of structure. Additionally, the play asks the question 'What is normality? What is this desire we often have as humans to feel normal?' In this instance the desire to have children or to have someone or something to care for seems to be an overriding theme and for the characters to achieve a 'normality' to their existence.

Scenes from Family Life bears certain similarities to my own upbringing. The world of the play is the world of a familiar council estate and the characters' often limited aspirations. I had always imagined the play to be set in a modern-day context and as the action becomes more surreal, the setting and environment could also become less realistic and more theatrical. Jack's metamorphosis into an animal is in many ways symbolic of there being nothing left in the world for him but to confront his loneliness.

Characters

Jack

Lisa

Stacy

Barry

Holly

Karen, Janine, Amy, Marta, Marie
a group of their female friends
from Holly's baby shower

Ryan
Holly's boyfriend

Three Soldiers

Mother
with an empty pram

Entertainer

A large group of
Parents and **Babies**

All the characters are aged sixteen to eighteen

Setting

Living room of Jack and Lisa's flat

For Marcus Nicolai

SCENE ONE

Living room of Jack and Lisa's flat.

Jack What's going on in your head?
Lisa Oh . . . I don't know.
Jack What you thinking?
Lisa Well . . .
Jack Tell me.
Lisa Well . . . happiness.
Jack Yeah?
Lisa Yeah. Happiness. You. Me. Baby.
Jack That all?
Lisa Yeah. That's all.
Jack You sure . . . ?
Lisa I can't tell you every feeling and –
Jack I want a feel.
Lisa Go on then.

Jack reaches out and touches Lisa's stomach.

Jack Oh yeah. Head and feet and . . . Tiny, but
  somewhere there's . . .
Lisa You thought of names?
Jack Not yet. Don't want to jinx it. Too soon. Barry and
  Stace in't chosen and they're in month eight. What's it
  feel like?
Lisa Different.
Jack Does it send you messages and stuff? Through your
  body?
Lisa I dunno. Maybe. Yeah.
Jack What messages? Tell me the messages. You gotta
  know.

423

Lisa No. You ready to be a dad?

Jack Totally ready. My mum, she says we're too young but I say I got a job, Lisa's got a job, we got the flat, it's time. I love you.

Lisa And I love you.

They kiss.

Jack Together for ever. Got you now.

Lisa Love it. Love you. See . . . there's a world out there of people and they're all odd. They seem odd. They have, like, freak-outs on buses and stuff. Talk to themselves. Punch strangers. I can't handle that. You're normal, aren't you?

Jack Reckon.

Lisa That's why I picked you. I gotta have a totally normal baby father.

Jack Come here.

Lisa Yeah?

They hug.

Jack You big kid. I'll get the tea.

Exit Jack. Whoosh, flash. Lisa vanishes into thin air. Re-enter Jack.

Lisa do you want white or the . . .? Lees? Lees? Lisa?

Pause.

Lisa?

Pause.

Lisa!

Pause.

LISA?

He hunts around the room.

424

Jack I'm gonna find you and when I find you I'm gonna . . .
Lisa?

He goes and checks in the bedroom.

(*Off.*) Lisa!

He enters from the bedroom.
She reappears – a re-materialisation.

Jack Oh my – Oh, my, oh, oh –
Lisa What? What?
Jack I . . . There was nothing there. It was frightening.
There was like this gap where a person should be and
I was calling out but there was nothing there. And
then you were there.
Lisa Stop messing around.
Jack I'm not, I – Lees. Where do you go? Where you just
been? Tell me.
Lisa Don't be silly. Forget it. Trick of the light. Kiss me.
Jack Listen, I . . . can't.
Lisa You're scared of me.
Jack No, just, I –
Lisa You are. You're scared of me.
Jack Of course if you can just –
Lisa I'm solid – I'm real – you see – you see – touch me –
touch me – what do you feel?
Jack Yeah, solid, real, yeah.
Lisa So I'm here. Nothing happened. Nobody's running
away. Nobody's fading. I'm here with you. We're gonna
have the baby together. We're gonna be together –
forever. Yeah?
Jack Lees. I'm not making it up. You did do it. You
vanished. Faded away and then . . . You're not gonna
do it again?
Lisa This is mad.
Jack I want you to stop doing that. I don't like it. Stop it.
Lisa I'm not doing anything.

Jack There's a place up there or down there or in there
or . . . somewhere, and you went there. You vanished.
You went somewhere. You came back. Tell me.

Lisa I've had enough of this. I've wanted this baby ever
since I was thirteen and now you, you – I'm going out.

Jack Where?

Jack Where?

Lisa I don't know. A mate's. Barry and Stacy's. Or
Holly's. She's having her baby shower. Everyone turns
up with presents now she's not far off. Yeah – Holly's.
I'll go there.

Jack No. I won't let you. Stay here. With the current
circumstances . . .

Lisa There are no . . .

Jack I'll look after you. Stay. Stay. Stay in the house.
How we gonna look after baby if you don't stay in the
house?

Lisa How can we if you keep going mad? We're
incompatible. You and me, we're –

*Whooshing, flashing, etc. Jack rapidly gets out his
mobile phone. Starts video recording. Lisa vanishes.*

Jack You're not gonna get me. I'll sort this. Come back,
Lees!

Whooshing flashing, etc. Lisa reappears.

Jack You did it again.

Lisa No, I never I –

Jack You did. Look.

*Jack rewinds the images, indicates to Lisa to have a
look on the phone.*

Lisa This is stupid, I'm not gonna just –

Jack Look when I tell you to look.

Reluctantly, she looks.

Lisa . . . Oh my God. Thin air and then I . . . Hold me.
Oh babe.

Jack (*holds her*) You see? Should have trusted me. I don't
lie. When I tell you something you have to believe me.

Lisa Am I solid now? I feel solid.

Jack You are. You're solid now. And I'm looking after
you.

Lisa What we gonna do? If I'm the kind of person who
just vanishes – I don't wanna be the kind of person
who just vanishes. I never heard of that . . . people
who just . . . oh. I want to be here for ever. You. Me.
Baby. For ever.

Jack Won't let you go again. I'm gonna put a stop to it.

Lisa Yeah?

Jack Find a way. You are never gonna leave my sight.

Doorbell.

Answer it. I'll watch you.

*They answer it. Enter Barry and Stacy, who is eight
months pregnant.*

Barry Will you tell her, will you tell her –?

Stacy Watch Barry. Just watch. That's what I'm doing.
Watching him all the time. In case –

Barry Will you two tell her –? Will you tell her – she's
got this idea, she's got this really stupid –

Stacy It's not a stupid –

Barry She says that I'm – listen to this, right? – vanishing.
Can you believe that? She says –

Stacy You do.

Barry I don't.

Stacy You do. You fade in front of my eyes – you go to
nothing. You leave me alone. There's gaps. It's been . . .
I can't sleep. Lie in bed. Look at him on the pillow.
Fading. Empty bed. Coming back. I'm not eating now.
Baby's calling out inside for food but still I can't . . .

Barry Will one of you, both of you, tell her that she is mad? Hormones.

Stacy I'm not –

Barry People don't just vanish. I try but I – it's the baby playing with her hormones, she doesn't . . . When women are pregnant they get these . . . your head gets muddled up. You cry and then you're happy and then I vanish. Few days you'll be happy again. Why don't you two go round Holly's baby shower? Jack – footie's starting.

Jack Barry, mate –

Barry Yeah?

Jack It's true. People vanish. Lisa's doing the same. I've seen her disappear.

Barry Jesus. World's gone mad.

Jack I never thought till today. But I've seen it. You can just . . . lose people. Look.

He shows Barry and Stacy the phone clip.

Barry . . . Oh my God . . . Is that what I . . . ?

Stacy Just the same. Same as you.

Barry Is this real?

Lisa Yeah. Real.

Barry But . . . I want to be in this world. All the time. I don't want to miss stuff.

Jack Maybe you're aliens.

Lisa You reckon?

Jack You go out with someone, you live with someone . . . You get pregnant with someone . . . and then . . . this. Aliens or ghosts. Secrets.

Lisa Hold me.

Jack Not now.

Lisa I'm not choosing to go – do you choose . . . ? I wouldn't choose . . . I want to be with you.

Stacy (*to Barry*) What if you vanish when the baby's born? Can't have you vanishing once the baby's born.

That's not a role model. I want a two-parent family.

Barry Course.

Stacy I gotta have . . . That's what it's about, isn't it?
A mum and a dad. I'm not gonna be a sad cow
pushing a kid round by myself. That's not what I want.

Lisa We're not aliens or ghosts. Stupid. Hold me. I think
we'd know if we were aliens or ghosts, wouldn't we?
And we'd let you know, so don't . . . Hold me. Hold
me. Hold me. I'm totally frightened. Don't just look at
me like that, staring. Come and hold me.

Jack . . . I can't. Not yet, babe. Sorry.

Lisa Oh. I just can't take this. It's doing my head in. I got
a kid on the way. Hold me. Kiss me. Kiss me. Kiss me.

Jack No. I don't know what you are.

Whoosh, flash. Lisa and Barry disappear.

Jack Oh.

Stacy Barry! Barry! This is doing my head in.

Jack How many times it's happened to you?

Stacy Four, five times since breakfast. This is my sixth.

Jack Does it get any easier?

Stacy No. Still hurts. In your gut. Your heart. Whatever.
Miss him.

Jack Yeah. Like they're punishing us. I couldn't ever get
used to a vanishing person.

Stacy Maybe we'll have to.

Jack I'm not. I gotta take control.

Stacy But if this is, like, the way it's gonna be –

Jack Then I just can't handle the way it's gonna be.

Stacy Well, at least I'll have the kid if Barry goes.

Jack If it's a stayer. Maybe the kid'll be a vanisher too.

Stacy Don't.

Jack If the dad's a vanisher then maybe the kid's a
vanisher too.

Stacy Stop. Stop. Scaring me.

Jack You still want it?

Stacy Yeah, only . . .

Jack You'll cope whatever, won't you? Vanisher or stayer?

Stacy I suppose, I don't . . . This is so new. Vanishers. Stayers. I didn't know there was a difference when I woke up this morning.

Jack We're not all the same. Terrible, innit?

Stacy Yeah. Terrible.

Jack This could be rest of our lives.

Stacy No. That's is too much. That is gonna drive me mad. I can feel my mind turning. I'm losing it. Losing it. Arrgghhh! Panic attack!

Jack Come on. Sssh. Sssh. They'll be back. Let me hold you. Come on. I'm here. We'll find out what's going on. Getting calmer?

Stacy Yeah.

Jack What's Lisa up to – up there? She could be doing anything. Aliens. Aliens experiment on you, don't they? Oh yeah. They abduct you, abduct you up to their spaceship and experiment. They could be putting an alien baby inside her. Taking out my baby and . . . I'm not letting her have an alien baby. I'm taking her up the hospital to get inspected.

Stacy You really having a baby?

Jack Yeah. Until I got a kid, I'm a kid. That's what I reckon.

Stacy Same for me . . . They've not come back.

Jack We're gonna stop this.

Stacy How we gonna . . .?

Jack They'll come back and then if we just hold on to them. Hold on to them really tight and don't let them go.

Stacy For ever?

Jack Well . . .

Stacy You can't just hold on to someone for ever.

Jack We could. Just till the vanishing's over.

Long pause.

Stacy Oh, he's not coming, he's not coming back . . . oh my God, he's not coming back. I've lost him. I had him and now he's gone. I think we should do something. (*To the sky.*) Give him back, send him back, and send him back to us . . . come on! Oh. This is stressing me so much. I'm only two weeks off my due date, I shouldn't be stressing like this. This can't go on for ever. Can't live days like this. What we gonna do? (*Clutches stomach.*) Oh!

Jack What?

Stacy Something. Baby moving.

Jack Can I listen? I'd like to listen. (*He listens.*) Oh yeah. Boy or girl?

Stacy Girl – oooo. Better not be – oooo . . .

Jack What?

Stacy Contractions. No. Not yet. I'm alright. Baz has gotta be here if –

Jack Yeah. I'll look after you if –

Stacy Yeah?

Jack Make sure you're up the hospital and that you know if you start –

Stacy But you're not the dad.

Jack No. I know that.

Stacy It's not the same.

Jack All I'm saying –

Stacy It has to be the dad. It has to be Baz.

Jack But if he's not here –

Stacy He's got to be here. I need him here. I want him here.

Jack Yeah, but all I'm saying, if he's vanished for ever –

Stacy He hasn't. Nobody vanishes for ever. (*Clutches stomach.*) Ooooo.

Jack 'Nother listen?

Stacy It's not a game. I don't want you to.

Jack But it's what I want. (*He leans into her stomach.*)
Dun't sound too bothered that her dad's a vanisher.
Stacy I am.
Jack Listen to baby. She's saying everything's alright.
Stacy Baz!
Jack There's only me and baby to talk to now.

Doorbell rings.

Jack Ignore it.

Doorbell rings again.

Stacy I want to get up the hospital.

Doorbell rings again.

Jack Wait till they've gone.

Doorbell. Banging on door.

Holly (*off*) Jack? Lisa? – it's Holly. You seen Stace?
Something weird's going on. There's sort of vanishings.
Are you there?

*Jack answers the door. Lets in a group of female
friends: Karen, Holly (heavily pregnant), Amy, Marta,
Marie, Janine. A couple of them have babies in buggies.*

Karen Stace – there you are. Listen. We were all round
Holly's house for the baby shower and then Holly
vanished. To nothing.
Holly That's right.
Karen But then Holly came back again, didn't you?
Holly That's right.
Karen But then it was Marie, Janine and baby Tyson, me –
Amy – and me.
Karen One at a time until it was like: who's next? Who's
going to go next? Stick together cos we don't know
who's going to go next. Nothing's solid.
Holly We are seriously frightened.

Holly Started off so happy – me baby shower. Vanishings? That's no world for me kid.

Enter Ryan, Holly's boyfriend, running after them.

Ryan It's happening all over the world, babe.

Holly Yeah?

Ryan Been on the news. Everywhere there's people fading away to nothing. They've got footage from China, America, India – everything. Nobody knows the figures. One in ten. That's what they're saying. One in ten people has already gone but the numbers keep going up – with every minute there's more and more.

Jack There could be nobody left soon.

Holly I wish I wasn't having this baby.

Stacy Don't. We gotta have the babies.

Jack In this world? By the end of today – nobody left.

Marie Let's pray.

Marta What's that gonna do?

Marie We gotta do something. I'm bringing mine up religious. So should you. (*Kneels.*) Oh wise one who created this world and made everything in it and is now taking away everything in it, have pity on us poor children. Spare us spare us spare us.

Marie continues to mutter a prayer under her breath.

Stacy I feel so close. Baby's telling me it wants out.

Jack Yeah?

Stacy It might happen. What if it happens? I don't want to have my baby like this.

Jack Ssssh. Whatever it is – we'll cope. I'll look after you.

Stacy I want Barry. BARRY!

Jack Stace – no – you musn't upset yourself – you'll bring it on – Stace!

Stacy BARRY!

Marie vanishes. General panic.

Holly Marie! Marie! When's it gonna end? This is my baby shower.

Megaphone (*off*) This is the authorities. Stay in your homes. I repeat: stay in your homes.

Janine Oh my God.

Megaphone Anyone leaving their home without authorisation will be shot. We are investigating the vanishings but you must stay in your homes.

Enter two Soldiers.

Soldier One Whose flat is this?

Jack Mine.

Soldier One The military has taken control. This country is now under military control.

Stacy Please. My baby's very close, I need to get to a –

Soldier One My orders say you stay here.

Stacy I want the hospital. Tell him, Jack. The hospital!

Jack You'll be alright here.

Stacy No, I won't I – I gotta get out – ah!

Soldier One (*raising gun*) Keep calm.

Jack Listen to what he says, Stace.

Soldier Two No harm will come to you if you do exactly as the army say.

Holly Come on, Stace – take it easy.

Jack I want to help sort out the emergency. What can I do?

Soldier Two Well . . . We are requisitioning a number of houses in which to herd the civilian population. I suppose . . .

Jack Use my flat. A suitable centre for civilians.

Soldier Two It's a bit small . . .

Jack Under the circumstances.

Soldier Two Alright. Let's use this place.

Soldier One (*who's been listening on an earpiece*) Shall I bring in the civilians?

Jack Yeah, definitely. Bring them in.

Soldier One (*calls off*) In here.

Soldier Two Your home is to be the base for the parents'
and babies' group. This way, this way.

*Soldier Three marches in a huge range of different
parents and babies: single parents and couples, papooses
front and back, and buggies, prams – some with twins,
triplets. The noise of crying babies fills the air.*

Jack That's it – make room, make room – if you squeeze
in – you gotta make room.

Stacy I don't want all them people.

Soldier One (*pointing gun*) Calm and orderly – that's it.

Stacy Take 'em away.

Holly Army orders, Stace,

Jack Room for everyone.

Finally everyone is in, but it's a very tight squeeze.

Soldier One (*with megaphone*) Right. Everyone sit down.
We have to keep order. We have to keep control. Each
parent must take responsibility for controlling their
baby. No baby is to crawl or in any way move from
their buggy or papoose. It is vital that we keep calm.

Jack Let's organise entertainment. (*On megaphone.*)
While the world crisis is being sorted, the babies have
got to be entertained. Can anyone juggle, dance or
offer any skills that might amuse the babies?

A man or woman comes forward.

Wo/Man Me.

Jack Right, entertain the babies.

Soldier Three That's an order.

*The Wo/man begins to breakdance or juggle, or play
the ukulele – or anything else that might entertain a
large crowd of parents and babies – but after a while:
whooshing, flashing, etc.*

Most of the people in the room vanish. There's just Jack, Stacy, a young Mother and a Soldier with an empty pram and a couple more parents and babies left. Panic.

Soldier One Quiet. Quiet. We'll wait here for further orders. Remain calm. (*To mouthpiece.*) Hello? Hello? It's just me and a small group of civilians left. Hello? Is there anyone out there?

Jack How's your baby doing?

Mother My baby? There's no baby. Look. The pram's empty. Look. Vanished. She was three weeks old. Now – empty. Me gut hurts now.

Jack It'll all come right. We'll sort it.

Mother You don't know.

Jack I don't – no – but . . .

Mother You? You're a kid. You don't speak my language. You got kids or you haven't got kids. And if you haven't got a kid you don't speak the language. I used to wander round the park looking at all them mums going: I'm a kid, I'm a kid. Got to be a mum, not a kid. Her dad was only around for a couple of weeks. But he did the job. All I needed.

Jack Yeah – but –

Mother Sorry. Kid. You don't understand.

Jack Maybe. But I'll understand – yeah. Very soon I'll understand when Lisa –

Mother You'll never get your chance. You missed your chance. This is it. No more people. No more babies, no more parents. End of the line. Kid.

Jack I'm not having it.

Mother You say your goodbyes. My pram's empty. All I want now is to vanish. Listen to them babies crying. Soon be gone now.

Jack No I've got to have her back. Want my baby. LISA! LISA! LISA!

Soldier One Order, order – we must have order.

Jack Lisa? Lisa?! Come back, come back.

Soldier One (*raises gun*) Steady.

Jack Lisa. I want a baby.

Soldier One Stop or I shoot – you're spreading panic.

Stacy Listen to him, Jack.

Jack But I have to have her. She's everything I need –

Soldier One (*raising gun*) I have permission to shoot troublemakers.

Jack Shoot me then, go on. What's the point? That's my future just vanished. Better shoot me now. They've got babies. You've got babies. That's what I want. Give me a baby. Give me a baby. I want Lisa back so we can have our baby and fill up the world again. I'm not a nutter. Just cos you got your babies. Could be me. Should be me with a baby. Give me a baby. Give me a baby.

Jack goes to grab a parent's baby. They try to fight him off.

Parent My baby. My baby. My baby. Not your baby. Off.

Jack gets the baby.

Jack My baby now. Come on, baby. Look at me.

Soldier One Return the baby (*Gun to Jack.*) Return the baby.

Jack I wanna look after –

Soldier One Return the baby.

Jack hands back the baby.

Parent Animal, you animal. You're a total. (*To baby.*) Alright, alright.

Whoosh, flash – total darkness.

Mother Here we go. We're fading away. All fading away. Yes, yes. Thank you. Thank you. It's the end. We're vanishing.

The room empties of people. Silence. Utter darkness.

Jack Hello? Hello? Anyone there? Anyone at all?

Jack uses a lighter to create a little bit of light.

Is there anyone left? Or am I the only person left in the
world? No, please don't do that. I don't want to be
the only person left in the world. That's horrible. See,
I won't know what to do if it's just me cos I need
people to talk to and to do things with. I don't exist if
there's no one else. I'm nobody without other people.
What are they all doing in the other world? Is there
another world? Come on – take me there – I don't
want to be like this for ever.

*He finds a candle and lights it. He bumps into the
empty pram.*

Jack Pram. Baby. Yes. (*Feeling inside.*) Nothing. No.
Empty pram. Dad to nothing.

Stacy Jack – is that you?

Jack Stace – over here.

Stacy Have they all gone?

Jack I reckon.

Stacy (*calls*) Hello? Hello? . . . They've all gone. . . . Jack –

Jack Yeah?

Stacy I'm contracting.

Jack You mean like . . . ?

Stacy The baby. My contractions.

Jack Are you sure?

Stacy Yeah – oh – oh – yeah – I'm sure.

Jack How long have we got?

Stacy Few hours. Oh. Maybe they'll come back. Maybe all
the doctors and nurses and midwives and everything'll
be back in time.

Jack Maybe.

Stacy Oh. Bigger contractions. (*To sky.*) Please – come

back. All of you – come back . . . Oh. I'm just about to
have . . . Oh – once my waters break, that's it.

Jack Then I'm gonna have to –

Jack cuddles Stacy.

Alright, alright. You . . . breathe and calm and when
you're breathing and calm and – I'll take care of this.

Stacy You can't. They'll be mess and pain and everything.

Jack I know. (*Beat.*) Stace. Do you think this was how it
was meant to be?

Stacy No, I don't. Do you?

Jack I don't . . . Yes. I think this was how it was meant
to be.

Stacy No – this is not supposed to be. This is not normal.
This is . . .

Jack The last thing in the world?

Stacy Yeah.

Jack We're all alone now. Just you and me. Listen to
that. See? If you really listen. Nothing. No babies, no
mums and dads. Nothing. I reckon there's no one.
Anywhere. Just you and me. We're the world. Just us
now.

Stacy And a . . . Oh! New one on the way.

Jack Not a problem.

Stacy No?

Jack No problem. I can deliver a baby.

Stacy Yeah?

Jack It's inside your soul. Doing a birth. Instinct –
human instinct. Every man's got it if he knows how.
I've got the instinct.

Stacy I want a doctor and a midwife.

Jack Lie back, Stace.

Stacy You're not up to this, Jack.

Jack I am.

Stacy Come back, all of you! Come back!

Jack Lie back, Stace. I'm in control. You got to trust me.
I'm gonna be inside you.
Stacy Oh . . .

She gets on all fours with the pain.

Jack Big breaths – come on – listen to me – big breaths –
Stacy So frightened.
Jack No need. I'm here.
Stacy This was supposed to be Baz. A hospital.
Jack Gone. Everything gone. Just me.
Stacy Arrrgggghhh!
Jack I'm everything now.
Stacy I don't want this.
Jack This is the best way. We're having a baby. That's it.
A baby's on the way. Once upon a time there were
people. The world was full of people. But it got too
full of people. Too many of them. So they had to go.
And everything started all over again. With just you
and me.
Stacy No, I –
Jack Lie back and listen. We were chosen, you and me.
Must be. Got to be a reason. We're the special ones.
Chosen to stay behind. And inside you is a special
baby. And tonight is a special night when the special
baby gets born. I'm gonna make that so special for us.
Stacy I – I – I –
Jack Forget the others. All gone now. New start. We're
just beginning. We're gonna fill up this empty pram
today, alright?
Stacy Alright.

SCENE TWO

*The living room, six months later. Jack, and a baby in the
pram.*

Jack (*to baby*) And once upon a time there was a brand new world. And the world had no people. Until – pop – there were two people. And they were called Jack and Stacy. And they were happy but they wanted more people. And then there were three people in the world cos along came a baby. And they called that baby Kelly. You're lovely, aren't you, Kelly? Yes, you are. Your mum's out there hunting somewhere and your mum'll be back soon. And we'll be back together. Family. Cos that's what we are, we're a –

Enter Stacy, with a rucksack on.

Jack Hey. How do you get on?
Stacy Yeah. Not bad.
Jack Baby's good. Took her feed. Nice sleep. Show me what you got.

Stacy opens the rucksack for his inspection of contents.

Jack More beans? It's always beans.
Stacy Yeah. Sorry. But – look.

She holds up a packet of nappies.

Jack Well done. Brilliant. At last.
Stacy Yeah.
Jack You get attacked by them escaped lions again?
Stacy No – there's dogs though. They gone feral. Started hunting in packs. There's a load of them live up the multi-storey car park. You have to watch yourself.
Jack You got blood.
Stacy It's nothing.
Jack Show me.

Stacy shows her hand.

Stacy There was a cat and a load of kittens sat on the nappies. We had a fight.

Jack See. Told you. The animals are still breeding.

Stacy S'pose.

Jack She must have met a tom. We gotta look after that.

Stacy It's nothing.

Jack I'll bandage it.

> *Exit Jack. Stacy takes out a tin of rice pudding from the rucksack and a tin opener and opens the tin. Enter Jack with plaster, TCP, etc.*

Jack You gonna eat that cold?

Stacy I been hunting all day.

Jack Still no sign of any humans?

Stacy No.

Jack See. I told you.

Stacy Got to keep looking.

Jack Six months – if there was anyone else we'd have found them by now.

Stacy I suppose.

Jack Come on, Stace, there can't be –

Stacy Don't you want people? Don't you want the world?

Jack You could have microwaved that.

Stacy This can't be just . . . Why would it just be us?

Jack Luck. Fate.

Stacy A thousand – a thousand thousand – miles – there's someone else.

Jack No. Just you and me and . . . baby. Stace – don't you think we should give her a name?

Stacy No.

Jack I mean six months – 'baby' – it'll stunt her development, something.

Stacy I know, only . . .

Jack How long you gonna wait?

Stacy I want to choose it with Baz.

Jack I don't miss humans. Humans were noisy.

Stacy Those elephants down the road make noise.

Jack Just a few of them. They're lonely. But billions of human beings. That was terrible. It's good that they went.

Stacy Don't you miss Lisa?

Jack Sometimes.

Stacy You were having a kid.

Jack Yeah, well, she's gone now.

Stacy But if you're having a kid –

Jack After six months, you move on.

Stacy Move on? There's nobody to . . . Ugh! She needs her nappy changing.

Jack I'll do it. (*To baby.*) Come on, Kelly, we're going to –

Stacy What did you call her?

Jack Dun't matter.

Stacy You called her something. Kelly?

Jack She needs a name. It's not good for her.

Stacy Oh no, oh no. That is not Kelly, right? That is 'baby'. And I'm not having you doing anything different? Understand? Understand? Give me baby.

Jack I'm gonna –

Stacy Give me baby – now. Come on, baby, let's clean you up.

Stacy and baby exit. Jack opens a box of cornflakes from the rucksack, starts eating with his hands. Whoosh, flash. Barry appears.

Barry Stace? Stace?

Jack Baz? No. You can't come back.

Barry Stace. I want Stacy. Gotta speak to her. She had my baby? Must have been born now. They alright?

Jack Baz, she's –

Barry She had the baby yet, Jack? (*Sees the pram.*) Where's the baby?

Jack Barry, mate –

Barry Stace! You tell Stace I gotta see her. I gotta see my baby. I'm slipping back. You tell her, Jack. Baz is looking for her.

Jack I don't want you here, you can't just . . . Baz, I like this world now. It's brilliant. Perfect. Me, Stacy, baby. Everything. I love that, I can't –

Barry I can't stay now. But I'm coming back. Back for Stacy and my baby.

Whoosh, flash. Barry disappears, Stacy re-enters with baby.

Stacy Where's them fresh nappies?

Jack Stace – let's go somewhere. Now. The whole world's empty. We could live anywhere. Buckingham Palace. Yeah – let's move. Find somewhere else.

Stacy We're fine here. She's used to it.

Jack No – we got to move now. I'll get some things.

Stacy Don't be mad.

Jack Make a head start before it gets dark.

Stacy I'm not going anywhere.

Jack It's dangerous here. It's not safe.

Stacy Alright. You go if you want to.

Jack Stace, you don't understand –

Stacy Go.

Jack By myself?

Stacy Jack, I know what you're up to.

Jack You reckon?

Stacy Playing families.

Jack It's not a game. Pack your bags.

Stacy Well, you're not Dad, see?

Jack I know, but –

Stacy So keep away from her. She's my baby. Mine. You keep off her, Jack. Piss off. Piss off, you – piss off and leave me and my baby in peace. You're a kid and I'm a mum and me and baby don't want you.

Jack Right – I gave you a warning. This is what we're doing. I'm taking charge. We're moving on. Pack a few things and get down here in ten minutes and we move on or I –

Stacy What?

Jack I –

Stacy See? Nothing.

Jack (*grabs her*) This is a perfect world. This is my world. I'm in charge. Not having that ruined. You're not spoiling it for me.

Stacy Get off.

Jack It's just you and me and me and Kelly.

Stacy She's not called –

Jack She's called Kelly.

Jack reaches into the rucksack and pulls out a bread knife.

Jack (*waves knife*) Alright?

Stacy No, I don't wanna –

Jack Somebody's gotta make decisions in this family. She's called Kelly.

Stacy Baby. Baby. Baby. She's called. Baby.

Jack No. Kelly. I name our child Kelly. Kelly – tonight from this moment on, now and for ever more you are christened Kelly. Kelly. Kelly. (*To Stacy, wielding knife.*) Yes? Yes? Yes?

He holds knife to her throat.

Stacy . . . Yes. Kelly.

Jack That's it, Mummy. Say hello to Kelly.

Stacy . . . Hello, Kelly.

Jack Thank you, Stacy. I didn't want to lose it only . . . Stace – I get lonely in my bed.

Stacy Can't help that.

Jack Sleep with me, Stace.

Stacy No.

Jack We don't have to do nothing – just share the bed.

Stacy It'll lead to stuff.

Jack It won't. Last two humans – at least we could share the bed.

Stacy Forget it. It's not gonna happen.

Jack It's gonna happen. Tonight, Kelly – Mummy and Daddy are going to have a lovely meal of all the food that Mummy got up the shops then when Mummy and Daddy are feeling nice and tired they are going to go to a big house somewhere a long way away, somewhere like Buckingham Palace with a big double bed –

Stacy No.

Jack – big double bed, and they're going to take their clothes off and they're going to get into the big double bed. And they'll hold each other all night. Mummy's been too shy since you were born to sleep with Daddy but tonight she's not going to be shy. Tonight she'll get over that and she'll hold Daddy. And maybe if the mood's right they'll have sex. Yeah – maybe if it's an extra special night they'll have sex. Yeah. They'll have sex.

Stacy I'm not gonna do that.

Jack You'll do just what Daddy tells you to do or I'll – because this is all for Kelly, this is all . . . We got to be normal. Normal family. It's what happens. In a normal family – baby's got a name, Mummy and Daddy love each other, Mummy and Daddy have sex, Mummy and Daddy try for another baby.

Stacy No.

Jack Kelly all on her own. Not good. Not right. So we start working on a little brother or little sister for Kelly. We start working on that tonight.

Stacy It's not gonna happen.

Jack It's the normal thing.

Stacy Then I'm not going to be normal.

Jack You are.

He pulls the knife across her cheek.

Stacy Don't, Jack – no. Is there blood?

Jack A bit.

446

Stacy I'll go septic and die.

Jack No.

Stacy Yeah. I'll go septic and die, and then what you gonna do?

Jack I'm here for you. I'm here to look after us all. I'm gonna mend this and then you're gonna pack our stuff and we're gonna move on to our new place.

He dresses her cheeks with TCP and sticks a plaster on each.

Go and pack.

Stacy Can I change baby? Kelly. Don't hurt her. You can hurt me only . . .

Jack I'd never do that. She's everything to me.

Stacy Alright, as long as . . .

Jack I know what's best. I'm Dad.

Stacy Yeah.

Stacy exits with Kelly. Whoosh, flash. Barry appears.

Barry Where's Stace . . . ?

Jack Still . . . a long way away . . . hunting.

Barry My kid. Want to see my kid.

Jack Listen, Baz. I gotta tell you . . .

Barry Yeah?

Jack World's gone bad. Streets are full of wild animals. Baz, it's really bad here. You don't wanna . . . the world's such a bad place. Baz . . .

Barry Yeah?

Jack And . . . it's been six months. World moves on.

Barry Well . . . yeah.

Jack There's no one left in the world, Baz – 'cept me and Stace and Kelly. Oh yeah. We called the kid Kelly.

Barry But I wanted to –

Jack Sorry, mate. I delivered the baby, see, and now . . . we got a bond. Stacy. She's mine.

Barry No.

447

Jack And Kelly – we decided it was best, too confusing, see. Not gonna tell her about the world before, the vanished people. Decided to tell Kelly I'm her dad. Mummy, Daddy and baby.

Barry You bastard.

Jack So the rest of you can stay up there or down there or out there or whatever because we don't want you. You're not wanted here. So you stay right where you –

Barry No!

A fight between the two of them. Barry punches Jack in the stomach. Jack collapses. Barry kicks him.

My kid. My world.

Jack Don't want you. Stay in your world cos this world's better without you. I'm king here.

Whooshing, flashing. Barry vanishes. Jack is winded. Gets up.

Jack Alright, alright, everything's OK. Over now.

Enter Stacy, wearing a coat, and with a shopping trolley, fully loaded with bags, etc.

Jack Good girl. I don't like forcing you.

Stacy Funny way of . . .

Jack Only sometimes I just see. What's best. For the family.

Stacy Right.

Jack You'll like Buckingham Palace.

Stacy I'll do what you say.

Jack Stace – you gotta love me.

Stacy That an order?

Jack That should come natural.

Stacy Well – it's not natural.

Jack Give it time.

Stacy No. Anything you want you'll have to use that (*knife*).

Jack If I have to.

Stacy Yeah, you'll have to.

Jack Kelly's gonna have her own apartments when she's older. Her own wing. Kensington Palace.

Stacy Let her choose.

Jack She'll need guiding. Wagons roll.

Jack puts baby in the pram starts to push it.

Come on, Kelly. New home. New start.

Stacy Oh I –

Stacy staggers.

Jack What?

Stacy I – I – I –

She collapses.

Jack Gotta move. Gotta move on. Come on. Gotta get up. Come on.

Stacy Jack – I'm – oh!

Flashing. Brief vision of the hordes of the vanished.

Vanished
We are the vanished
We were once in the world
But now we're not in the world
Everyone gone
And we claim you.

They all point to Stacy. Whooshing. Dies down. Stacy has vanished. Just Jack and the baby left.

Jack Right. Right.

Pause.

(*To baby.*) Just you and me. Which is . . . this is . . . STACY? STACE?

Pause.

Just you and me. That's . . . yes . . . that's good.

Long pause.

Once there was a new world. And there was just me in it.
And I was all alone. And I grew up. And then one day
this baby – pop. I called her Kelly. I looked after her.
I fought off the animals. I hunted. I had meaning. I was
a king and there was a princess.
That's good, isn't it? We're the first and one day there'll be
– pop pop pop – from nowhere, more babies, but until
then . . .
Yeah. You and me. Empty world.
Always knew really – here – the gut – this was what my
life was – me – a kid – no one else – always knew that
was it.
Had a girlfriend once. What was she? Lees . . . Lees . . .
forgotten . . . forgotten . . . long time ago.
She didn't matter. Nobody mattered. 'Cept you and me.
This was what I wanted. All the others gone. Me and my
baby.

Goes to door.

Lions on the street. Shit. Looking hungry.
Right. We'll . . . sleep here tonight. We'll move on in the
morning.
Night, Kelly. (*Leans into pram, kisses baby.*) Night.
And we all slept sound, cos we were the only two in the
world and there was no fighting.

*Jack lies down to sleep, closes his eyes. Flashing,
whooshing. Jack leaps up.*

Kelly!

*Brief vision of Stacy and Barry carrying away the
baby.*

Don't take her, please.
Stacy But she's ours.

Jack You don't need her. There's millions in your world.

Stacy She came out my body.

Barry I'm the dad.

Jack But over there – the vanished – millions of you – but here – me – there's just me and her. Leave me her.

Stacy Can't have what don't belong to you, Jack.

Jack But this is the real world.

Stacy Not any more – we've all gone to the new world now. Passed through the door. This is just the old one.

Barry Come on, love, we got to go.

Jack Don't take her, no, don't. Love her like nothing I –

Stacy Bye, Jack.

Jack (*rushes with knife*) Give me give me give me.

Barry and Stacy raise a hand each. Power crackles from their palms, slamming Jack away from them. The knife falls from his grasp.

Stacy Thanks for doing the delivery, Jack, you were brilliant.

Barry Time to go.

Jack I'm not going to let you go. STOP! STOP!

He rushes and grasps at them. The crackle of energy. He falls, as dead.

Stacy Jack? Jack? Is he dead? The shock, he's . . . We might have killed him. Oh, Jack.

Barry We got to go back.

Stacy I want to stay. Oh, Jack. Jack. Jack. Wake up, Jack.

Barry Come away now.

Stacy I can't.

Barry You have to. Me, the baby. Stacy – what are you going to . . . ? You gonna stay here with him? Or you coming to your family?

Stacy . . . Sorry, Jack.

451

Whooshing, flashing. Jack is alone. He lies still for a while. Then he comes round .

Jack What is this place? (*Inspects pram.*) . . . Empty pram. Empty world.

Long pause.

The day that Jack was born . . . Yeah. I'll tell that one. The day that Jack was born.
I was born into this place of the animals and of the shops and the food and the houses.
And I was the only person. The first and the last.
And so I never thought about it. How could I ever think . . . ?
    If you never knew there were others, then . . .
    But sometimes I dreamt, I imagined there were others.
    Somewhere – others.
But . . . no. Can't remember the names of any others.
Can't remember anything the others ever did.
Something in this. (*Pram.*) Must have been something in this? What was it called? I. I. I. Can't remember.
But that was fantasy. Because the world is just me. Now and for ever. And on and on and good good good.
Only ever me.
So why the . . . (*pram*)?
A thing from long ago.

Beats the pram rhythmically.

Don't need you pram. Never need you pram. Don't know what you're for, pram. You're for nothing, pram.
Nothing. Nothing. Nothing. You are . . . a dead thing.

Kicks over the pram, carries on kicking it.

You are a totally dead thing.
    I am everything.
    I am the world.
    I am King.

So I . . .
Hunt. Eat. Sleep. Move on. This is my world.
And I . . .
No, if there were never others then there's no
     loneliness.
No lone— lone— lo— lo—
Lugh. Lugh. Lugh. Lee. Negh. Sssssss.
No feelings like . . . no feelings just –
(*A howl of emotion.*) Ooowwww!
(*Ape-like.*) Ugh ugh ugh.

He's becoming more animal, his centre of gravity moving down.

I ugh oh a oh a ooo m a ugh.
Me.
Me.
Me.

Pattern of movement, almost dancing.

Me.
Me.
Me.
And I.
And I.
And I.

Onto all floors, snuffling and whining. A great animal howl.

Hunt. Attack. Defend. Me.

Flashing, whooshing. Soldier One appears.

Soldier One Hello? Hello? (*To walkie-talkie.*) Anyone there? I'm back in the world. I've left the vanished. Is anyone else back? Am I on my own? Hello? Hello? I need orders. Am I on my own? Hello?

Jack snarls.

What the – ?

Jack growls, squats, ready to attack.

Steady. Alright – easy, easy. Don't be frightened. I'm a human. What are you?

Jack bares his teeth.

Animal. Now listen – I don't want to harm. Find civilians. Find a superior. Bring back order.

Jack snarls and barks.

I'm going now to bring order to the world.

Jack leaps and blocks Soldier's path.

I have to bring order to the world.

Jack is preparing to attack.

Step aside, or I will fire. You must not prevent me. It's vital the world is –

Jack comes from very close, snapping.
  Soldier One goes to fire.

You had your warning.

  Jack leaps at Soldier One, biting at him and snarling. A tussle on the ground. Jack is biting at the Soldier. The gun falls from the Soldier's hand. He retreats.

You've drawn blood – you animal. (*To walkie-talkie.*) Please – is there anyone there? Anyone out there I –?

  Soldier Two runs in from the street. Jack snarls.

Soldier Two Get back.
Soldier One Mate. It's not just me.
Soldier Two We're all coming back. People on the streets. World's filling again. What's that? (*Jack.*)

Soldier One I dunno. Looks human, but –

Jack has retreated. Whooshing, flashing.

Soldier Two Here we go. Told you. They're coming back!

The room begins to fill up with the vanished. Soon the room is full of the parents and babies, the soldiers, the friends and Barry, Stacy and Lisa. Everyone is talking, calling out. Mother with the empty pram steps forward.

Mother My kid. My kid. Where's my kid?

She disappears into the crowd, searching.
Jack is whimpering on the floor.

Lisa Jack.
Soldier One Keep away from him.
Lisa He'll know me.
Soldier One He doesn't know anything. Keep away.
Soldier Two What shall we do with him?
Soldier One Feral. Mad. Let me shoot him.
Soldier Two No – keep him there. We'll have him put away. (*On megaphone.*) Attention, everyone. Give me your attention. I have received instructions that it is over. The emergency is now over. The vanished have returned. You are to go back to your homes. There will be a period of transition in which the army will be guiding you. But democracy will return. Back to your homes. Go back home. Normality will be restored. The world is normal again.
Soldier Three Alright – come along everybody – back to your homes.

The room is clearing.

Lisa (*to Soldier One*) Let me talk to him.
Soldier One No point, he's an animal.
Lisa Please. Jack, it's me – Lisa. Do you know me – Lisa?

Jack Mmmmgrrrmmrrr.

Lisa Lisa.

Jack I. Me. Duh. Duh. Mad. Mad.

Lisa You're not mad, Jack. Look at all the people. Babies.

Jack Uh grrrroooo ooo.

Lisa No, Jack, speak words – I want a human. (*To Soldier One.*) Leave me with him.

Soldier One If he attacks –

Lisa I'll call the army.

Soldier One moves away.

Jack Grrrrrrr. Grrrrrrrr.

It's just Jack, Lisa, Barry, Stacy and the Mother with the empty pram.

Mother I got no baby. Pram's empty.

Lisa What you gonna do?

Mother Search. It hasn't vanished.

Lisa Could have.

Mother No. I'm a mother. I've gotta find her.

Exit Mother.

Lisa Jack. We're all back . . . Are you human? Come on –

Jack Human words. Please, Jack. I want a human.

Stacy Jack – what's happened to you?

Jack Grrrrrrrrrrrrrr.

Stacy You're frightening.

Barry Come on, love. Keep away.

Stacy Oooo. Felt something. I reckon this baby might come early.

Barry Shall we pick names?

Stacy Tonight?

Jack But you – you – you –

Stacy What's he saying?

Barry I don't know.

Jack You – you – you

Lisa What is it, Jack?
Jack You already – you had the baby already. I was there.
Lisa Don't, Jack.
Stacy Course I haven't – look. (*Shows her stomach.*)
Jack I lied attacked animal. I.
Barry Don't remember anything, mate.
Lisa We've been somewhere else.
Jack But you had a baby and you came back to –
Barry I don't remember –
Stacy It didn't happen.
Barry Come on, love. You need your rest.
Stacy Yeah. Night.

Exit Barry and Stacy.

Jack But but but but –
Lisa Alright, Jack. You're safe now. No one remembers. It's OK.

SCENE THREE

Lisa and Jack's living room, a year later. There's a pram. Jack is looking inside. Enter Lisa. She holds a wrapped-up present. She stands watching him.

Lisa How long you gonna stand there?
Jack I don't know.
Lisa You know how long you been there already?
Jack No.
Lisa Three hours now. He's not going anywhere.
Jack I know. But . . . new baby.
Lisa You never ate.
Jack I'm happy just watching.
Lisa You're mad.
Jack No. Our baby. You proud?
Lisa Course.

Jack Glad it was all normal – after all the vanishing and that.

Lisa Everything's normal. The whole world's normal. Everything totally back to normal.

Jack Yeah.

Lisa You coming round Baz and Stacy's?

Jack I want to stay here.

Lisa Come on – Lorraine's first birthday. You got to go to that. Baz and Stace are expecting you. Janine'll be round to babysit any minute.

Jack I just want to stay here.

Lisa He'll survive without you for a bit.

Jack I just like imagining what's going on in his head.

Lisa And . . .? What's in his head?

Jack All sorts. Other worlds.

Lisa Sign the card.

She hands him the card.

Jack Lorraine. That's a stupid name. Who calls a kid *Lorraine*?

Lisa It's not bad. You wanna tell Baz and Stace? What would you call her?

Jack What could I call her? I'd call her . . . Don't know. I suppose Lorraine's alright.

He signs, hands her the card.

Lisa I'm gonna go. Be back in time to feed him. You sure you're not coming?

Jack Lees. Where did you go?

Lisa I told you.

Jack I can't get it out of my head. Please. I was the only one. Where were you?

Lisa Like I said. Nowhere. Emptiness. It's a blank.

Jack Think. Underworld? Spaceship?

Lisa You can ask as many times as you like. When you vanish, there's nothing.

Jack Maybe you'll get flashes or dreams or . . .?

Lisa Jack. Empty.

Jack It'll come back. One day you'll know what there is.

Lisa Maybe.

Jack You'll tell me. It's important.

Lisa I gotta go. You don't have to stand there the whole time.

Jack I want to.

Lisa You'll frighten him.

Jack How can I frighten him? I'm his dad.

Lisa Still . . . What did you do?

Jack Eh?

Lisa Six months on the planet. What did you do?

Jack I don't know . . .

Lisa You're the only human being who knows. Stacy knows nothing.

Jack I –

Lisa Yeah?

Jack Did what I could to survive. Went out hunting. Did what I could for Stace and the baby, for Lorraine. I kept things going. Fought. Protected.

Lisa Like an animal?

Jack You have to. Do you think it was aliens?

Lisa Stop.

Jack Maybe if you tried drawing or . . .

Lisa Just stop.

Jack Hypnosis to –

Lisa Stop. Stop. Stop. Listen. You are never going to know. Face it. It's not going to –

Jack The mother of my – everyone's been there. Secret. And I don't know it. It's impossible. Can't live with that.

Lisa There's no choice.

Jack I want to see inside their heads, their memories –

Lisa No.

Jack Cut 'em open: where did you go? Where did you go? Where did you go?

Lisa Stop it, Jack – you're horrible.

Jack How am I supposed to spend the rest of my life with you if you got a secret?

Lisa I'm going to Baz and Stace's. I won't be long. Janine'll be here any minute. If you want to come on –

Jack Maybe later.

Lisa Alright.

Exit Lisa. Jack watches the pram for a while, then picks up the baby from the pram.

Jack And everyone in the world had a secret. Everyone had been to the same place. And one day Daddy was going to find out where that place was.

Doorbell rings.

Sssssh. Sssssh. Keep quiet till they go away.

Doorbell rings again.

Sssssh. Soon be over.

Doorbell rings.

Janine (*off*) Jack? Lisa? I'm here for the babysitting. Jack. Lisa. Hello?

Long pause.

Jack That's it. Just you and me for ever more. Sssshhhh.

The End.

Production Notes

SCENE ONE

The beginning of play to Lisa's first vanishing:

- What is Jack and Lisa's existing relationship?
- How many months pregnant is Lisa?
- What is Lisa's attitude towards Jack?
- How long has Lisa felt the way she has about Jack?
- Out of one to ten, how much does Jack want a baby?
- Out of one to ten, how much does Lisa want a baby?
- What's the flat like that Jack and Lisa live in?
- How is it furnished? Is it sparse or is it cluttered?
- Has anything for the flat been passed on to them by their parents?
- Do Lisa and Jack work?
- What are Jack and Lisa's aspirations?
- How long have Jack and Lisa lived together?

Mark: 'I have always felt it necessary to keep this play open to interpretation. However, the background to where they live is, in my mind, a council flats area, and I wanted to make a true observation of the people who live ordinary and simple lives there . . .'

Lisa's vanishing and after:

- What traits are we seeing in Jack's character?
- Does Lisa have a sense of her disappearance?

- How does Jack react to Lisa vanishing?
- Why is Lisa with Jack?
- What has changed in their relationship with the future expectancy of them having a baby?
- What are Jack and Lisa's fears and desires?
- What do they both want from life?
- What does Lisa mean when she talks about 'normality'?
- What do they mean by something being 'real' and 'solid'?
- What does a baby represent for Jack and Lisa?
- What are their ideals?
- How do their desires motor the scene?
- Who instigated Jack and Lisa's relationship?
- What's Lisa's response to being told she has disappeared?

Mark: 'Try some games of parent and child. Hot-seating could be useful here. All the clues you need are in the text.'

Enter Barry and Stacy . . .

- How does Barry and Stacy's entrance affect the scene?
- What energy do they bring to the scene?
- What's the difference between Barry and Stacy's and Jack and Lisa's relationship?
- What does the word 'stayer' mean in the play's context?
- Does the word vanishing have a negative connotation?
- How do you perceive Jack and Stacy's relationship?
- What does Stacy want from Jack?

- Is Jack looking for an immediate replacement from Stacy, following Lisa's vanishing?
- What does a 'long pause' mean in the text?

Roxana Silbert: 'With a pause it often helps to give an actor an internal dialogue – a story to engage an actor to help us (the audience) believe in the truth of the situation.'

Mark: 'I wrote a long pause because I feel Stacy is really willing Barry to come back and thus needs emphasising . . . Try different lengths of pause and see what you find . . .'

Enter Karen, Amy, Tony, Marta, Marie and Janine . . .

- What religion is Marie practising?
- Has Marie always been religious or has she suddenly decided to become religious?
- What is a baby shower?
- What could the costumes be for the baby shower?
- Who is Holly's role model?
- Are these characters happy to be pregnant?
- What time of year is it?

EXERCISE   A good exercise is to ask the actors who they think their character's role-model is and to act it in a short improvisation.

NOTE   A 'baby shower' is an American idiom. Female friends come round to have a party and 'shower' presents on the future mother.

Mark: 'Marie's religious practice could vary in accordance with your school's social and religious status . . .'

Arrival of the soldiers . . .

- What do the soldiers represent?
- What happens when the soldiers arrive?
- What are the staging challenges when the mothers and babies enter?
- How can you differentiate between the mother and the other characters, if the actors are the same age?
- How can you create chaos and at the same time have order on stage?

Mark: 'The soldiers represent the authority which is here to maintain order – they represent an element of state control. They are also incorporated into the play to add to the dramatic element of the vanishings that are occurring . . . They could be young, as in Iraq – say seventeen.

'The mother should be of the same age as the rest of the cast and it's more important to focus on her status and qualities as a character . . . In many ways the mother is the most realistic character in the play.

'The show provided by the children's entertainer should be a joyful and vibrant moment and can include unique or interesting skills that the cast have.'

Jack alone . . .

- Who is Jack talking to when he is alone?
- What does Jack's speech suggest about his vulnerability?

Mark: 'Despite Jack's controlling nature, it's his underlying vulnerability that should make an audience engage in his personal struggle.'

SCENE TWO

- Out of one to ten, how happy is Jack at the beginning of the scene?
- Out of one to ten, how happy is Stacy at the beginning of the scene?
- How do their states differ from those at the beginning of the play?
- How does Barry's appearance affect Jack and his situation with Stacy?
- Is there a change in Stacy, now that she has had a baby?
- What's the significance of having a knife on stage?
- How frightened is Stacy of the knife?
- Do you feel Jack would actually use a knife?
- What are Stacy's needs now that she has had a baby?
- What are the problems of staging a fight on stage?
- How does the arrival of the 'vanished' affect the form of the play?
- What does the vanished world suggest or symbolise to you?
- Why does Jack never vanish?

Mark: 'Jack wants to be a mother more than a father. He is more interested in the mother role.

'At this point in the play, we begin to see that the "vanished" are now beginning to form an identity and a sense of the place where the "vanished" come and go . . .'

Roxana Silbert: 'In my mind, the world of the vanished is a painless world.'

Jack alone and his transformation into an animal . . .

- What do you feel Jack's speech is about?
- How do you keep Jack's speech active?
- Does Jack actively choose or resist becoming an animal?
- How do you achieve an actor becoming an animal on stage?
- Does Jack choose loneliness?

Mark: 'I feel that we (as humans) are "social beings" and not "individuals" and we are governed and formed by our social interaction with others. In the context of the play and in terms of Jack's loneliness, I wanted to ask these questions:

'What is it to be human and to be lonely?

'Do animals feel abandoned or fear loneliness?'

SCENE THREE

- What has changed in the relationship between Jack and Lisa at the end of the play?
- How has the flat changed?

Mark: 'In terms of the vanishings that occur during the play, don't be intimidated by what appears to be a difficult challenge in staging. Keep the vanishings simple to maintain the forward thrust and momentum of the play. Be careful in using stage effects as they may hold up the pace of the play.'

The way in which people vanish on stage affects the story and its message enormously.

What would be the difference if:

- The actor did actually vanish on stage?
- The actor just turned his back to us on stage?
- The actor froze?

Directors should be encouraged to look at various alternatives for the vanishings before making their final decision.

Mark: 'I feel the more you work on the play the funnier it gets. The play should be allowed to be funny . . . so have fun!'

From a workshop led by Roxana Silbert
with notes by Max Key

A VAMPIRE STORY

Moira Buffini

Moira Buffini's plays include, for the National and in the West End, *Dinner*; *Blavatsky's Tower* and *Gabriel* at Soho Theatre; *Silence* at Birmingham Rep; *Loveplay* at the RSC; and *Dying For It* and *Marianne Dreams* at the Almeida. Films include *Presence*, *Gabriel*, *The Enlightenment*, *Dibbuk Box* and *Jane Eyre*.

Author's Note

We love vampires because, of all the gods and monsters we have made in our own image, they are the most feared and the most sympathetic. They have no reflection; yet they hold up a crooked looking-glass through which we can question what it means to be human.

My vampires (if vampires they are) have survived for two hundred years. Perhaps they are sisters. Perhaps they are mother and daughter. Vampires, in our British tradition, are always aristocrats. But mine (if vampires they are) are two females who should never have been vampires in the first place: a prostitute and a schoolgirl.

I started writing convinced that Clara and Eleanor were vampires. But as they emerged on the page, I began to wonder. The pain that they were feeling and denying was so clearly human. It began to seem more and more possible that they were lost girls.

A Vampire Story is a very funny play. But it is not a comedy.

I wrote it for my sisters, Fiona and Nuala, and for my daughter, Bridie.

Characters

Ella
aged sixteen, present day

Eleanor
aged sixteen, nineteenth century

Claire
aged twenty-one, present day

Clara
aged twenty-one nineteenth century

Frank
Briggs
Moon
schoolboys, present day

Debit
Point
schoolgirls, present day

Mint
a drama teacher

Fillet
a food technology teacher

Marianne
a child prostitute

Ruthven
a gambler

Darvell
a stranger

Tina
Frank's mother

Geoff
Frank's father

Letty and **Harriet**
schoolgirls, nineteenth century

Bettina
a maidservant

Mint and Fillet can be played
by male or female actors

Setting

A town, somewhere in Britain.
Present day

Scenes

SCENE ONE

*Eleanor is sixteen. She is dressed in a costume of 1822.
She is on stage almost all the time. There is a small
writing desk where she occasionally sits and writes,
although her focus should always be on the action.*

Eleanor People will always believe the most fabulous tale
you can tell. It's the one that they secretly long for. It
must be unprovable, impossible, fantastical. To believe
it then becomes an act of faith. An act of faith.

Ella Scene One. A Train.

*Ella and Claire are dressed in modern-day clothes. Ella
is sixteen, Claire, twenty-one. Claire is very fashionably
and stylishly attired. Ella dresses as if the whole concept
of fashion is confusing and alien to her.*

Claire Guess what your name is

Ella I can't

Claire Go on

Ella Just tell me

Claire You'll never guess

Ella Don't make me

Claire It's fun

Ella No

Claire Come on, it's interesting

Ella No

Claire I'll give you a clue. My name's Claire

Ella Claire what?

Claire Wythenshawe

Ella Claire Wythenshawe

Claire And you're my little sister, Eleanor

Ella Oh

Claire Isn't that great? I thought you'd be pleased with that

Ella Eleanor Wythenshawe

Claire That's right. And I'm Claire

Ella You found two sisters called Eleanor and Claire?

Claire Fancy that

Ella What happened to them?

Claire Killed in a car crash. Identities there for the taking

Ella What about their parents?

Claire They only had a dad. And I'm afraid he recently died

Ella How?

Claire blandly shrugs.

Don't you feel anything?

Claire Like what?

Ella For them

Claire I feel glad we got away. You didn't think we would, did you?

Ella One day, we won't

Pause.

So where are we going, Claire?

Claire A lovely small town

Ella I told you; no more small towns

Claire They're the best places

Ella They're a nightmare

Claire We're going to a lovely British small town surrounded by beautiful countryside

Ella I'll be sick

Claire No you won't

Ella I'll go mad

Claire You always say that

Ella I'll kill myself

Claire You could try

Ella I could kill you

Claire Then you'd be all alone. I love these small towns, Ella. The people are lovely

Ella So gullible

Claire I've rented us a nice little flat and I'll get a job in a bar or something

Ella You're a very sad person

Claire I thought you had doubts as to whether I was a person at all. (*She looks out of the window.*) Look at those lovely little gardens. The way the sun dapples the patios. They've planted magnolias in the multiplex car park – and the bins – they're rainforest green. It's going to be good for us here, I can feel it

Ella You said that about the last place

Claire That town we just left? I've already forgotten it

Ella So what am I going to do in this dump?

Claire There are two schools –

Ella Not school again!

Claire What else can I do with you? You refuse to grow up; you won't behave like an adult –

Ella I feel ancient

Claire Well, the effect is utterly teenage. You don't know how lucky you are; all that knowledge you've got, all that education. One day, Ella, you'll put it together and calculate the most important thing. How to survive

Ella Fine. School, then

Claire Don't do English Literature again. It makes you depressed. What about Computing?

Ella Done it

Claire Music, then

Ella No thanks

Claire Art

Ella Done it

Claire Or that subject where you make benches

Ella That is not a subject

Claire Can you do Espionage at A Level?

Ella No

Claire What about Cooking?

Ella You mean Food Technology?

Claire About time you learnt to cook

Ella What's the point?

Claire Ella, you don't have to eat all the stuff. Do it for me

Ella Food Technology

Claire And what else is there? A nice, light subject. You could do with a laugh. I know –

Ella I won't do it

Claire What's wrong with you?

Ella You can't make me

Claire I haven't even said / what it is yet

Ella I know what you're going to say. And how can I do that? It's all about laying yourself open to vicious attack, exposing your soul, performing like a flea in a / flea circus

Claire Oh, come on. What subject can be so terrible?

SCENE TWO

Eleanor Scene Two
Frank A Level Drama

Frank has sensitive eyes and a nervous demeanour. Mint is full of fervour and frustration. Mint's students, Briggs, Point, Debit and Moon, have perfected an air of cultivated boredom. They look as if they haven't had any fresh air in years. They look in fact, like detached, fashionable, effortlessly nonchalant vampires.

Mint So, same old spoilt rebels and fashion victims as last year. Not allowed to swear with disappointment or I would. Briggs

Briggs Mint

Mint I'm gutted to see you; I thought you'd be shovelling fries for the rest of your life. And Debit

Debit Hello, Mint

Mint You actually passed an exam?

Debit Might have

Mint So there's a brain somewhere under all that hair spray

Debit It's mousse

Mint Well, let's see how long you last

Point No, Mint, why don't we see how long you last?

Mint We're off to a great start already. Now, I'm more than delighted to see that we have some new blood. What are your names?

Ella Eleanor Wythenshawe

Mint And?

Frank Frank Adam Stein

Mint OK, Ella and – one name will do – Frank. I'm going to throw you in at the deep end. What's the first rule of making drama? Come on! First rule of making drama?

Debit Just say 'Yes'

Mint Thank you, Debit. 'Yes'. Yes to an idea, yes to each other, yes to the energy, to the communal experience, yes to the mighty, universal 'yes'. That's what we aspire to in this class, isn't it?

Moon No

Mint So. The hot seat. Frank – let's start with you

Frank What?

Mint takes Frank to a seat apart from the group.

Mint We're going to put you on the hot seat

Frank What for? Why?

Briggs To scald your arse

Mint The hot seat, guys, is a place of discovery, OK? Now we usually use it when we're 'in character', but

479

I'm going to do something we've never tried before.
I'm an instinctive teacher and my instincts are saying,
'Go, Mint, go.' So I'm going to throw away the code
of good practice and hot seat you as yourself

Moon That's psychological torture, Mint

Mint It's going to be fun, OK?

Moon You could leave him permanently scarred

Mint Frank, the rest of the group will ask you questions

Moon You're infringing his human rights

Mint And your only job is to be truthful

Moon These are torture chamber conditions

Mint It's a simple question and answer exercise. Are you
being tortured, Frank?

Frank Um

Mint Now, think about everything that has bought you
to this moment in time. People, when I clap my hands
we're going to begin – so have your questions for
Frank ready

Frank is full of dread. Mint claps.

Moon Do you feel that in doing this, Mint is infringing
your human rights?

Frank Um

Briggs What's your name?

Frank I've already said it

Briggs I didn't listen

Frank Frank

Briggs Frank what?

Frank Stein

Briggs What's that short for?

Frank Franklin

Moon Your name's Franklinstein?

Briggs (*laughing*) Are you lying?

Frank My dad thought it was funny too. In fact, it was
his last big joke before his sense of humour calcified
and had to be removed

Point Are you a monster?

Frank Probably

Briggs Are you a wanker?

Mint Briggs!

Debit What school were you at before, Franklin?

Frank I'm home-educated

Debit What?

Frank My mum and dad have been teaching me at home

Briggs How long for?

Frank Since I was a foetus

Moon You've never been to school?

Frank No

Point Why not?

Frank You'll have to ask my parents that really

Point No thanks

Frank Perhaps they were worried that I might grow up
normal if I went to school so they decided to concentrate
all their efforts on turning me into a freak

Point Why?

Frank Well, they're freaks, so I expect they just wanted
me to fit in

Mint Frank, I can understand your defensiveness, but
just try to be open. Say yes

Frank Well, to be fair on my mum and dad – that's Tina
and Geoff – I think they had high hopes. They wanted
me to fulfil my potential

Point What potential is that, Franklin?

Frank Tina and Geoff thought that if I learnt everything
there is to know by the age of sixteen I might turn out
to be a leader of men or a genius or something but I
eventually had to point out the flaw in their plan and
say, 'Tina and Geoff, if you don't let me go to school
and talk to some other people, I'll end up in a nut
house before I'm twenty,' and to drive home my point
I painted my bedroom black and drowned Tina's pot
plants so, given that I've got four 'A's at A Level

already, they decided to let me come. They see it as a
bit of a gap year, I think

Moon Did you say you were a genius?

Frank No, I'm a great disappointment

Briggs Are you gay?

Mint Question not allowed

Moon Is God a man or a woman?

Frank Pardon?

Mint I think he means are you religious?

Moon No, is God a man or a woman?

Frank Um, if there was a deity or creator I'd say it would
be unlikely to have recognisable genitalia

Debit That's rude

Frank God probably transcends gender. The deity is
probably asexual or even polysexual

Point Is that what you are, Frank?

Frank It may even be formless, dare I say it, non-existent
and therefore imaginable in any form

Debit I think you're shy about sex

Frank Is that a question?

Debit That's cute. You got any diseases?

Mint Not allowed

Debit Have you got a girlfriend, Frank?

Frank No

Briggs Have you got any friends at all?

Frank Yes, no, well, it depends what you mean by
friends. If you mean actual living people who like me,
then no

Debit That's a bit sad, isn't it?

Frank I used to have an imaginary friend, but he moved
out. He was great; really funny; much more daring than
me. He used to subvert Geoff's quizzes and put lighted
matches in the bin, but in the end he had to go

Moon Why?

Frank It turned out he was hiding pornography under
the bed and Tina found it. She had a massive row with

him. He came in to tell me he was leaving and I haven't
seen him since

Ella Do you miss him?

Frank Yes

Debit So what d'you do for fun, Frank?

Frank Fun?

Moon Apart from the pornography

Frank That wasn't mine; it was imaginary

Mint One last question: what made you choose Drama,
Frank?

Frank Um, my parents think it's a totally useless subject
so it seemed like the obvious choice

Mint OK. Well done. Respect. Round of applause

Only Mint and Ella clap.

Briggs Frank

Frank Yes?

Briggs I love you

Frank flinches as if he's about to be hit.

Mint Eleanor, we're going to do something different with
you, OK? We're going to play 'Lifegame'. Are you
ready?

Ella No

Mint Learn to say yes. OK, you barbarians, get off your
chairs. Eleanor, I'm going be 'in role' as the interviewer.
(*To the rest of the group.*) And from what I glean in
the interview, you lot are going to act out episodes in
Ella's life

Point Bore me to death

Mint Someone's already beaten me to it, Point. Move
these chairs

Ella and Frank move their chairs.

Ella That was brave

Frank No, it wasn't

Ella I've never told the truth about myself
Frank Why not?
Ella Because no one would believe it
Mint I said move your chairs

The others move their chairs.

Frank I would

Ella looks at him. Eleanor joins her. Remains close by.

Mint Right. Welcome to 'Lifegame'. Today we have as
our special guest Eleanor Wythenshawe
Moon (*without enthusiasm*) Yo
Mint And we're going to be recreating, before her very
own eyes, episodes from her true-life story. Eleanor,
let's take a journey back to your early childhood. Can
you share with us one of your earliest memories?
Eleanor Yes
Ella I'm at Miss Skullpepper's school. It's a rainy night.
I'm about six years old and I'm in bed with two of my
friends
Point What sort of a school was this?
Ella It was a private orphanage. We all had benefactors
who paid our fees. Most of us didn't know who they
were. It's hard to describe really; such places don't
exist any more
Mint When was this?
Eleanor/Ella Must have been 1812
Mint Eleanor, I think I can feel some improvising going
on here, which, in a different exercise would be totally
cool but as this game's about the Real You, just stick
to the truth for now, OK?
Ella I have a clear memory of celebrating the rout of
Napoleon in Russia, that's why I'm so sure it was
1812. It was night
Briggs What were you doing in bed with two girls?
Ella Space was short and in winter the house was so cold

Briggs Were you naked?

Ella No

Debit What were your friends called?

Ella Harriet and Leticia

Mint OK, in the spirit of saying yes, we're going to go along with Ella's impro

Ella It's not an impro – it's a memory

Mint Point, you play Eleanor, Debit, you play Harriet, and Briggs, you're Leticia

Briggs No way

Mint I beg your pardon?

Briggs I'm not playing a girl

Mint Get over it, or get out. You're three in a bed

Briggs Tell me about my character

Ella Leticia was very shy and sweet

Briggs Was she buff?

Ella Pardon?

Briggs Cos I'm not playing a dog

Ella She was dark and slight. I thought her beautiful. Her mother had died on her way home from the Gold Coast, after giving birth to her child of shame

Briggs Her what?

Ella Leticia was a child of shame. We all were. Harriet was the daughter of a tea merchant. Her mother was a whore, like mine

Debit Did you just say my mother was a whore?

Mint Eleanor, this certainly shows you've done some very interesting reading

Moon If this was 1812, why haven't you decomposed?

Eleanor/Ella I freely confess that I have stayed alive for all these years by drinking human blood

This causes a sensation; from shock to laughter.

Moon Yuk

Point Oh my God

Briggs That's disgusting

485

Debit You fucking weirdo

Mint Language

Point That is so freaked out

Moon Are you saying you're a vampire?

Ella Yes

Mint Eleanor, you know sometimes, when we've gone through a traumatic event, maybe bereavement or parental divorce, we retreat into fantasy to try to make sense of it all. Now, I don't think that's wrong. You've found a sympathetic ear here / OK?

Debit No she hasn't

Point Is this supposed to be a drama lesson? Because it's like stepping into someone's nervous breakdown, Mint

Mint Let's have a tableau

Moon A tableau of what?

Mint Of Eleanor's story. She's at school, in bed with her friends, Leticia and Harriet

Moon What about me?

Mint You're the bed

They form a tableau. Point, as a vampire, is trying to suck Briggs's blood. Briggs swoons, girlishly. Debit does Munch's 'Scream'. Moon attention-seeks as the bed.

Mint Eleanor, is that how it was?

Ella No. We were six years old. They were asleep

Mint You two – you're asleep. You're six years old.

Briggs What is the point of being asleep? Are we supposed to learn something, being asleep?

Mint I ask myself that question every time you enter this Studio

Point We've spent enough time on this freakish shit

Mint Language! Eleanor, you've got a great imagination – and that's a vital tool for making effective theatre. Now, I don't want to finish yet, OK? I don't want you to walk out of here feeling that you've failed

486

Ella I won't

Mint I want you to leave this studio with your head held high, OK?

Ella I will

Mint Let's fast-forward to the present, to the twenty-first century here and now, and find out about the real Eleanor

Debit How many people have you drunk?

Briggs Do you suck anything else apart from blood?

Mint Who do you live with, Eleanor?

Ella Claire

Frank Who's Claire?

Ella She's my legal guardian

Debit What about your mum and dad?

Ella My father was a sperm. I never knew him

Mint And your mum?

Eleanor/Ella My mother is a vampire

Point She is a mental emergency, Mint

Mint OK, thank you, Eleanor. One final question: what made you choose Drama?

Ella giggles at their consternation.

Ella My hilarious sense of fun

SCENE THREE

Fillet Scene Three

Moon Food Technology

Fillet And so, we begin our exploration with the humble root vegetable. They grow and thrive in the darkness, down in the rich heart of our mother earth. Gastronauts, have your peelers at the ready. Today, we're going to discover the science of mash

The students start peeling their root vegetables. Ella is working next to Frank.

Frank One thing's puzzling me; it's daylight

Ella Yes

Frank So if you were a vampire you'd be a little pile of dust. And I'm surprised you haven't cringed away from me shrieking by now

Ella Why's that?

Frank Because Tina made me garlic sandwiches for lunch

Ella True vampires live and move in society just like everyone else

Frank You haven't even got pointy teeth

Ella We don't die in daylight. We're not scared of garlic. We can use our teeth but we find it more effective to let the blood with a knife

Frank You don't look like someone who's committed countless motiveless killings

Ella I do have a motive – my own survival

Fillet Make sure every blemish is removed. We need perfect specimens

Frank Eleanor, if you really were a vampire, why would you tell us?

Ella I've carried the secret for so long. When I told it I thought – I don't know – the walls would come crashing down. I might have known that no one would believe me. It was a mistake. No one usually notices me and now I've put myself in their sights

Fillet As we boil, we are going to observe the physico-chemical alterations of cell-wall constituents. What is the behaviour of the vegetable during cooking? Does it scream with pain?

Frank Well, if it cheers you up, I don't think I made any friends either. I don't know how to be in groups. I bring out the worst in people. They can probably sense that there's something not quite right about me

Fillet Let us meditate on the fate of the potato

Ella What's not right about you, Frank?

Frank I see the world too clearly

Ella Do you?

Fillet This humble tuber will lead us to ponder the
morals of the food chain

Frank It's all in fragments but I see everything all the
time, splintered, fractured, all of creation, the beauty,
the horror, the madness, the inescapable ride towards
destruction

Ella Yes

Frank The, the machinations of far-off power, the
monsters of –

Ella Yes

Frank The terrible and ridiculous monsters of –

Ella Monsters of what?

Frank Sorry. Monsters of my own making. My own
thoughts

Ella That's not what you were going to say

Frank No. Some days I think we're so monstrous that
we'll destroy this earth, that's all

Ella You think humanity is monstrous?

Frank I don't know. Just asleep, maybe. Otherwise
they'd do something

Ella They're happy, Frank; that's what it is. They appear
asleep because they're happy

Frank How can you be happy in a world like this?

Fillet The subject of food on this planet is like a door,
a metaphysical door opening between worlds: the
scientific, the political, the environmental, the culinary
and yes, the spiritual. Gastronauts, today, by peeling
and boiling this potato, you will be taking your first
step into a bigger universe

Frank So, where d'you keep your coffin, anyway?

Ella smiles.

Ella No one ever got around to burying me

Frank smiles.

Frank They're giving me an appointment to see the
school shrink
Ella Me too

Eleanor comes forward.

Eleanor 1812. I am six years old. At night, I sleep in
a bed with two other abandoned girls. They are my
friends, Letty and Harriet.

Clara enters. Claire enters.

One night, I wake up in the dark to see a lovely woman
in a shining dress sitting on our bed. She is staring at
me, as if I am something precious. 'Who are you?' I say
Clara/Claire I'm your mother
Eleanor She replies, and I am glad because my mother is
dead and now I know she is an angel

SCENE FOUR

Clara Scene Four

Clara exits.

Claire Happy Hour

*Claire's bar. A spectacle in which the whole company
except Ella and Eleanor can take part.*
*Friday night happy hour. The bar staff are busy, the
dance floor already crowded. Socialising, hedonism,
drink; male behaviours and female behaviours. The
spectacle is full of energy and charge. People are already
dancing. Moon plays the fool, Briggs shows off his
wares, Point plays hard to get and Debit is drunk.*
*Claire watches from behind the bar, pulling a pint
in slow motion, her serenity a counterpoint to all the
movement – as if time is standing still for her. She*

*focuses on Briggs, taking note of everything he does.
Point tries to attract Briggs's attention. But Briggs has
seen Claire staring at him – and now he's staring back.
Point becomes angry. She yells:*

Point Let's go
Briggs I can't
Point Why not?
Briggs I'm staring at her

*Point looks at Claire and back to Briggs. Briggs ignores
her.*

Point Loser. Boy band loser

*Point throws her drink at him. She exits. Briggs tries
to wipe the alcopop off his face. Claire holds out a
napkin. As Briggs takes it, the bar falls silent and all
the movement continues in slow motion – as if Briggs
has joined Claire in her pocket of time.*

Claire What's your name?
Briggs Dave Briggs
Claire Well, Dave Briggs, I'm Claire Wythenshawe
Briggs Wythenshawe? Shit – have you got a sister?
Claire Might have
Briggs What's her name?
Claire Eleanor
Briggs I don't believe it
Claire D'you know her?
Briggs She is something else, isn't she?
Claire Is she?
Briggs Well, you know; she's a bit –
Claire Bit what?
Briggs Well, not meaning to disrespect your family, but
   she's a fucking mentalist
Claire Oh
Briggs I'm not knocking her but –

Claire Yeah, she's a strange one

Briggs What a looper. I can't believe she's got a sister like you

Claire How d'you know her then, Dave? You at school with her?

Briggs We both do Drama. Man, she is so crap. I mean, I know she's your sister and everything but you should see her trying to act. It is like watching a door trying to walk. Honestly, what a freakoid

Claire Well, that's strange because Eleanor's only in Year Twelve

Briggs Yeah?

Claire So, you're in here underage drinking, aren't you, Dave?

Briggs No

Claire I take a very dim view of that

Briggs How dim?

Briggs has one of his hands spread out on the bar. Claire leans forward, digging her elbow into the back of it. It brings her very close to him. The action in the bar has been going slower and slower. It now freezes.

Claire I could lose my job for serving you

Briggs I'm eighteen

Claire Show me some ID

Briggs I haven't got any. I never get asked cos I look so mature

Claire Get out

Briggs You see, you're saying that, but then you've got your elbow digging into the back of my hand so I can't actually move and so I'm getting mixed messages, you know? You smell lovely. What did you say your name was again?

Claire Claire

Briggs Claire, I know there's an age difference between
us, but –

Claire You going to give me some bullshit, Dave?

Briggs Yeah, I was going to try

Claire About how you could prove you were all grown
up by giving me the shag of a lifetime?

Briggs I was going to put it nicer than that

Claire Shall we cut to the chase?

Briggs Are you chasing me, Claire?

Claire I'm always in pursuit of pleasure, Dave. I like to
live in the moment, in the eternal second of present
time

*Claire clicks her fingers. The bar suddenly empties.
Briggs and Claire are alone.*

D'you get me?

Briggs Yeah

Claire It's what I exist for. The present that I seek is
random and indiscriminate and when I find it, there
is no guilt or consequence. Just gratification and a
moment of bliss

Briggs Wow

Claire Do you consent?

Briggs To what?

Claire To be my next pleasure

Briggs I think that's the best offer I've ever had

Claire Is that a yes, then?

Briggs You don't mess about, do you?

Claire Never

Clara takes the tray of drinks from Claire.

Clara Scene Five

SCENE FIVE

Ella is sitting at a small desk.

Eleanor Coursework

Ella Write a short scene incorporating some of Brecht's techniques of alienation. Subject matter: a secret

Ella starts to write. Characters enter and position themselves as she speaks.

A smoky, opulent room. Bodies lie drunkenly scattered in slumber. Ruthven, a gambler and Darvell –

Eleanor It is him

Ella – are at a card table. They are deep in their game. Clara Webb serves them with drinks.

Ruthven and Darvell are at a card table. Clara serves them with drinks.

Clara, to us –

Clara This game of cards has been going on for the last five hours

Ella Ruthven –

Ruthven (*to Darvell*) I'll see your hundred and add two

Ella Darvell –

Darvell As you wish, My Lord

Ella Darvell puts the last of his money on the table

Darvell puts the last of his money on the table. Marianne, little more than a child, is cradling a drunk.

Marianne (*to us*) You're in a house of ill-repute. That's to say a brothel. That's to say a whorehouse, a fleshpot, full of sluts, trollops, tarts, strumpets, whores / and men

Eleanor And men

Ella writes, concentrating deeply.

494

Marianne You're lucky to be here – and so am I for that matter because it's one of London's finest. It is run by a woman called / Clara Webb

Eleanor Clara Webb

Marianne That's her. She survived her brutal childhood to become, at the age of just twenty-one, London's pushiest and most ambitious whore

Clara Have you given that man what he's paid for?

Marianne I don't think he's capable, really

Clara Chuck him out on the street and see to someone else

Marianne Clara Webb is a hard-faced slag if ever there was one, but she pays alright. She won't let them beat us and there's always a doctor on call for our clap. What more could a prostitute ask for? It's 1816, after all – our life expectancy's only twenty

Ella Marianne exits, dragging the unconscious lord

Marianne What do I say next?

Ella Nothing

Marianne Is this it? Is this the whole of my part?

Ella Yes

Marianne But I'm an interesting character

Ella This story is not about you

Marianne exits, dragging the unconscious lord.

Clara My business turns over two thousand a year, all of it tax free. I plough a lot back in, providing the gentlemen with the very finest service in these decadent surroundings. The profits I make, I secrete in a trust for my daughter

Ruthven has put more money on the table.

Ruthven So what are you to do, sir? Where do we go from here?

Clara My daughter is the only thing in the world I love. When the midwife put her on my chest it was like a

revelation. I had never known what love was until
I felt her thundering heartbeat and smelt her tiny,
bloodied head. Everything I have done since then has
been for her

Darvell You'll need to accept a credit note. I've no more
cash on me, My Lord

Ruthven You're mistaking me for an idiot

Darvell Then what will you accept?

Ruthven Admit defeat. To go on is past reason

Clara My daughter's at a little school, where she'll learn
how to marry and have a safe life. She's been told that
her mother is dead. And the fiction will soon be true.
In my profession we don't last long; even us clever
ones. My lungs are rotting by inches – and I'm so
angry about it I am spitting blood

Darvell I have something far more valuable than cash.
Perhaps we should play for that

Ruthven What is it?

Darvell I have a secret

Ruthven Don't waste my time

Darvell I am offering you Time. I possess the knowledge
of a place where one can find life everlasting

Ruthven I'm insulted

Darvell Lord Ruthven, I can give you immortality. Where
is the insult in that? I have seen it

Clara remains in the shadows, watching, fascinated.

Ruthven Immortality?

Darvell You could move through time without aging,
young forever

Ruthven How?

Darvell I was travelling through Asia Minor –

Ruthven When?

Darvell Last spring. I was with an old friend of mine. We
were nearing Byzantium –

Ruthven Constantinople, surely?

Darvell – Byzantium, when he caught a fever and fell
  gravely ill
Ruthven What friend? His name, please
Ella/Darvell I have sworn never to reveal his name
Ruthven Then your story is full of holes
Darvell We were up in the mountains when his fever
  heightened and I knew that he would be dead before
  I could get him down. We came upon a high, deserted
  cemetery overshadowed by an ancient ruin, a temple
  with a half-blasted statue – of Artemis the huntress. In
  the heat of the day, the birds circling above, I laid him
  down to die
Ruthven Your powers of fiction are most compelling,
  sir

*At some point during the next speech, Ella stops
writing. She looks up, as if she is seeing what Darvell
describes. Some of the sleepers begin to wake and
listen.*

Darvell He begged me for water. I got it and when I
  returned, I saw on a rock nearby a great bird with a
  serpent writhing in its beak
Ella/Darvell It was looking at me.
Darvell I shouted a curse. The bird tossed the serpent
  into the air and devoured it. Then it spread its great
  wings and flew with slow grace over the graves

Ella and Eleanor spread their arms as if they are wings.

I gave my friend water. Upon his neck was a mark, red
  and angry – like the two-pronged bite of a snake. 'A
  miracle,' he whispered. With the last of his strength he
  made me swear to tell no one of his death – an oath
  that I am breaking now – and he said that in a month's
  time, when the moon rose –
Ruthven (*laughing*) What a fabulous tale. This is too
  fantastic!

Darvell stands.

Darvell You don't deserve my secret. The thought of bestowing that priceless gift on you – you'd waste it

Darvell looks straight at Clara.

I'd do better offering it to this girl. It'd be a fine thing, don't you think, to have an immortal whore? She could reap vengeance on mankind for ever more

All of the sleepers are now awake, listening.

Ruthven What happened to your friend?
Darvell My friend died
Ruthven He whispered the secret and died – perfect
Darvell I held him until he was cold as the rock he lay on
Ruthven And then what?
Darvell I dug his grave. The bird watched as I worked, perched on the broken goddess, a hunched silhouette. In the shadows, it seemed to have a human shape. I buried him and then ran, stumbled through the night. At first light I saw the coast and found a town. I lay in a fever for a month, hallucinating terrors. I sent letters to Byzantium, requesting aid
Ruthven Constantinople, surely –
Darvell And then, the evening that my boat was due to sail, I saw him – my friend – walking down by the harbour. At first I thought it was an apparition, but he approached and gripped my arm. A strange light was in his eyes, a cold burning as if everything he looked upon was a source of wonder
Ruthven A cold burning; very nice
Darvell He shook me by the hand and thanked me for my care of him. He was freezing
Ruthven I don't believe a word
Darvell That's because you have no faith. But you're longing for it to be true. My secret for your fortune.

I will tell you all: the location of the cemetery, the
significance of the bird and what befell my friend
Ruthven Where is he now?
Darvell Do we play?
Ruthven We play
Clara I hardly dared breathe, hoping that the stranger
would –

Frank has entered. He stands just behind Ella.

Frank Hi

Ella startles. The characters in her scene freeze.

Ella, sorry, did I scare you?
Ella No
Frank What are you doing?
Ella Drama coursework.
Frank Oh, how's it going?
Ella Fine. I'll put it away

*She closes her book. Eleanor clicks her fingers. The
characters in the scene disappear – except Clara.*

Frank Mine's crap. I don't know what the hell he's
talking about
Ella Who?
Frank Brecht. I mean, what's alienation anyway? Will
you go out with me?
Ella What?
Frank Don't say yes. Forget I asked. I've just come from
my session with the shrink
Ella Oh
Frank Yes, he wants to refer me
Ella To whom?
Frank More shrinks. Have you seen him yet?
Ella No
Frank Don't tell the truth, will you? It's a bad mistake
Ella Thank you

Frank I've been watching a lot of vampire films

Ella What for?

Frank Oh, you know, thought I'd try and get to know you better. They say some great stuff. I mean, once you get past the cape era you start wondering what they're a metaphor for; you know, it might be Aids, heroin, anorexia, it might be the whole spiralling chaos of western society; not knowing the difference between good and evil – I mean not even being able to define the terms. And they're sexy and heartbroken and mostly Californian and they keep coming out with fantastic clichés like, 'It's easier to succumb to the darkness within than to fight the darkness without,' and you get the feeling that if it wasn't for their nihilistic disregard for human life, they'd be the nearest thing we've got these days to gods

Ella Could you say that again?

Frank They used to be there just to terrify, as if the forces they represented had to be crushed by the righteous, but we don't want to crush them now. They fascinate us. Perhaps we are all becoming vampires. I mean, the way we devour everything. (*Pause.*) Can you see your reflection in a mirror, by the way?

Ella Not properly, no

Frank That must be disturbing

Ella It was at first. I'm used to it now

Frank I love your psychosis, Ella. It's epic. It's amazing

Ella You don't listen

Frank I'm having a party. It's not really a party. I'm only inviting you. But it's my birthday. Will you come?

Ella Yes

Frank Great

Ella I love the way you speak

Frank Do you?

Ella You're so human

Clara The great thing about being a whore is that no one remembers you're there. I could have been furniture that night.

Eleanor/Clara The stranger lost

Clara He forfeited his secret – and it fell right into my eavesdropping ear. Lord Ruthven soon departed for the East. I said that if he took me with him, he would get my constant service, free. By the time we reached Byzantium, my lungs were seeping blood. I prayed that I would live to see my daughter grow

SCENE SIX

Eleanor Scene Six

Geoff Franklin's Party

Tina Every year, since Franklin was five, he's had a geography quiz on his birthday

Tina is offering Ella a plate piled high with Jammie Dodgers.

Geoff Which African nation was known until recently as Zaire?

Tina makes a buzzing sound.

Tina

Tina The Congo

Geoff I'm sorry, it's the Democratic Republic of Congo

Tina Silly me

Geoff What phenomenon produces opposite weather conditions to El Niño?

Tina Don't you like Jammie Dodgers, Eleanor?

Ella No thank you

Tina picks up another plate. Frank makes a buzzing sound.

Geoff Franklin

Frank La Nina

Geoff Ten points. Name two languages of Eritrea

Tina These are luncheon-meat wrap-arounds. I made them myself

Ella No thank you

Geoff Come on, languages of Eritrea

Tina Oh!

Tina makes a buzzing sound.

Geoff Tina

Tina Tigrinyan and Arabic

Geoff Correct. One step closer to those chockies, Tina

Tina How exciting

Tina exits with her plates.

Geoff If I was looking at a Sprite, where would I be?

Frank sighs. He buzzes.

Franklin

Frank You'd be in the middle of a lightning storm above the clouds

Geoff Ten points. Name the debris deposited by a receding glacier

Ella Terminal moraine

Geoff I'm sorry; strictly speaking it's just moraine

Ella Oh

Frank Will you give her the points?

Geoff I was looking for the generic term

Tina enters with a plate piled high with tinned peach halves.

Frank Give her the points, Geoff

Geoff Besides, I can't give her the points because she didn't buzz. You've got to buzz, Eleanor

Tina (*to Ella*) Do you like tinned peach halves? Franklin
only gets them as a very special treat

Frank Dad, will you please give Ella the points?

Tina Have a peach half

Ella No thank you

Geoff I'm the / quizmaster

Frank You're totally unfair

Ella It doesn't matter

Frank Yes / it does

Geoff I can't award points unless they've been properly
won according to the rules

Tina Go on, Eleanor – they're yummy

Ella No

Tina What's wrong with them?

Geoff Name three different / kinds of –

Frank Right, I'm not playing

Geoff Franklin, I've bought these chocolates specially
and I've spent time and effort compiling a question
list. We do a geography quiz every year and we do it
because you like it

Frank But I'm seventeen –

Geoff And I've taken that into account with my choice of
questions. Now pull yourself together and name three
different kinds of igneous rock

Frank I've had enough

Tina Pumice

Frank I don't want to play

Geoff Buzz, Tina, buzz

Tina makes a buzzing sound.

Tina

Frank Shut up

Tina Pumice, soapstone and –

Frank Shut up now, or I'll swear

Geoff How dare you

Frank I don't want to do a geography quiz. I don't want
  peach halves. I don't want you or Tina at my party

Tina Franklin, how could you say that?

Geoff You are so ungrateful. We did everything right

Frank Oh not / this again

Geoff We devoted ourselves to you. We could have had
  careers, holidays, fulfilling adult lives, but no. We
  exhausted ourselves ensuring your development. You
  had a reading age of twelve by the time you were six
  years old and one day you'll appreciate what that
  meant

Frank It meant I was alone, always

Ella Let's go for a walk in the car park, Frank. The
  magnolias are coming into bloom

Frank Yes

Ella And the bins are rainforest green

Frank takes Ella's hand.

Frank Eleanor's a vampire

Tina Are you?

Ella Yes

Frank She's been alive for over two hundred years

Tina Have you?

Ella Yes

Tina I thought there was something about you, some
  whiff of depression

Frank Let's go

Tina I know what it is. You're an anorexic

Ella No

Tina I've got no patience with anorexics. I think you're
  rude and freakish. What's wrong with food?

Frank Come on

Ella I'm coming

Geoff Wherever you're going, young lady, whatever
  weird, starvation-induced visions you might be having,
  don't pull our son down with you

Tina She won't even eat peaches, Franklin. She is embracing death. Keep away from her

SCENE SEVEN

Frank Scene Seven

Claire Car Park

Ella Embracing death?

Frank They won an award for designing this car park. I'm not surprised; if it wasn't for the cars you'd think you were in nirvana

Ella I'm not embracing death

Frank That was my best party yet

Ella I feel alive. I feel like I'm burning all the time. I feel raw with it

Frank Yes

Ella Something's going to happen. I can feel it coming; some terrible change

Frank What if it's not terrible? What if it's good? What if it's amazing?

Frank tries to kiss her. Ella breaks away.

Ella I have to go

Frank Where?

Ella Back to Claire

Frank I'll come with you

Ella You can't

Frank Why not?

Ella Claire won't like you

Frank Doesn't matter

Ella You won't like her

Frank Why not?

Ella Because she'll tell you lies. Claire will try and tell you that I'm only sixteen. She'll try to tell you that our mother died three years ago of cancer. She'll try to tell you that they couldn't trace our useless sperm of a father so they put me in a care home. Claire will tell you I got raped there. She came and found me all withdrawn and suicidal. She'll tell you how she fought for me, rescued me, breathed her life force into me. Since then, she has been my mother. She'll tell you that we go from town to town avoiding social workers and police, and that she sticks at low-paid jobs because they give her opportunity to steal. She'll tell you how her magpie heart is satisfied by simple, little pleasures. She'll say she lives each moment to the full – and so she does. My sister-mother is ruthless Frank, and so am I

Frank You're not ruthless

Claire enters, laden with bags from fashion stores.

Ella Why don't you believe me? I keep telling you the truth

Claire So who's this, then?

They startle.

Frank Hi

Ella This is Frank. He's my friend

Claire Your *what*?

Frank Are you Claire? Great to meet you. I hear you're really good at shoplifting and identity theft

Claire (*to Ella*) They've called me into your school. Why would that be?

Ella I expect it's because someone tried to put a stake through my heart

Claire Come indoors. Now. (*Referring to Frank.*) And send that home

She exits.

Ella You'd better go

Frank Why?

Ella She doesn't like you
Frank So what?
Eleanor/Ella I don't want to hurt you
Frank I wouldn't care if you did
Ella Scene Eight
Frank Kiss me
Ella Scene Eight
Frank That's what vampires do, isn't it?
Claire Scene Eight

SCENE EIGHT

Eleanor Costume Cupboard
Claire You can call me Claire
Mint Thank you so much for coming, Claire
Claire This is a nice classroom
Mint It's a drama studio
Claire Lovely and dark. What's this over here?
Mint The costume cupboard
Claire Oh I like dressing up, don't you?

> *Claire picks up Marianne's costumes. Eleanor is
> watching from the shadows.*

Mint Claire
Claire These are just like the real thing
Mint How long have you had sole care of Eleanor?
Claire Since I was legally able. When our mother died
three years ago, Ella was put in a care home. I got her
out as soon as I could and she's been with me ever since
Mint That's a great responsibility for someone so young
Claire There were monsters in that care home. I couldn't
have left her
Mint Well – respect
Claire Sorry, what's your name again?
Mint The kids like to call me Mint

Claire You've got very nice hands, Mint

Mint Thank you

Claire Can't help noticing. Elegant fingers

Mint I'm sorry I had to call you in

Claire What's she been up to, Mint?

Mint It's hard to know where to start. Because usually she's fine at school. Usually, I'm not bothered

Mint As part of their coursework the kids have to write a short scene

Eleanor clicks her fingers. Ruthven enters. He is looking for something. He is not aware of Mint and Claire.

Mint Some kids just do little monologues, but Eleanor's written the best part of a play – which is great / don't get me wrong –

Claire A play? Isn't she clever?

Mint The reason I've asked you to come in is the subject matter. Eleanor is quite convinced that she's a vampire

Clara enters. She watches Ruthven, unaware of Claire and Mint.

Claire I'm sorry?

Mint Yes, and not only that; she thinks you're a vampire too

Claire What?

Mint She says that you're not really her sister at all. She says you're her mother

Claire A vampire mother?

Ruthven (*to Clara*) What are you looking at?

Clara Nothing, My Lord

Mint She says you were a nineteeth-century hooker

Claire She never did

Mint And you became a vampire when she was just six years old – youth everlasting

Claire Unbelievable

Ruthven (*to Clara*) Are you laughing at me?

Clara I wouldn't dare

Mint It's a really amazing story. I'm giving her an 'A'.
  She's got you following some lord to a ruined cemetery
  near Constantinople

Claire Istanbul, surely

Mint Lord Ruthven, she calls him. It's a name ripped
  off from an early vampire story. You're dying of
  consumption, looking for the secret of eternal life

Ruthven I've searched every rock and stone in this
  godforsaken ruin and no revelation has come. He lied
  to me. The secret is not here

Clara You don't see it, do you?

Clara is laughing. She is physically frail.

Ruthven Why are you laughing? What did he tell you?
  Where is it?

Clara shakes her head. Ruthven grabs her, furious.

You know how to get it, don't you? You'd better tell me,
  or by God you'll regret it

Mint He becomes totally incensed

Ruthven If you make a fool of me, I swear I'll kill you

Mint And he strikes you – very violent, quite disturbing,
  actually. In your weakened state, he kills you

Clara is dying – but smiling, triumphantly.

Clara Eternal life will only come to those prepared to
  die

Ruthven Then die

Mint He lobs you into a tomb and leaves you. By the
  next full moon, he's preparing to sail for home and
  you find yourself reborn

Claire Wow

*Ruthven has picked up Marianne's costume. He
embraces it, as if it is a girl.*

Mint You wake with a terrible thirst and set out to find
Lord Ruthven. He's in a hotel room with a little girl
he's paid to entertain him

Clara My Lord

Ruthven Clara

Clara touches him. Ruthven is terrified.

You're cold

Clara I'm burning

Mint You realise that the worst fate for him would be
to die slowly of all the sexually transmitted diseases
he's picked up over the years

Clara takes Marianne's dress from Ruthven.

Clara Your own corruption will kill you. You'll never be
immortal – but this girl will

Mint And you kill and drink his innocent prostitute right
in front of him. Just to show him how powerful you are

Claire I'd never do that. No way. I'd never kill an
innocent –

Mint Eleanor says you're indiscriminate

Claire She must hate me

Mint You show no mercy

Claire Mint, I'm stunned

Mint Can we come out of the cupboard, please?

Eleanor clicks her fingers. Clara and Ruthven exit.

Claire How could she write about me like that?

Mint The trouble is, her vampire delusion is so carefully
maintained and so convincing that the rest of the
group has completely rejected her. It doesn't help that
one of them recently disappeared – a kid called Dave
Briggs. Ran away from home, we think

Claire Dave what?

Mint Briggs. D'you know him?

Claire Never come across him

Mint Eleanor had taken an active dislike to him and now the others are accusing her of macabre and outlandish crimes

Elsewhere. Point, Moon and Debit enter. They are wheeling a trolley on which Ella is tied, Hannibal Lecter-style. She has a sock shoved in her mouth.

Debit What have you done with him?
Point Where's Dave, you freak?

Point is brandishing a wooden stake. Ella tries to speak.

Debit Don't lie to us, you bloodsucking bitch – where's he gone?
Point He'd never disappear like that
Moon He was too boring
Point And we were in love
Debit So tell us where he is before we put a stake through your heart

Ella is furiously trying to make herself understood.

Moon If you took the sock out of her mouth she might talk. Otherwise it's just mindless torture and I'm a member of Amnesty, OK, so I'm a bit uncomfortable with this
Point (*pulling out the sock*) Where's Briggs?
Ella You have no idea how hard I'm fighting not to use my powers, not to tear through these bonds and make a bloodbath of your flesh. You have no idea how much self-control and godlike compassion I am exercising
Debit That is so pathetic
Point What did you do to Briggs?
Ella Nothing
Point He was beautiful
Ella He was an idiot – just the kind of moron I'd love to have killed, but I didn't
Point Where is he?

Moon There's a very real possibility that he just ran away. You know how much he wanted to be interesting

Point He'd never have gone without me. We had dreams. We were going to live in a van and write songs about meaningful sex

Ella I wish I had claimed him as prey, I wish I'd gorged on his every last corpuscle – but I didn't

Point Something terrible has happened to him

Ella I'd have done humanity a service in culling him, but I didn't

Debit You're going to pick us off one by one, aren't you?

Point Unless we finish you first – mutant

Debit Stake her

Point Watch her age two hundred years. She'll decompose before our eyes

Debit Her scream will rip out her throat

Point raises the wooden stake.

Moon I'm freaking out! I'm freaking out! I don't know what to do! We need a teacher

Moon hurriedly wheels Ella off.

Debit Bring her back here, Moon

Point I want violence! Violence!

Point and Debit exit after Moon.

Mint We found her outside the staff room, still tied to the trolley. There was a wooden stake shoved down her cardy

Claire I've tried so hard to be a mum to her – and a sister

Mint I'm sure you've done everything you could

Claire She's my whole life, Mint

Mint I've been speaking to the head teacher and to her counsellor. He's keen to refer her to psychiatric services

Claire You're not sending her to shrinks. They'd split us up

Mint Maybe a short stay in a residential –

Claire NO WAY

Mint Look, we're very sympathetic, but we can't ignore her problems. Eleanor needs more help than this school can currently offer

Claire Mint, if they took her away from me – my heart would break; right here

Claire has taken Mint's hand and put it on her heart.

Mint What are you doing? Let go of my hand please, Claire

Claire moves closer.

Claire You want to help me, Mint; you know you do. Look at me

Mint Claire, I made a decision a long time ago that relationships, feelings, human interaction; these things would only happen in the theatre for me – because real emotion doesn't come near the wild spectacle of the stage. I live for creating drama. I've made it my life

Claire You must be so alone

Mint No, anything can come out of this darkness, any character, any marvellous scene. I've been happy to wear down my health in the service of theatre

Claire You're so devoted

Mint Yes – and the pinnacle of my achievement is A Level Drama. It sustains me every year. Claire, the worst thing about all of this, about your sister's breakdown, Briggs disappearing, the traumatising bullying, the very worst thing –

Claire What is it?

Mint – the group won't work together. They are saying 'No'. Please try to understand

Claire I'll try

Mint If I don't get Eleanor out of my class, they'll get a
bad mark in their practical. They might even get 'D's

*Claire looks at Mint in utter disbelief. She moves
closer.*

Claire My heart bleeds for you. It really does

SCENE NINE

Eleanor is sitting at Ella's desk. Ruthven is behind her.

Eleanor Scene Nine
Ruthven Education

Eleanor writes.

Eleanor Third of January 1822. Beloved diary, I love
your clean white pages. They're like sheets in which
my lonely thoughts can lie. Today I am sixteen

Ella enters. She is wearing a modern, pink nightdress.

Ella Sixteen

Eleanor rises. Ella sits in her place and starts writing.

Ella/Eleanor Perhaps I will prick my finger on a spinning
wheel and die
Ella Leticia and Harriet enter. Bettina, a maidservant,
follows

Letty and Harriet enter. Bettina, a maidservant, follows.

Letty Eleanor?
Harriet There's a gentleman to see you –
Letty A gentleman in our school
Eleanor A gentleman?
Harriet He said

Ruthven I'm here for Miss Webb

Letty For you, for you

Bettina (*taking Ruthven's coat*) I got to take his coat, and as he gave it to me he said

Ruthven Thank you, child

Bettina And his hand brushed against my wrist, like a feather and, oh, it was like lightning, miniature lightning rushing up my arm

Eleanor Who is he?

Ella Lord Ruthven

Harriet/Letty Lord Ruthven

Bettina Him

Eleanor But I don't know him. I've never heard of him

Bettina Mrs Skullpepper led him into the library. She asked him the purpose of his visit. He said –

Ella/Ruthven I have news of her mother

Bettina Mrs Skullpepper tried to question him, but he sent her away

Ruthven My time is precious

Harriet He wants to see you alone

Letty Alone

Harriet/Letty We're so jealous

Eleanor He has news of my mother?

Bettina He touched me right there

Ella/Eleanor My mother is dead

Letty Look at his jacket

Harriet The best tailoring – just the best

Bettina Smell it

Harriet Oh, you can't!

Bettina Late nights

Letty Tobacco, some kind of faint scent

Harriet Don't! He'll be able to tell

Letty It smells of male

Bettina Did you see his boots?

Harriet Spattered with mud from his manly life

Eleanor My mother is dead. Why is he here?

Harriet It must be something dreadfully important

Bettina His expression

Letty It was grave, Ella

Bettina Dark and brooding

Harriet As if he's prey to some cureless inquietetude of mind

Eleanor Some what?

Harriet Inquietetude. He looks dangerous

Eleanor All men look dangerous when you're us. We've never seen any men

Letty He looks somehow blighted, too

Bettina Like a poor, wounded beast

Harriet Full of dark mystery

Eleanor Oh, stop it

Bettina When he touched me, it was lightning I felt. I'll never, never be the same again

Bettina, Harriet and Letty exit. Eleanor approaches Ruthven.

Eleanor My Lord? I am Eleanor Webb

She curtsies.

Ruthven Eleanor Webb. Look at you. I know your mother

Eleanor My mother is dead, My Lord

Ruthven Nonsense. I've been searching for her this past decade – ever since she stole my secret – and last week I found her. She is living not two miles from here and doing what she does best

Eleanor My Lord?

Ruthven Keeping a brothel, a kennel, a dungheap, a whorehouse – do you understand me, child? Your mother sells human flesh

Eleanor (*to Ella*) Stop writing

Ella No

Eleanor Stop now

Ella/Ruthven And she preys on her customers like a
carrion crow – picks them off one by one

Eleanor You know how it ends; please stop

Ella I don't understand you. My mother is dead

Eleanor (*to Ruthven*) I don't understand you. My mother
is dead.

Ruthven Is that what they've told you?

Eleanor (*to Ella*) Don't make me go on!

Ruthven My dear, they have nourished you on lies

Ella/Eleanor What do you mean?

Ruthven I'll be brief with you, Miss Webb. Your mother
stole a secret from me and I'm here to steal something
from her

Ruthven takes hold of Eleanor.

Eleanor Let me go

Ruthven Imagine my delight when I discovered you
existed. Her precious, treasured daughter, the jewel
she's hidden away for all these years

Ella/Eleanor My mother is dead

Ruthven Your mother believes that the pact of blood she
made with the gods and monsters makes her invincible.
But I will cause her pain. I will make her rage – as I
raged when she stole my secret

Eleanor (*to Ella*) Don't let him touch me

Ruthven I am dying, Miss Webb. I could have lived for
ever but I'll soon be dead. Your mother robbed me of
life and I will rob you. You will share my disease

Eleanor Mother –

Ruthven A terrible disease for an innocent to catch. For
there is only one way to catch it, Miss Webb

Eleanor Mother –

Ruthven And when I have finished with you –

*Ella and Eleanor close their eyes and put their hands
over their ears. The action freezes. Claire enters.*

Claire What are you doing? Ella

Claire takes Ella's hands from her ears.

I've just been to see your teacher. Why are you telling
  people that we're vampires?
Ella Leave me alone
Claire They will cart you away to the nuthouse
Ella Get out
Claire Why are you like this?
Ella YOU MADE ME LIKE THIS

Claire grabs Ella's script.

Claire You are condemning yourself. They will section
  you. And once they write 'personality disorder' on
  your notes they will throw away the key. I am fed up
  trying to save you
Ella Suppose I don't want to be saved?
Claire Is this your play?
Ella Yes
Claire How dare you

Claire reads the scene.

Ruthven Eleanor Webb. I know your mother
Eleanor My mother is dead
Ruthven A dungheap. Carrion crow
Eleanor I don't understand
Ruthven Nourished on lies
Eleanor My mother is dead
Ruthven A secret
Eleanor Let me go
Ruthven Disease
Eleanor Mother
Ruthven Terrible for an innocent
Eleanor Mother
Ruthven And when I have finished with you

Claire stops reading.

Claire Very clever. What comes next?
Ella I can't write it
Claire A rape scene without a rape?

She drops the script.

Why are you calling him Ruthven?

Ella doesn't respond. Claire exits. Ruthven releases Eleanor.

Ruthven Welcome to the adult world. Welcome, Miss Webb. Welcome to a slow death. Welcome, you whore

He throws a coin at her.

Give my regards to your mother

Ruthven exits. Ella goes to Eleanor. They cling to each other.

Ella Eleanor, he didn't kill you
Eleanor I'm still dying
Ella He didn't kill you
Eleanor I'm dying
Ella Why have you let him win?

Eleanor fights her way out of Ella's arms. She exits. Ella is shocked that she has gone. Claire returns with a suitcase.

Claire Right. Get packing

She starts putting Ella's things in the case.

Ella What are you doing?
Claire We have to go
Ella Why?
Claire Because you've been telling people we're vampires!
Ella (*suspiciously*) What have you done, Mother?
Claire Don't call me that. I'm your sister
Ella What have you done?
Claire Nothing

Ella Then I'm not leaving

Claire We have to

Ella Why?

Claire Because you're right. This place is killing you. You're going small-town crazy. We'll go to London, wherever you like –

Ella I want to stay here

Claire Why?

Ella The magnolias are blooming. The bins are rainforest green

Claire When did you last eat?

Ella What's that got to do with anything?

Claire When did you last feed yourself? (*Pause.*) You're so unique, Ella, you're so amazing. When are you going to start living? Look at you, you're starving

SCENE TEN

Point Scene Ten

Fillet The Beast

The students of A Level Food Technology gather themselves. Ella is ill, withdrawn.

In order to do my proper duty to you as a teacher of Food Technology –

Frank Eleanor

Fillet – I have been trying to teach you about every edible thing on this planet. We've gone into the Earth and returned bearing fruits

Frank I'm leaving Tina and Geoff. Come to London with me. We'll find somewhere to live, even if it's a protest tent on Westminster Green

Ella I can't

Frank Yes, you can

Fillet We've spent many weeks delving into the vegetable.
And now we must encounter the beast

Frank We can get crap jobs and at nights we'll lie there

Fillet A new heading. Meat

Frank Trying to find stars in the light pollution, thinking
up ways to attack the consumerist system

Fillet Franklin Stein! This lesson may bring you learning
that will affect the rest of your life. I want you
young people to leave my class secure in the
knowledge that if society broke down and all the
supermarkets closed, you could walk into a field,
butcher an animal and prepare enough food to feed
a village for a week

Debit (*to Point*) Have you heard about Mint?

Point What?

Fillet I'm harking back to a purer time, when we didn't
consume meat from factory abattoirs, vacuum-sealed
in plastic; I'm harking back to a time when we stroked
and petted every beast we ate

Debit Found this morning; dead as a doornail in the
costume cupboard

Point No! Poor Mint

Fillet If we killed it, we'd respect it

Debit They're trying to tell us it was a stroke

Point No

Fillet I am going to teach you to respect the beast. And
one day, when order breaks down into violence and
chaos and starving hordes are roaming the land, you
will be the one who can hold up your cleaver and say,
'I did A Level Food Technology. I can save humanity!'
So today, adults of tomorrow, we shall begin our study
of the beast by investigating its life force. We are going
to make blood pudding

Moon faints. Fillet arranges the ingredients.

Fillet Onions finely chopped, a kilo of diced pork fat, two metres of intestine, a litre of double cream, oatmeal, barley, salt, mace

Fillet lifts a bowl filled with pig's blood onto the table. Ella stares at it longingly.

And here is our pig's blood. Pig's blood is identical to human blood by ninety-eight per cent. Isn't that a strange fact? We are only two per cent different from a pig. Mint is dead. Mint, my comrade, your teacher, has fallen. We shall have a minute's silence at the end of the lesson but for now, contemplate this: GOD, WHY DID YOU MAKE US ONLY TWO PER CENT DIFFERENT FROM A PIG? Forgive me. I'm wreckage this morning. I loved Mint. Mint was an innocent. You get gallons of blood from each mature beast, but here I have just two litres

Frank Eleanor –

Ella has walked up to the desk as if in a trance.

Fillet Now, the pudding sticks better if the blood is warm. Get back to your seat. Get back, I said. What are you doing?

Ella Forgive me

Ella lifts the bowl. She puts it to her lips.

Starving

The class erupts into screams. Pandemonium, as Ella drinks the blood.

Point It's her!
Debit Her!
Point She killed Briggs
Debit She killed Mint
Debit/Point Vampire!

A cacophony of screaming. Frank is watching, aghast.
Blackout.

SCENE ELEVEN

Clara Scene Eleven

In the darkness:

Eleanor Deathbed
Clara Eleanor
Eleanor Who's there?

Clara strikes a light. She is sitting on the end of
Eleanor's bed. Eleanor is wearing Ella's pink nightdress.

Who are you?
Clara My name is Clara Webb
Eleanor I've seen you before. When I was a child
Clara You're right
Eleanor You are an angel
Clara I used to climb in through your window and watch
  you while you slept
Eleanor My mother
Clara My girl
Eleanor I'm dying
Clara There's no need to die. I'll take you away with me
Eleanor A man was here
Clara I'll teach you how to live
Eleanor He has killed me
Clara You shall not die
Eleanor Mother
Clara I'll never leave you. Never leave you again

Clara gently bares Eleanor's neck. She blows out the
light.

SCENE TWELVE

Claire Scene Twelve

Darvell Immortal

Ella Let me out of here! Let me out!

Fillet You stay in that drama studio, down there in the darkness where you belong. My lab looks like carnage; apocalyptic. I'm not letting you out until they're here

Ella Who?

Fillet The mental health-care professionals, those in authority, those with absolute power

Ella You've got no right to keep me

Fillet Mint had files on you. Mint knew something was wrong

Ella What files? I demand to see them

Fillet Mint was trying to help you, and look what you did

Ella I've done nothing

Ella looks down at her bloodsoaked clothes. She cries. Elsewhere, Claire is robbing a till.

Frank Claire

Claire Who's asking?

Frank I'm Frank, your sister's friend

Claire Her what?

Frank You've got to come. They've contained her – locked her in the drama studio

Claire What's she done?

Frank She drank blood

Claire You're lying. You're sick for saying that

Frank She needs to get away. I want to take her to London with me

Claire You what?

Frank I'm running away from my parents

Claire How teen and cute

Frank I want to take Ella with me

524

Claire You're just her type, I must say. Earnest, clueless, about as sexy as a pair of sandals. But I know what's best for Eleanor. We're leaving now. And no one at that shit-heap school will ever hear of us again

Claire slams the till and makes to go.

Frank Maybe that's why she did it
Claire Did what?
Frank Drank the blood – an act of protest
Claire Against what?
Frank You. Eleanor's written a story where she's spent two hundred years with you. So that must be what it feels like
Claire Ella couldn't survive without me
Frank I think it's the other way round. I think you rely on her for everything. You don't let anyone near her, do you? You're worse than my parents.
Claire If it wasn't for me she'd be dead
Frank Personally, I think you're slowly killing her
Claire Are you in love with her, little Frank?
Frank Do you know anything about Mint's death?
Claire I beg your pardon?
Frank When we met you in the car park you were on your way to meet him. And next morning he was dead. And Briggs. Point saw you talking to him the night he went away
Claire You're playing a very dangerous game, little Frank

Frank makes his fingers into a crucifix.

Frank Are you threatening me?
Claire I'm just giving you a warning. I am by nature indiscriminate. I learnt to be promiscuous when I was still a child. But with Ella, it's all about love
Frank What do you mean?
Claire It's tragic really. It's like the saying with her: 'Each man kills the thing he loves'

Frank Ella's not a man

Claire When she's finished with you, you'll be left
hanging like a cheap suit on a washing line. We use
people up. That's what we do. We're survivors

*The drama studio. Ella has dressed up in a costume
from the costume cupboard.*
      Eleanor enters, wearing Ella's pink nightgown.

Eleanor People will always believe the most fabulous tale
you can tell. The fabulous tale is the one that they long
for. It must be unprovable, impossible, fantastical. To
believe it then becomes an act of faith

Ella An act of faith. Every prisoner should have the
means to write. It says so in the Geneva dramatic
convention. I demand a pen and paper

Eleanor Enter Darvell. He is dressed as a Doctor of
Psychiatry

Darvell enters. He is dressed as a Doctor of Psychiatry.

Darvell Eleanor? My name is Darvell

Ella What do you want?

Darvell I'm a doctor

Ella What kind of doctor?

Darvell The kind who seeks to heal

Ella Do I know you?

Darvell I'd like to help you, Eleanor

Ella May I have a pen and paper?

Darvell In due time, you shall have everything you want

Ella I need to finish my story

Darvell Of course you do

Ella It's about a girl. She meets a boy. He's a genius, but
every bit as friendless as she. The girl has been alone
for a long time. The boy tries to bring her back to life.
But her past is gone; the present hurts; she has no
future. She is the beetle who crawled into amber

Darvell What do you mean?

Ella I cannot die, though I know I am dead. I am hungry all the time but I cannot eat. My desires are destructive. I live off others. I am alone. I am a vampire. / Do you believe me?

Eleanor Do you believe me? Am I mad?

Darvell I don't know what madness is. There is only pain and our ability to bear it. Sometimes, when the pain is too great, the mind can no longer withstand it, and it breaks

Ella When we devour, it's because it's our nature

Darvell But our natures are able to change. Change can be painful. It can feel like a mortal blow

Ella It hurts

Darvell All pain can be relieved

Ella I feel immortal, sir, but not alive

Eleanor clicks her fingers. Claire and Frank enter.

Claire She's sixteen. She's a sixteen-year-old kid. You can't legally section her – she's too young

Darvell In order to help her, I need to take her away

Frank Ella, he's from a secure institution. Don't go with him. There's nothing wrong with you

Claire (*to Frank*) Listen, you tank-topped desperado, you've got no right to be here and nothing to say. This situation is none of your business

Frank Yes, it is

Claire I'm her legal guardian. She's mine

Darvell Eleanor is free to come with me

Claire Ella, he thinks he's God in a white coat

Ella Mother –

Clara My girl

Claire I'm not your mother. Don't leave me

Clara Please

Claire/Clara I got nothing else

Ella (*turning to him*) Frank –

Frank I want nothing from you

Darvell You're under my protection now
Ella Frank –
Frank Run. This way. Quick
Ella No – through here

Eleanor clicks her fingers. The action freezes, as if Frank and Ella are alone in a pocket of time.

Frank This isn't the exit
Ella I know
Frank Where are we?
Ella The costume cupboard. Lock the door

Clara, Claire and Darvell exit.

Frank We're trapped, Ella. Why didn't you run for the exit?
Ella I love it in here. You can be anything you like
Frank Come to London with me
Ella We'll protest
Frank Yes
Ella Against what?
Frank Ella, unless we act, unless we stop devouring everything, unless we try to understand what it means to be human, in two hundred, a hundred, in fifty years' time . . . we'll be nothing. We must protest, even if we're inarticulate, even if our only word is 'No'. There's so much to do. Don't hide away in your pain
Ella I love the way you speak

Frank tries to kiss her. She stops him.

I'm writing a story, Frank. It's a vampire story
Frank I know. But it's just a story. It isn't real. You're real
Ella Frank
Eleanor (*writing*) Frank, you can't have a vampire story
Ella You can't have a vampire story
Eleanor Unless

528

Ella Unless there are vampires in it
Eleanor I'm sorry
Ella I'm so sorry
Frank Don't be sorry

Frank and Ella kiss. A beautiful kiss, straight from a Gothic tale. As the kiss goes on, Ella gently bares Frank's neck. Eleanor watches them.

SCENE THIRTEEN

Darvell Scene Thirteen
Eleanor Byzantium

Morning light. Birdsong.

Darvell Good morning, Eleanor
Eleanor I've finished my story, Doctor
Darvell Well done
Eleanor I worked all night. Right though the darkness
Darvell That's very good. I look forward to it. You have a wonderful flair
Eleanor Thank you
Darvell Now, you've been alone in here long enough. It's time to come down. Your sister is coming to visit
Eleanor My mother?
Darvell Your sister. Did you forget?

Eleanor turns away.

Perhaps you'll try and eat a bit of something for her today

Eleanor nods.

That's very good. Now, what would you like to wear? Eleanor, will you choose some clothes?
Eleanor I'd like to wear my costume, please

The End.

Production Notes

Vampire *noun.* **1.** Ghost or reanimated body (usually of criminal, heretic, prostitute, wizard, etc.) supposed to leave grave at night and suck on the blood of sleeping persons; person who preys ruthlessly on others. **2.** (Theatr.) Small spring trap door used for sudden disappearances.

DIRECTING THE PLAY

Read the play closely. • Write down a list of questions which the text throws up. • Who are Ella and Claire? • Are they really vampires? • What connection do they have with Eleanor and Clara? • Is the play Ella's story, Eleanor's story, or Moira's story? • What effect do the observers have in the play?

Although your reading may invite many questions, one of the most important ones is: *who is watching whom and why?*

It's vital that, as a director, you quickly develop your own answer to this question. As soon as you've done that, you can begin to work out the logic of this imagined world and set up your own conventions. Your unique answer will begin to offer you some unique possibilities in terms of staging.

Moira Buffini: 'An audience will buy into it as long as you know your own intentions.'

Anna Mackmin: 'The earlier your audience are

introduced to your world, the quicker they will accept your conventions.'

EXERCISE *Split into groups. Go through the play together and make a list of any reference to watching, or being watched. Note anything that relates to watching. Find quotes. Discuss.*

The importance of setting up the rules and conventions of your imagined theatrical world is twofold. Primarily it will govern your staging, allowing you to address moments without being swamped by the theory behind it. Secondly, though, setting up conventions throughout the play allows for truly gut-punching moments in later scenes when you deliberately break from the conventions. What effect does it have when Eleanor and Ella finally touch? What similar moments will you include?

EXERCISE *In early rehearsals, try over-stylising the focus of the scene. Make absolutely sure that the audience is looking where you want them to at each moment. What does the scene look like if all the characters' heads turn together to focus on an area or character? If the focus is that precise then it makes for very exciting theatre.*

At this stage don't concern yourself with how real a gesture feels to a character. Be authoritative: 'Stand here.' 'Look there.' Your job as director is to tell the story clearly. Enforce focus in the early stages and the framework will be established. Within that framework you are then free to explore your characters and design.

COMEDY

Be prepared for laughs at both expected and unexpected moments.

Do make sure everyone in your cast knows how to hold and maintain the energy of the comic moment while the audience laughs.

Anna Mackmin: 'A laugh is a fantastic tool, but if not controlled, it can leave a lull in energy behind it.'

VAMPIRES

Vampires have always offered an abundance of material for script writers and novelists. The following examples (most available free online) might be worth a look:

AUGUSTUS DARVELL, *Byron*   Introduces us to the Darvell character.

THE VAMPYRE, *Dr John Polidori*   Polidori's Lord Ruthven seems to be the first appearance of the modern vampire: an undead, vampiric being possessing a developed intellect and preternatural charm, as well as physical attraction. Uses a small letting knife instead of his teeth.

CARMILLA, *Sheridan Le Fanu*   Introduces us to a young female vampire. This story inspired Moira's play. She asked herself: 'What would happen if Carmilla survived the end of her own story? What if her mother returned and they went off together into the future – an immortal mother and daughter? What if one of them was moral and the other amoral?'

DRACULA, *Bram Stoker*   Victorian conditions, vampire women, the ultimate gentleman bloodsucker. Anyone with a passing interest in vampires must give this tormented account of the world of the immortal count at least a passing glance.

TITHONUS, *Alfred Lord Tennyson*   The goddess Eos asks for her human lover, Tithonus, to become immortal, but she forgets to ask for eternal youth. While not about vampires, lines from this tragic poem have been used in many vampire stories. It's a beautiful mediation on the horrors of immortality.

INTERVIEW WITH A VAMPIRE, *Anne Rice*   A modern classic in the vampire canon. Its depiction of an non-ageing young vampire girl, Claudia, gives insight into the boredom and depression which vampirism might induce.

In the late nineteenth century, a frightening statistic suggested that a third of working women in London were prostitutes. Stories of violent bloodsuckers transmitting a demonic communicable disease, with undertones of sex and death, struck a chord in a society where tuberculosis and syphilis were common.

Despite this, the vampire was often an attractive figure, over-romanticised, epitomising the breaking of taboos, the embracing of the other, the challenge to authority, power versus passion and immortality.

LANGUAGE

Moira has been very careful with her choice of language, and clues can be gathered from her precise vernacular and use of punctuation. At a fundamental level, her use of short lines and quick interchanges necessitates speed and pace.

EXERCISE *Encourage two actors involved in a fast-paced piece of dialogue to learn all their lines like a speech. Let the lines flow quickly, overlapping. Practice passing the energy of the lines rather than just the words. The lines have a musical quality to them; try closing your eyes and listening to how the rhythm is passed.*

Moira has created at least two separate time periods in her play and has furnished each of them with its own form of language.

HEIGHTENED LANGUAGE This occurs in the historical sections. Moira suggests that in this era everything people are saying is being said for the first time. The language is full of poetic imagery and is very articulate.

WOUNDED SPEECH This is modern vernacular, spoken ineloquently by a contemporary society. Its poetry is in its rhythms.

Moira's punctuation, or lack of it, is also revealing:

Moira Buffini: There are no full stops at the end of human dialogue.'

It's hard for an actor not to play a full stop at the end of a line, but its presence always results in a drop in energy. The absence of full stops necessitates the energy and pace which characterises the whole piece.

STAGING

Think of transitions as scene-links rather than scene changes. It's a no-let-up play. It has an urgency. Other aspects of staging to consider in terms of maintaining pace and energy are the ways of making people arrive on stage, and you should make a theatre of your entrances and exits. Follow the golden rule of farce: energetic entrances and exits.

Whilst experimenting with rapid scene-links and high-energy entrances, you will be considering the body of each scene. The energy should still be high, but the blocking and setting is dependent on your reading. Explore the elasticity of the play. It goes in and out; small intimate scenes are followed by large theatrical pieces, and then back to intimacy again.

EXERCISE   *Experiment with the elasticity of the scenes. Perhaps play intimate scenes across the whole acting space, and play big scenes in small intimate ways – e.g., Fit the entire first drama scene into the costume cupboard.*

DESIGN   The play's design possibilities are plentiful, and with scenes set on distant mountainsides, in Victorian whorehouses and in a surreal asylum, this should be a designer's dream. Always remember, however, to adhere to your conventions. If it is Eleanor's story, told from the past, then should the present-day scenes be less naturalistic in their design? Or should the heightened language of the Victorian scenes be mirrored in an overly theatrical design concept? And always remember the need for pace!

SCENE ONE

A girl stands before the audience. She is trying to grab her moment, grab her life and explain it to us. She manages a few words, then suddenly a train is there, and we are relocated in a flash. Claire seems to be delighted in the

535

present; she is not jaded or bored. Ella, on the other hand, seems to be seeking some kind of sanctuary, some kind of asylum.

Unpack their different objectives. Conflicting aims are always dramatic. Their language is naturalistic and fast. What effect is created in the scene by Eleanor's presence as an observer? This is when you must start setting up your conventions.

SCENE TWO

A general sense of everyone wanting to have the last word. Status is at play hugely in this scene, which is also the audience's introduction to the comic elements of the play. If you wish to make use of laughter later, it's important that at this stage you make it clear that it is acceptable to laugh.

SCENE THREE

This scene is about finding someone who can listen to you.

As Frank and Ella talk, Fillet lectures us on the concept of consumption: 'What's your food?', 'What do you devour?' How much attention will you draw to these background indicators?

SCENE FOUR

Make use of the strong location shift: after the mesmeric potato-peeling scene, the bar should explode into movement, music and light. The music should be short and concentrated.

All through the play, characters refuse to listen to each other. In this scene Briggs blurts out 'You smell lovely' to Claire, unable to hold it in. Briggs thinks he's seducing her, but she's actually hunting him. To what extent is this play about breakdowns in communication?

It is Claire's snap of the fingers that empties the bar. In line with the alienation effects used throughout, when Claire's fingers snap, all masks of character can drop away and the actors can cross over, elegantly exiting the stage.

Moira Buffini: 'You have full licence to have actors on stage as actors rather than characters.'

SCENE FIVE

We are introduced to concepts of theatrical creation by Ella writing a short scene. As she explores alienation techniques, we are transported to a new world, a smoky, opulent room. Remember that Byzantium, Constantinople, and Istanbul are the same place in three different eras.

The staging of this whole scene needs command of focus and control. There is a great deal of direct audience adrress. The audience becomes the confidant of the characters. There is also storytelling from Darvell. How can you stage this intimate scene in a darkened room so that it draws us in.

It is a common misconception that the alienation effect requires constant objective acting. Indeed, sometimes alienation can be more powerful if an audience is brought into the world of the characters and then detached instantly at a powerful moment – which is, in fact, just what happens in the scene. Clara states, 'I hardly dared breathe, hoping that the stranger would . . .' and in bursts Frank. What effect does Frank's speech about vampires have on Eleanor and Clara?

SCENE SIX

Frank wants to escape, and he does so by vindictively throwing 'Eleanor's a vampire' at his parents. He wants to escape from what has become in effect a dead home. Tina and Geoff suck the life, the teenage vigour, out of their son. Does Ella give it back to him, in the form of confidence to stand up to his parents? If so, it is a reversal. Tina and Geoff are the devourers, feeding off the life of their house and son. Ella, a vampire, gives life back. In taking her hand, Frank becomes an active character.

SCENE SEVEN

What does Eleanor think about Ella's revelations? What effect does it have on her when Ella conveys Claire's version of their life story to Frank?

SCENE EIGHT

Claire's account to Mint here, must be utterly sincere. There's a level of emotional wreckage behind it. If Claire's story is played with utter sincerity, then we feel her pain and frustration in both eras. The seduction which she attempts afterwards is a desperate last resort. Don't play the effect, play the cause.

Claire also says, 'I'd never kill an innocent.' How do we equate this with her treatment of Briggs and Mint? The scene should have a sense of impending claustrophobia, an air of trapped animals. Are Ella and Claire permanently escaping entrapment? What if this whole scene was playing within the confines of the costume cupboard – with lots of energy, but people pressed up against each other? Both the ridiculous and the menacing are pushed into such close proximity.

SCENE NINE

Every choice the director makes about the imaginary world of the play should culminate in this scene. All the conventions which have been set up are confirmed here. Make sure everything is addressed in the embrace between Ella and Eleanor in which we perceive the full extent of the trauma suffered, and her pain.

Identities get more confused as we near the end. Eleanor is referred to as Ella as Ella sits and writes at Eleanor's writing desk. Ella forces the revelation and Eleanor panics, instructing her to 'Stop writing'.

The energy of the 'slew' of revelations must never falter. The lines are short and snappy and rapid switches between past and present will produce really exciting theatre. Moira also made it clear that the threat in the rape scene is all that is needed. There need be no depiction. We feel the threat and we see the aftermath. That is enough.

SCENE TEN

Fillet's reappearance is not mere comic relief. It is central to the themes of the play. Fillet's extreme emotional state and bleak vision of the future are very important. Fillet's confession of love for Mint should be played as a devastating truth. It will still be very funny. The more blood (the full two litres please!) and the more screaming, the better.

≤ SCENE ELEVEN

This can be set up during Scene Ten, so no break in the action need happen.

SCENE TWELVE

The flow of energetic exits and entrances will make this almost work. The appearance of Darvell is very important. Perhaps links can be made to his previous appearance in the play with the use of music.

SCENE THIRTEEN

Simplicity and gentleness will give this scene great power. What does Darvell think of Eleanor's desire to wear her costume? Is he in agreement? Or does it sadden him? Think very carefully about the final image of the play.

STAGE BLOOD

This is a recipe for edible blood. There are very striking fake-blood recipes which use washing up liquid as their base, but as Ella needs to drink it, they're probably not appropriate!

4 oz flour
2 litres of water

4 tsp gravy granules
Red food colouring (add a drop of green if needed)

Sieve the flour into the water and get all of the lumps out. Bring to a boil and simmer for about thirty minutes. Add gravy granules for extra thickness. Let it cool and stir in the colour.

From a workshop led by Anna Mackmin
with notes by Simon Evans

Participating Companies

360 Youth Theatre
Ackworth School
Alderbrook School
Arcola Youth Theatre
ArtsOne
Astor College for the Arts
Bablake School
Balerno Youth Theatre
Bedford College
Bexhill College
Bilimankhwe Young Company
Bishop Thomas Grant School
Bishops Stortford College
Blue Coat CE Comprehensive
  School
Blyth Community College
Boston Spa School
Bournemouth School For Girls
Bournside School
Brewery Youth Theatre
Bridgend College
Bridlington School Sports College
Bristol Old Vic Theatre
Brockhill Park Performing Arts
  College
CAPtivate
Cardinal Newman RC School
Castell Alun High School
Castleford High School
CATS Youth Theatre
Centre Stage
Chaucer Business & Enterprise
  College
Chellaston School
Chelmsford New Model Spec Sch
Chorlton High School

City College Norwich
Clacton County High School
Claremont High School
Clean Break Theatre Company
Coleg Sir Gar
Coln House School
Coulsdon College
County Carlow Youth Theatre
Craigholme School
Cre8
Dartford Grammar School for
  Girls
Denbigh High School
Diverse
Dumont High School
Ealing Hsmith & W London Coll
Encore Youth Theatre
Falkirk Youth Theatre
Francis Combe School
Freebird
George Abbot School
George Green's School
George Heriot's School
Glenthorne High School
Grenville College
Hall Garth School
Hampstead Theatre Youth
  Theatre (Years 12 & 13)
Harlow Fields School
Harrogate Youth Theatre
Hatfield Visual Arts College
Hemel Hempstead School
Hemsworth Art and Community
  College
Hendon School
Hertswood School

Hornsey School for Girls
Huish Episcopi School
Ian Ramsey CE Secondary School
Independent Youth Theatre
Kennet School
Kent Youth Theatre
Kernow Youth Theatre
Kidbrooke School
Kildare Youth Theatre @
    Crooked House
Kinetic Youth Group
Kingsmead Secondary School
Kingston College, School of
    Performing Arts
Lammas School
Langley School
Latimer Community Arts College
Leyton Sixth Form College
Lightbulb Youth Theatre
Lingfield Notre Dame School
Little Actors Youth Theatre
Llanelli Youth Theatre
Longcroft School
Longley Park Sixth Form College
Looe Community School
Lyceum Youth Theatre
Lyndon School
Malmesbury School
Manor College of Technology
Marple Hall School
Monks Dyke Technology College
Morehouse School
Nelson Thomlinson School
New South Wales Public Schools
    Drama Company
Newcastle College
North Kesteven School
North Walsham High School
Northampton School for Girls
Notre Dame Senior School
Nower Hill High School
Nuffield Youth Theatre
Perfect Circle Youth Theatre

Peshkar
Peter Symonds College
Peterborough High School
Players & Faces @ BW
Preston Manor High School
Princess Royal Performing Arts
    Centre
Pump House CYT
Queen Elizabeth Community Coll
Radley College
Razed Roof
Regent College
Retford Little Theatre Youth
Roundabout Youth Theatre
Royal and Derngate Youth
    Theatre
Royal Scottish Academy of Music
    and Drama
Saffron Walden County High
    School
Saint Martins School
Sandbach School
Sedbergh School
Shaftesbury School
Shenfield High School
Shotton Hall Theatre School
Sir Frederic Osborn School
Skelmersdale and Ormskirk
    Colleges
South West Youth Theatre
Southfields School
Southwark College
St Aelred's RC Technology
    College
St Elizabeth's Centre
St George's RC School
St Joseph's RC Comprehensive
    School
St Martin in the Fields High
    School
St Mary's School Calne
St Monica's RC High School
St Paul's Catholic High School

PARTICIPATING COMPANIES

St Catherine's School
St Mary's Youth Theatre
St Peter's School
Stage By Stage
Stagecoach Ormskirk
Stephen Joseph Youth Theatre
Stockport Garrick Theatre
Stopsley High School
Sudbury Upper Sch & Arts College
Tarleton High School
The Academy at Peckham
The Arnewood School
The Barn Theatre
The Blue Coat School
The BRIT School
The Castle Youth Theatre
The Commonweal School
The Crestwood School
The Daydreamer Youth Theatre
The Elizabethan High School
The Garage
The Harrodian School
The Howard School
The Lindsey School and
    Community Arts College
The Park High School

The Petersfield School
The Plume School
The Priory LSST
The Television Workshop
    Nottingham
Theatre Royal Bury St Edmunds
    Youth Theatre
Thomas Lord Audley Sch Lang
    College
Thomas Tallis School
Unicorn Youth Theatre
Uppingham School
Walthamstow Academy
Watford Palace Theatre
West Exe Technology College
West Thames College
Wilmington Entreprise College
Windermere St Annes School
Woolston Community High
    School
Wortley High School
Yew Tree Youth Theatre
Young Actors Company
Young Actors Theatre
Ysgol Aberconwy
YUF Theatre Shetland

PARTNERSHIP THEATRES

Bath Theatre Royal
Brighton Pavilion Theatre
Edinburgh Lyceum Theatre
Kendal Brewery Arts Centre
Kildare Riverbank Arts Centre
London Arcola Theatre
London Hampstead Theatre
Mold Clwyd Theatr Cymru
Newcastle Theatre Royal
Northampton Royal and Derngate
Norwich Playhouse and Garage
Plymouth Theatre Royal
Salford Lowry Centre
Scarborough Stephen Joseph Theatre
Southampton Nuffield Theatre

545

The Connections Series

NEW CONNECTIONS 2008

SHELL CONNECTIONS 2004: NEW PLAYS FOR YOUNG PEOPLE
Bedbug by Snoo Wilson, *Boat Memory* by Laline Paull, *Dead End*
by Letizia Russo, *Discontented Winter: House Remix* by Bryony Lavery,
Eclipse by Simon Armitage, *Headstrong* by April De Angelis,
Moonfleece by Philip Ridley, *The Musicians* by Patrick Marber,
Where I Come From: Scenes From Abroad by Mike Williams,
The Willow Pattern by Judith Johnson

SHELL CONNECTIONS 2005: NEW PLAYS FOR YOUNG PEOPLE
Blooded by Isabel Wright, *Burn* by Deborah Gearing,
Chatroom by Enda Walsh, *Citizenship* by Mark Ravenhill,
Just by Ali Smith, *Lunch in Venice* by Nick Dear,
Mugged by Andrew Payne, *Samurai* by Geoffrey Case,
Seventeen by Michael Gow, *Through the Wire* by Catherine Johnson

SHELL CONNECTIONS 2006: NEW PLAYS FOR YOUNG PEOPLE
Broken Hallelujah by Sharman Macdonald, *Feather Boy: the Musical*
by Nicky Singer and Peter Tabern, *Liar* by Gregory Burke,
The Miracle by Lin Coghlan, *Pack Up Your Troubles: the Musical*
by Snoo Wilson, *Pass It On* by Doug Lucie, *School Journey
to the Centre of the Earth* by Daisy Campbell with Ken Campbell,
The Shoemaker's Incredible Wife by Federico Garcia Lorca,
Shut Up by Andrew Payne, *The Spider Men* by Ursula Rani Sarma

NT CONNECTIONS 2007: NEW PLAYS FOR YOUNG PEOPLE
Baby Girl by Roy Williams, *The Black Remote* by Glyn Maxwell,
A Bridge to the Stars by Henning Mankel, *DeoxyriboNucleic Acid* by
Dennis Kelly, *Red Sky* by Bryony Lavery, *Ruckus in the Garden* by
David Farr, *Scary Play* by Judith Johnson, *Show and Tell* by Laline Paull,
A Year and a Day by Christina Reid

The Chrysalids
adapted by David Harrower from the novel by John Wyndham

More Light by Bryony Lavery

After Juliet by Sharman Macdonald

Gizmo by Alan Ayckbourn & *Don't Eat Little Charlie*
by Tankred Dorst with Ursula Ehler

Eclipse by Simon Armitage & *Friendly Fire* by Peter Gill

Cuba by Liz Lochhead & *Dog House* by Gina Moxley

Brokenville by Philip Ridley & *The Pilgrimage* by Paul Goetzee